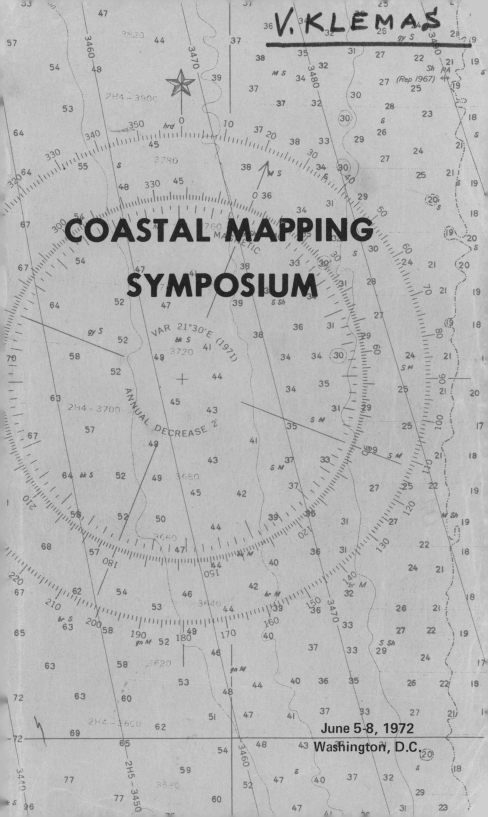

V. KLEMAS

COASTAL MAPPING

SYMPOSIUM

June 5-8, 1972
Washington, D.C.

PROCEEDINGS OF A SYMPOSIUM
ON
COASTAL MAPPING
Washington, D. C.

June 5-8, 1972

Sponsored by

American Society of Photogrammetry
Potomac Region
Photogrammetric Surveys Division

With the cooperation of

NOAA, National Ocean Survey

American Congress on Surveying and Mapping
Marine Surveying and Mapping Committee

Marine Technology Society
Coastal Zone Marine Management Committee

U. S. Geological Survey

Library of Congress Catalog Number
72-82726

PREFACE

The papers presented in this volume have been assembled and
printed prior to presentation at this Symposium. The Program
Committee requested reproducible originals, in a standard format from all authors, and those papers that were received in
advance are included in this volume.

The papers are bound in order of their presentation. The index
is alphabetical according to author.

The Symposium Committee wants to thank the many authors who
made both this volume and the Symposium possible.

SYMPOSIUM COMMITTEE

Director . . . . George M. Ball - NOAA-NOS

Arrangements . . . . Don Conway - ETL

Finance . . . . Thomas A. Hughes - USGS

Publications . . . . John T. Gerlach - NOAA-NOS

Staging & Visual Aids . . . . . Walter L. Sappington - USGS

Program Coordinator . . . . . . Lawrence W. Fritz - NOAA-NOS

Program Staff . . . . Jerome C. Ives - BLM
                                James E. Gearhart - NOAA-NOS
                                Robert C. Stirling - NAVOCEANO
                                Louis Kaufman - USCofE

INDEX OF AUTHORS

W M

THE ROLE OF THE UNITED NATIONS IN COASTAL MAPPING

Mr. Chris N. Christopher
Chief, Cartography Section
Resources & Transport Division
United Nations Secretariat

Mr. Christopher and his staff at the United Nations deeply regret to inform the participants at the Coastal Mapping Symposium that they are unable to present a paper. They are, at this moment, at the United Nations'Conference on the Human Environment in Stockholm, Sweden, (June 5-16, 1972) which will parallel in theme many of the important coastal problems being discussed here. The following is an excerpt from Mr. Christopher's letter to the Symposium committee:

..."The following is a brief outline of the various offices and agencies which are involved with programmes that may include surveying and charting of the coastal regions. These agencies and offices work in close cooperation with each other.

1 - a programme on the exploitation of marine resources carried on by both the United Nations and the Food and Agriculture Organization (FAO) to promote research and organize concerted actions for Member States to ensure the necessary framework for rational exploitation;

2 - a programme on the development of mineral resources, by the United Nations to organize scientific international projects involving exploitation of marine mineral resources;

3 - a programme involving several agencies dealing with the legal questions related to scientific investigations of the ocean and its resources with appropriate support by all bodies concerned to help reach international agreement;

4 - a cooperative study of the Kuroshio and adjacent regions. This programme undertaken cooperatively by FAO and the United Nations Educational, Scientific, and Cultural Organization (UNESCO) supports and facilitates the attendance of participants from developing countries, including the implementation of field work;

5 - two agencies (UNESCO-FAO) are conducting cooperative investigation in the Caribbean;

6 - the United Nations, together with FAO, UNESCO and the World Meteorological Organization (WMO) are concerned with a programme on the use of satellites and remote sensing for marine sciences;

7 - the United Nations, as well as, the United Nations Specialized Agencies are involved in various types of work to control the pollution in the marine environment.

I have tried to outline the types of programmes which would normally have need for coastal mapping, as well as, bathymetric

7

mapping of open sea areas. There are three United Nations'
specialized agencies concerned with the training of personnel in coastal region pollution control, which involves
mapping. I expect that we will in our future cartographic
conferences in surveying and mapping give careful consideration to coastal mapping, emphasizing its importance to the
developing countries"...

ROLE OF FEDERAL GOVERNMENT IN COASTAL MAPPING

Rear Admiral Don A. Jones, NOAA
Director, National Ocean Survey
National Oceanic and Atmospheric Administration
Rockville, Maryland 20852

BIOGRAPHICAL SKETCH

Rear Admiral Don A. Jones received a B.S. degree in Civil
Engineering from Michigan State University in 1933 and is a
graduate of the U.S. Armed Forces Staff College at Norfolk,
Virginia. Adm. Jones joined the Coast and Geodetic Survey
in 1933 as a civilian employee and was commissioned an ensign
in the Coast and Geodetic Survey in 1940. As a commissioned
officer, his duties have encompassed all types of geodetic
control surveys as well as hydrographic and photogrammetric
surveys. In World War II he was transferred to the jurisdiction of the U.S. Army and served from 1942 to 1944 as a
coast artillery staff officer, surveying and mapping officer,
and submarine mine planter commander. From 1944 to 1946, he
served with the Office of Strategic Services (OSS). Upon
transfer back to the Coast and Geodetic Survey at the end of
World War II, he served aboard various survey ships and was
chief of the Alaska Arctic Coast survey. From 1957 to 1961,
Adm. Jones was chief of a geodetic project establishing
ground control for water resources mapping of the headwaters
of the Blue Nile River in Ethiopia, Africa. In April 1966,
he became Associate Director, C&GS, Office of Hydrography and
Oceanography; January 1, 1967, he was appointed Associate
Administrator of the Environmental Science Services Adminis-
tration; and on September 1, 1968, Director, Coast and Geodetic
Survey. With the creation of the National Oceanic and Atmos-
pheric Administration, the Coast and Geodetic Survey became
National Ocean Survey October 3, 1970, with Adm. Jones as
Acting Director. President Nixon appointed him Director of
National Ocean Survey on February 22, 1971.

ABSTRACT

The Coastal Zone is defined. Its importance to the great
natural environmental systems represented in the zone and its
recognition as a political frontier are described. The responsibilities of the federal, state, and local governments to
share in the development of a coastal zone plan are outlined.
The federal role in the coastal zone is largely uncoordinated
between the various federal agencies concerned with coastal
zone problems. The diffusion of responsibility within state
governments represents an area which affects performance at
the federal level.

Many federal mapping and charting agencies recognize the
necessity of concentrating resources insofar as feasible in
the coastal zone in support of overall missions. Recommendations are made for mapping the zone.

INTRODUCTION

The Coastal Zone has been defined as that part of the land which is affected by its proximity to the sea and that part of the ocean which is affected by its proximity to the land. The area is difficult to describe geographically because it includes different areas for the economist, the social scientist, the geographer, and so on. There are various scientific and legal opinions as to what, precisely, is the coastal zone.

As related to mapping and charting, the coastal zone may be defined as that comprising waters to the outer limits of the territorial sea and lands beneath those waters, and adjacent terrain extending to the inland heads of tidewater as delimited by tidal estuaries forming an onshore belt averaging about 50 miles in breadth. Along most of the East Coast, the zone varies in width from less than 10 miles to nearly 100, and along the New England coast and the Pacific coast, including Alaska, the coastal plain is practically non-existent but the coastal zone may be considered as extending inward as far as tidewater surges.

The coastal zone is where the people and the seas meet and where an ever greater percentage of the nation's population tends to congregate. The 30 coastal and Great Lakes states contain more than 75 percent of our population--more than 85 million people live in the U.S. coastal counties. It's an area of great cities and harbors, of great expanses of open ocean, of shipbuilding and shipping centers, of nursing and feeding grounds for fish and shellfish, of very high property values, and of great and varied natural beauty.

The great natural environmental systems of the coastal zone-- air, water, land, and life--all interact, sometimes violently. Each system has its own interacting subsystems, so that none remains the same in time or from place to place. The meteorologist, oceanographer, geologist, and biologist all realize that this is like a web in which a change may have far-flung and unforeseen effects. The sea and air interact. The sea and the seabed and coast interact. And the fact of being alive requires all organisms to interact constantly with the environment.

The hundreds of activities of man focused in this area also result in changes which have lasting effects. Where shorebirds and fish once ruled, we now find factories, warehouses and docks; oil derricks, ocean platforms and refineries; marinas and power plants; and acres of real estate development. We level sand dunes, destroy vegetation, dredge and fill and pollute as we go. The very difficult and complex problem is to achieve and maintain an orderly regimen of both preservation and use.

Today more than ever, man is becoming aware of the potential wealth of the sea. One need only look at the millions of dollars at stake in controversies involving offshore oil wells to extrapolate the amounts of money involved as the resources of sea become exploitable to technologically advanced man. It is not just the sea and the underlying seabed, however, which yield potential wealth. The shoreline and shorefront property become increasingly important as recreational development and an increasing population drives property values ever upwards. The recent environmental concern for the preservation of the ecological balance of both the sea and the shore is yet another value which makes these areas important to man. You

may wonder what monetary and ethereal qualities have in common
with the job of a surveyor. Simply stated, no matter what considerations make a particular territory of value to an individual,
the individual must always be able to define the territory he
wishes to protect or develop. One might only speculate on the
number of cases in property law that would never have had to be
resolved in court had precise boundaries been available for the
property in question.

The coastal zone is, therefore, a political frontier where a
nation's rights give way to freedom of the seas, and where
seaward jurisdictional boundaries are for the most part indefinite, yet looming more and more significant: seaward boundaries between adjoining nations, between the Federal Government
and the States, between adjoining states, and between the state
and private property owners.

NOS is the leading federal agency in the establishment of seaward boundaries defining the territorial waters and the lateral
boundaries between our coastal states. Federal, state, and private boundaries in the coastal zone must be determined for the
proper planning and management of the coastal zone environment.
Photogrammetric and geodetic surveying techniques are employed
by NOS in the field of marine geodesy. The increased interest
of the coastal states in marine environment activities has
resulted in the formation of special commissions or advisory
groups working with federal officials in solving seaward boundary
problems.

Federal, state, and local governments share the responsibility
to develop for the coastal zone a plan which reconciles or, if
necessary, chooses among competing interests and protects long-
term values. Effective management to date has been thwarted
by the variety of government jurisdictions involved, the low
priority afforded marine matters by state governments, the
diffusion of responsibilities among state agencies, and the
failure of state agencies to develop and implement long-range
plans. Until recently, navigation--over which federal authority
is pre-eminent--has tended to dominate other uses of the coastal
zone, and perhaps for this reason, states have been slow to assume
their responsibilities.

The federal role in the coastal zones has grown haphazardly.
Closely related functions are discharged by the U.S. Coast
Guard, Army Corps of Engineers, Department of Housing and Urban
Development, a number of bureaus of the Department of the Interior,
and several other federal agencies. The Federal Government spon-
sors planning activities in certain coastal areas through river
basin commissions, established pursuant to Title II of the Water
Resources Planning Act of 1965, and in certain others through
regional commissions established under Title V of the Public
Works and Economic Development Act.

At the federal level, the Committee on Multiple Use of the
Coastal Zone of the Marine Council considers the broad aspects
of coastal management and seeks effective and consistent federal
policies. The Water Resources Council, a cabinet-level coordinating and planning group analogous to the Marine Council
but chaired by the Secretary of the Interior, also has an
interest in the coastal zone, although its work is primarily

directed to inland waters. But, of course, neither committee
can be concerned with the detailed management of particular
coastal areas.

The diffusion of responsibility has been reflected within
state governments, within which individual agencies deal
directly with their counterparts at the federal level. Too
often states lack plans of their own based on an appraisal
of all state interests in their coastal resources. In these
cases, states have tended only to react to federal plans.

In varying degrees, the states possess the resources, administrative machinery, enforcement powers, and constitutional
authority on which to build. However, they will need federal
assistance and support, and the Federal Government must assure
the protection of national interests in the coastal zone.

The Federal Government cannot and, of course, should not com-
pel a state to develop a special organization to deal with its
coastal management problems. However, it can encourage such
actions, provide guidelines for the functions of such organizations, facilitate federal cooperation with state authorities,
and provide appropriate assistance.

In support of NOAA's program for description, prediction, monitoring, and related research to detect, assess, and predict the
effects of natural and man-made changes on the quality of marine
environments, the NOS is concentrating more and more of its
resources on the coastal zone. All of this is in line with the
President's recent creation of the Environmental Protection Agency
as an independent enforcement mechanism which will rely heavily
on NOAA's mapping, charting, research and scientific capabilities
to monitor the marine environment effectively.

First, before any effective monitoring can be accomplished, we
must establish certain baselines in the coastal zone. One such
baseline results from datum-plane determination and the associated
low water line mapping which has been conducted over the years
to support the production of nautical charts. This work is now
being accelerated to meet new requirements for seaward boundary
demarcation and for settlement of land ownership disputes. The
sea boundaries of the territorial waters and many of the boundaries
between our coastal states are referenced to the mean low water
line. Determination of location and form of this baseline and
other tidal boundaries utilizes two fundamental surveying procedures: (1) establishment of tidal datum planes, which involves
the vertical component; and (2) the horizontal delineation of
the shoreline at the accepted datum-plane elevation. The first
procedure is accomplished by use of tide gages, and the second
by means of aerial photomapping where the state-of-the-art in
photogrammetry provides the required accuracy and the best
alternative for the accomplishment of the boundary mapping task.

National Ocean Survey is engaged in a long-term program to systematically map the geophysical characteristics of the continental
margins of the United States and portions of the adjacent deep
oceans. A major effort, relatively new in concept and techniques,
is now being mounted to collect marine geophysical information.
Specific data collected at this time include bathymetry, mag-
netics, gravity, and seismic information. All of these may be
collected concurrently in an underway mode. Surficial sediment
data is also used to prepare maps.

It is planned that two series of maps will be produced--one
at a scale of 1:250,000 for the continental margin, and another
at a scale of 1:1,000,000 for the deep oceans. Each map unit
will contain bathymetry as a base map, with magnetic, gravi-
metric, and seismic properties as contoured overlays. Addition-
ally, reports and other products will be produced. Control will
be the best available. Coverage will be based upon a grid system--
nominally five miles at 1:250,000 and 10 miles at 1:1,000,000.
The deep sea work is presently being undertaken as part of the
President's International Decade of Ocean Exploration (IDOE).
The continental margins will be surveyed in part by NOAA ships
and possibly by private contractors. The data will be available
to users through the Environmental Data Service of NOAA. We
hope that future programs will allow regional map atlases to
be developed, including sediment properties, heat flow data,
basement structure, and various physical parameters.

Conceptually, the program has been initiated in response to
various studies indicating the need for marine geophysical
data for planning, resource evaluation, and environmental
related problems. We as a nation need to preserve the marine
environment as well as exploit it intelligently for the good
of our people, and make the necessary decisions involving the
total management of marine areas off our coast. To understand
the geophysical processes that allow meeting of these goals,
we must first measure them and do so logically and systematically.
It is this objective that the NOS marine geophysical mapping
program undertakes to accomplish.

The need for a systematic program of geophysical data collection,
plus generation of data onto maps, lists, tapes, reports, etc.,
has been recognized for resource purposes, fishing, engineering
aspects and similar reasons. However, two factors of relatively
recent emergence pointed out the urgency of geophysical relation-
ships--environmental needs and pollution control matters, and
the overall coastal zone planning now recognized as necessary
for a total view of uses of the sea. One further fact should
not be overlooked--work on ocean tectonics and drift theories
are dependent upon availability of marine geophysical data. It
is now recognized that before man can gauge the effects and the
significance of marine geophysical data, he must measure them
and do so systematically and to necessary densities and accuracies.

I would like to discuss briefly a project recently completed
in a zone immediately adjacent to the coastline--that of an
estuary. During the 1969 and 1970 field seasons, a comprehensive circulatory survey was conducted in Penobscot Bay, Maine.
It consisted of approximately 180 current stations, 1,000
salinity-temperature-depth observations, and 10 tide stations.
Instrumentation consisted primarily of self-recording and tele-
metering current meters capable of being interrogated by either
ship or satellite, sampling at 6-minute intervals for periods
from 5 days to as long as 5 months. As the system is completely
automated, the limitation on simultaneous observations is restricted only to the number of sensors available.

The importance of this survey is that it represents a new concept in field operations of the NOS. The emphasis is now being
placed upon circulation with the objective of predicting estuarine
flushing rates and not solely on navigation as has been past

practice. However, the navigational information will also be involved and updated as a result of this new initiative. NOS is working closely with other components of NOAA to arrive at an even more meaningful National Coastal and Estuarine Studies Program. Preliminary analysis has been made of data obtained by the Penobscot Estuary survey. Raw current meter data are now available for many locations.

The second phase is now underway along the coast of South Carolina. A comprehensive circulation survey has been underway since February. Remote sensing has been integrated into the survey which will add synoptic detail impossible to obtain from instrumented arrays. A third phase of the program involves cooperative efforts of NOS with potential users. The user is afforded the opportunity to provide input directly into the program thus aiding in avoiding duplication of effort.

The technique employed in the circulatory surveys has been developed by NOS whereby surface currents could be described by photogrammetric methods. The first serious application of this technique was in 1962 in Charleston Harbor and a new survey has been tied into the previous work. The refined technique now in use is far superior to the earlier work. Surveys of this type will be extremely useful for prediction of the distribution of surface pollution such as oil spills.

In addition to the photogrammetric measurements of the surface currents, infrared photography will be taken for the purpose of tracing the temperature distribution throughout the tidal cycle. This will hopefully lead to increased detail of the water mass movements within the estuary as a result of correlation with the in situ measurements of current, temperature, and salinity.

This total program represents a unique capability of the NOS. Under one roof lies the ability to perform conventional oceanographic measurements, conduct synoptic photogrammetric surveys of the surface currents, obtain infrared imagery for mapping thermal characteristics, and to gather related ground truth.

In view of the critical nature of the pollution problem and the success of the trial program, NOS plans to continue and significantly expand these operations contingent upon federal/state cost-sharing arrangements. Positive state response will help determine our priorities and it will enable the states to participate actively in the operations.

NOS, as successor to the Coast and Geodetic Survey, is responsible for charting the coastal frontiers. NOS nautical charts are produced from detailed surveys of the shoreline margins and of the adjacent water depths. These surveys are made at much larger scales than the publication scale of the nautical chart. The nautical charting program of the nation has been in effect for a century and a half with each succeeding decade creating new and more refinements to provide critical information for safe and efficient navigation.

The vast store of pertinent data in the NOS archives provides a wealth of information needed for coastal zone mapping, coastal engineering, and alongshore economic development. In addition to original hydrographic and topographic surveys, the data include comprehensive tidal information, tidal datum planes, geodetic survey records, and aerial photography. It is a formidable task to acquire the great number of qualitative and quantitative measurements and observations needed to produce the required coastal zone graphics.

At the present time approximately 23 federal agencies are engaged in oceanographic or marine-oriented activities. The Department of the Interior has responsibilities for geological studies, particularly in connection with the offshore extraction of oil and other minerals. The Departments of Commerce and Defense have primary responsibility for carrying out extensive and comprehensive programs in ocean exploration, mapping, and charting. Within DOD the Naval Oceanographic Office conducts extensive surveys to provide naval operating forces with environmental data they need to operate effectively Navy ships and weapons systems contributing to the security of the nation.

The Corps of Engineers also has specific responsibility for obtaining environmental data for the planning, designing, construction, operation, and maintenance of non-military projects. Unlike the Navy programs, the Corps of Engineers work is principally in the harbor or harbor approach area of the country and areas of coastal erosion and along intracoastal and inland waterways. The Corps of Engineers, because of the needs of its civil works programs and its responsibilities for protection and maintenance of the coast and waterways, has developed the nation's primary competence in coastal engineering. The Coastal Engineering Research Center is the key element of federal capability in this field.

The National Shoreline Study recently completed by the Corps of Engineers provides an excellent inventory of shorelines and adjacent features. This report is designed primarily in the interest of solving coastal erosion problems and develops information on the impact of erosion, proposes possible corrective measures and their costs and guidelines for the development of shore protection and management programs.

Within the Department of the Interior, the Geological Survey carries on the large-scale topographic mapping of the coastal zone. Together with the Office of Water Resources Research, programs are conducted in the maintenance of research and information on coastal zone waters. The Geological Survey provides background information for optimum management of coastal zone activities. Collection and appraisal of basic water data are carried out covering such factors as source availability, dissolved mineral content, and organic matter.

The primary purpose of the Geological Survey topographic mapping program is to provide topographic maps uniform as to scale, accuracy, and content. These maps are essential to military and civilian planning and construction projects that involve land descriptions and identification. They also are essential to the investigation and appraisal of natural resources and serve as a base for inventorying the geographic distribution of materials and resources.

The Geological Survey is the principal federal agency concerned with an extensive and systematic program of topographic mapping designed to serve a general combination of map needs. The Geological Survey mapping program is supplemented to some extent by limited topographic mapping by the Forest Service, the Tennessee Valley Authority, the Mississippi River Commission, and NOS. The Mississippi River Commission mapping is of the lower Mississippi River and the maps are also distributed by the Geological Survey.

The U.S. Coast Guard has specific responsibility in the national waterways which requires close coordination and cooperation with National Ocean Survey. The Coast Guard provides information regarding aids to navigation and contributes substantially to the depiction of these features on nautical charts. In this area controlling depths and related information of navigable rivers and channels are supplied by the Corps of Engineers.

Bridge clearances, dredging, and other pertinent information are furnished by the Department of Transportation and other federal, state, and local government agencies as well as private contributors. Mapping and charting of the United States portion of the Great Lakes, Lake Champlain, and the St. Lawrence Seaway and River became the responsibility of NOAA when the U.S. Lake Survey was transferred to NOAA by the President's Reorganization Plan No. 4 in October 1970.

The Department of Health, Education, and Welfare has specific need of detailed mapping in selected coastal zone areas which is supplied by National Ocean Survey. The Bureau of Land Management is concerned with the coastal zone in connection with the leasing of offshore petroleum drilling permits. The Department of Justice has a continuing interest in coastal zone graphics in connection with law enforcement matters. The Department of State has sole responsibility for international boundaries and in this connection is basically concerned with the seaward boundaries of the United States.

The mounting concern over the coastal zone leads to the needs of specific actions and studies. The states have a profound concern for defining the seaward limits of their area and also for defining lateral boundaries between states. NOS, under a cooperative agreement with the State of Florida, is conducting an accelerated program to determine and map the private-state-federal coastal zone boundaries of Florida. This project combines standard hydrographic, photogrammetric, and coastal mapping techniques and exploits the use of color, infrared, and panchromatic aerial films in developing general procedures for coastal boundary mapping operations. Extensive tide observations are used to establish local mean high and mean low water tidal datums; the national vertical control net is being expanded; coastal zone aerial photography is being flown to meet aerotriangulation and compilation requirements; and a special map series of approximately 450 coastal boundary photomaps at 1:10,000 scale is being published, along with supplemental tidal data required for establishing the boundary lines on the ground. Under this program approximately 20 map sheets have been completed; some 50 tide gages are now in operation in preparation for new segments of the coastline.

Effective management and development of the nation's coastal zone are dependent upon accurate determination and mapping of coastal zone parameters. NOS is recognized by state and federal authorities for its technical expertise, particularly in determining tidal datums.

Coastal zone mapping is envisioned as a cost-sharing cooperative undertaking whereby the states and the Federal Government derive mutual benefits from the data acquired. It is proposed that with the increasing demand for this type of coastal zone graphics, an enlarged federal program will be forthcoming to satisfy the needs of all coastal states.

NATIONAL MARITIME BOUNDARIES: CONSIDERATIONS
FOR COASTAL MAPPING

Dr. Robert D. Hodgson
The Geographer
Department of State, Washington, D.C.

BIOGRAPHICAL SKETCH

Robert D. Hodgson was born in New York City on June 7, 1923. He
received his A.B., M.A. and Ph.D degrees in Geography from the University
of Michigan. After teaching at the University of Michigan from 1947 to
1951, Dr. Hodgson joined the United States Government. He has served
as Geographic Attache in Bonn, Germany (1952-57) and in the Department's
Bureau of Intelligence and Research (1957-Present). Since 1969, he has
been The Geographer to the Department and Director, Office of the
Geographer, Bureau of Intelligence and Research. He is the author of
numerous articles on maritime jurisdictional boundaries.

ABSTRACT

The Geneva Conventions on the Territorial Sea and the Contiguous Zone
and on the Continental Shelf have placed increased responsibilities on
coastal mapping agencies. Charts, originally designed as aids to
mariners, now must depict accurately the basepoints for the measurement
of the territorial sea as well as the bases for the limits of national
jurisdiction on the seabed. To accomplish these vital missions, the
National Ocean Survey must alter certain of its existing practices. An
augmentation in the Survey will be necessary to accomplish the new tasks.

INTRODUCTION

About a year ago, I had the pleasure of participating in a panel program
of the ACSM/ASP on Marine Surveying and Mapping.[1] At that time, I
discussed in detail the potential marine boundaries which the world's
coastal states will have to develop or negotiate in the near future.
In the interim, I have participated in the construction of a set of
provisional baseline maps for the 50 states of the United States.

Although international law concerning these limits is still in a
developmental or evolutionary stage, it is possible to enumerate briefly
the limits which the United States will have to delimit:

1) the national baseline from which all mileage zones and boundaries
must be measured. This baseline may be the low-water coastline as
represented on officially-recognized charts or, where certain geographic
conditions prevail, a system of straight baselines closing juridical
bays, river mouths, indented coastlines or connecting offshore islands
with each other and/or the mainland baseline. Other derived points may
by utilized as basepoints, as we shall presently see;

2) the seaward limit of the territorial sea which is measured from the
national baseline. Currently, the United States claims a three nautical
mile territorial sea although attempting, in New York and Geneva, to
negotiate an international norm of 12 nautical miles. In either
instance, the territorial sea boundary is situated so that every point
on it is precisely three (or 12) nautical miles seaward of the nearest
point on the national baseline.

1. Hodgson, Robert D., "Limits in the Seas", Surveying and Mapping,
    September 1971, pp. 397-409.

3) the seaward limit of a contiguous zone or zones, also measured from the national baseline at a set distance (or distances). Currently, the United States claims a 12 nautical mile exclusive fisheries zone; i.e., a three nautical mile territorial sea of sovereign territory and an additional nine nautical mile zone of exclusive jurisdiction for fisheries (and customs control).

4) the seaward limit of national sovereign jurisdiction on the continental shelf when it is delineated precisely by a depth and/or distance criterion.

5) other submarine limits between national and international jurisdiction when, or if, they are defined;

6) the limits of these zones between the United States and adjacent and opposite states; and

7) the limits between Federal and state jurisdictions over these zones, if any.

How then do these boundaries relate specifically to coastal charting and surveying? The negotiators of the Geneva Conventions on the Territorial Sea and the Contiguous Zone and on the Continental Shelf, in their infinite wisdom or in ignorance, relate these limits to officially-produced and recognized charts of the coastal state. In the United States, we are fortunate to possess, in the National Ocean Survey, a superior organization with technical competence in all aspects of coastal surveying, mapping, geodesy, photogrammetry, tidal determination, etc. However, we must recognize that most coastal states do not have such an organization, or, if one exists, it is often of a limited competence. All too often, these developing states must rely on charts produced by the former metropole states or by others which have little or no direct relationships with the coastal state.[1]

The international lawyers and diplomats, unfortunately, were either not cognizant of the true state of affairs or they felt that they had no real alternative but to select existing and "officially-approved" charts for these boundaries. The policy-makers have directly or indirectly placed requirements on national coastal survey organizations, such as the N.O.S., which these organizations had not envisioned. Their responsibilities have normally been limited to the production of nautical charts and books for navigators.

Nautical charts are probably as old as sailing, although the first "charts" may have been perishable lines scratched on the sands of the shore. Detailed and accurate coastal charts, such as we have today, evolved from the Portolano charts of the early Middle Ages. Accurate and possessing great artistic beauty, these charts were designed, as is the modern chart, to aid navigation, to make sailing safer and more efficient. While the modern N.O.S. chart portrays the navigator's "reefs and shoals" at larger scales and with greater precision and intensity, the essential purpose and design of the chart have remained static.

---

1. See UNESCO Sixth United Nations Regional Cartographic Conference for Asia and the Far East, E/CONF.57/L.1, 27 May 1970, "Report on the Meeting of the Ad Hoc Group of Experts on Hydrographic Surveying and Bathymetric Charting" for an excellent summary on the status of coastal surveying and survey organizations of the world.

What new requirements then have been placed upon these nautical coastal charts? The most logical way to analyze the increased demands is to relate the charts to the various limits in the seas previously outlined.

THE NATIONAL BASELINE AND THE TERRITORIAL SEA

The first group of limits includes the national baselines and the limits which relate directly to them. The Convention on the Territorial Sea and Contiguous Zone defines the national baselines, in part, as "...the low-water line along the coast as marked on large-scale charts officially recognized by the coastal state."[1] In addition, the territorial sea of an island, defined as a "naturally formed area of land, surrounded by water, which is above water at high tide", is measured in accordance with the provisions of the Convention.[2] Finally, a low-tide elevation, defined as a naturally-formed area of land which is surrounded by and above water at low tide but submerged at high tide, may be used as a basepoint if it is situated at a distance equal to or less than the breadth of the claimed territorial sea from a point on the national baseline including islands.[3] (The question of straight baselines will not be developed in this paper.)

Using these enumerated provisions, among others, a Committee of Experts of the Federal Government has established a provisional baseline, territorial sea and contiguous zone for the area of the 50 states of the United States. I stress the word "provisional" because the committee faced many problems which proved to be insurmountable with available charts and other data. It is well to remember, at this point, that the United States is fortunate to have the excellent National Ocean Survey, staffed with trained, competent and dedicated scientists and technicians. For most other nations, the problems of establishing accurately their national baselines must be infinitely greater. We are also fortunate to have a considerable tradition of coastal charting which has led to coverage at large or medium scales, 1:50,000 to 1:200,000 of most US coastal areas.

Even with these benefits, the Committee could not produce a totally definitive baseline for the United States. The "fault" does not rest with the N.O.S. but with requirements placed upon the Survey.

The first problem to face the Committee involved the lack of consistency on the representation of the low-water coastline of the country. On certain older sheets, or in areas of imprecise surveys, the low-water coastline could not be identified readily. All sheets symbolized bathymetry to the proper low-water tidal datums, but only newer editions represented a distinctive and easily determinable low-water line to serve as the national baseline. The absence of the low-water line does not detract from the utility of the charts for navigational purposes; only for their use as boundary sheets may they be considered deficient.

The second problem, the most serious one we faced, involved the symbolization of certain small rocks and shoals which might serve as

1. Shalowitz, A., Shore and Sea Boundaries, Vol. I, Appendix I, p. 371, "Convention on the Territorial Sea...", Article 3.

2. Op. Cit., Article 10.

3. Op. Cit., Article 11.

natural basepoints. The rocks caused the greatest difficulty and will be the hardest problem to solve in the boundary question.

To the mariner, rocks just above, at, or slightly below the tidal datum all constitute dangers to navigation and are, regardless of their horizontal position, within a matter of feet, to be avoided at all costs. He gains no consolation from knowing that he may have run aground or torn the ship's bottom on a potential basepoint for the territorial sea or on a non-usable submerged rock. Consequently, and incidentally due to cost factors as well, the N.O.S. charts symbolize, with an asterisk, points which may be within one of four categories:

1) rocks immediately below the low-tide datum;

2) rocks awash at this level of the sea;

3) true drying rocks situated between the low and high tide datums; and

4) true islands which are situated slightly above the high tidal level.

All of these categories are navigational hazards; the latter two may be used as basepoints for the territorial sea.

Original T-sheets and H-sheets may note the precise category of the rocks. However, very often they do not. As a result, we were forced, in making the provisional baseline charts, to ignore these symbols unless additional data on the chart or on other sources could substantiate the precise nature of the rock. Remember, at this point, that the Convention requires the baseline to be represented on officially-recognized charts. Compilation data and other archival materials may not affect the baseline except in instances of obviously gross inequities. The passage of a hurricane through the outer banks of the Carolinas or the Mississippi delta area may lead to great and obvious changes in coastal configuration which must be considered in relation to the basepoints during the interim period between revisions.

However, the problem of rocks, and their relation to tidal datums, has another facet in the baseline problem. Obviously, where a large number of these rocks exists, perhaps too many to show individually, the chart maker must generalize, and he selects those rocks which are most seaward or which he may perceive as the greatest threat to navigation. These rocks, which may not be usable as basepoints since they may be submerged at low tide, have led to the omission of other points which might serve as basepoints.

The third problem which the Committee faced involved the relevancy and currency of certain coastal data. Some charts in areas of considerable coastal change, e.g., the Mississippi Delta, were quite out-of-date. Sheets covering the Chandeleur Islands, for example, would show the effects of the hurricane of several years ago on one sheet but would fail to do so on the adjacent sheet. Often, inland data were very old or lacking for areas which were deemed non-navigable. Yet the shorelines were vital for the determination of juridical bays and their closing lines, for example.

Finally, a brief note should be made that truly large scale charts are missing for large portions of our coast. The Pacific shores and Hawaii, for example, do not have complete coverage at the same scale as the East and Gulf Coasts.

THE CONTINENTAL SHELF AND SEABED

The current definition of the continental shelf is "elastic" relating to waters 200 meters deep or beyond where the exploitability criterion may be met. These are limited by an undefined factor of adjacency.[1] As a consequence, lawyers and statesmen are attempting to revise the current Convention definitions affecting national limits on the seabed. The United States has proposed that this limit beyond the territorial sea (of 12 nautical miles) be the 200 meter isobath.[2] We have further suggested that a trusteeship zone be established which, although under the administration of the coastal state, would be part of an international seabed zone. No specific seaward limit for this zone has been proposed although the original concept related to the geological margin of the continents, again undefined.

Ten years ago, to establish a 200 meter isobathmetric boundary for the United States would have been difficult but not impossible. Most charted depths related to points; bottom contours were not drawn because they were deemed of little value to the navigator. Recently, the N.O.S. has added these to standard charts as they are revised and has produced special maps, at medium scale, extending to relatively deep waters. The areal coverage of these charts, however, is not complete. Should the 200 meter isobath be accepted as the limit of national sovereign jurisdiction on the seabed, the United States will be in a relatively good position for the determination of its shelf limits. The major problem would be one of conversion from feet or fathoms to the more universally accepted metric system.

The limits, however, are by no means certain. The original concept related to a geographic-geologic feature--the continental shelf. The depth criterion was selected as a convenient measure for the depth of the feature throughout the world. In most areas, of course, the feature and the depth do not relate. The Convention, in adding the exploitability and adjacency clauses, compounded the confusion beyond measure. Some proponents claim the right to the entire continental margin for the coastal state while others say that adjacency places an absolute, but undefined, distance limit on the seaward claims of national sovereign rights to the seabed.

If a geographic-geologic criterion is retained and a depth or slope equivalent is again substituted for deeper waters, great problems may arise in locating the limits.

Depth surveys of a reasonable degree of accuracy are a recent phenomenon. As Beazley has pointed out so well,[3] these modern surveys may be accurate only in comparison with older surveys. He cites problems involving accurate positioning, corrections of bathymetric data and differences in spheroids. These factors may all combine to produce great errors in depth/positioning relationships of considerable magnitudes.

---

1. Whiteman, M. Digest of International Law, Vol. 4, p. 923, "Convention on the Continental Shelf", Article 1.

2. U.S. Draft Proposal, August 1970.

3. Beazley, P.B., The Relationship of Deep Bathymetric Surveys to the Determination of Limits of National Jurisdiction on the Seabed, Paper 402.2, p. 3.

Again, the United States possesses competence and equipment (velocitymeters, satellite navigation, inertial guidance navigation, etc.) to produce accurate and precise surveys. However, not all survey ships are so equipped and not all surveys have relied on these modern craft.

Obviously, the developing nations face even greater problems and their level of expectation, in relation to the promised wealth of the seabed, is much higher even than ours. Will we have to assist them in determining these depths for their offshore areas? Will they trust our results and technology? Many have little faith in the developed states and prefer a transfer of technology. Can we train the local personnel to perform these surveys? Can we transfer the technology even if the training is possible? These and many other questions may need to be faced before a viable ocean regime may be envisioned.

ADJACENT AND OPPOSITE BOUNDARIES

Due to the shortage of time, I will not develop fully the problems of establishing boundaries with our neighboring states. The following, however, will be required:

1) two territorial sea boundaries with Mexico which we, with the able assistance of the National Ocean Survey, have negotiated and established in the Gulf of Mexico and the Pacific Ocean;

2) two continental shelf/seabed boundaries with Mexico to continue these territorial sea boundaries to the limits of national jurisdiction;

3) a continental/shelf seabed boundary with Cuba;

4) a continental shelf/seabed boundary with the Bahamas;

5) four territorial sea boundaries with Canada in the Atlantic, Pacific and Arctic Oceans;

6) four continental shelf/seabed boundaries with Canada;

7) a territorial sea boundary with the U.S.S.R.; and

8) one or two continental shelf boundaries with the U.S.S.R. Other limits, of course, will be needed for the U.S. overseas territories and possessions.

All negotiations will require large-scale maps which will portray accurately and precisely common tidal datums, basepoints and bathymetry. More factors may also be demanded depending on the final limits still to be defined. We may eventually require an oceanic, geodetic network such as Mourad had described.[1]

CONCLUSIONS

Obviously, these limits of national sovereignty and sovereign jurisdiction are of paramount importance to the United States and to the coastal nations of the world. Valuable resources of the sea, the seabed and the subsoil may accrue within the limits. Accurate charts will form the bases for the delimitations and negotiations and will be vital for the

---

1. Mourad, A.G., "Marine Geodesy", Battelle Technical Review, Feb. 1965.

peaceful and accurate delineation of these limits. New and more precise baseline surveys will be required; perhaps even new types of charts will have to be designed to satisfy the boundary demands. These charts must reflect the requirements of the Law of the Sea Conventions and the Supreme Court decisions which affect our national baseline and maritime limits. Among others, the charts must distinguish between permanent harbor works, on one hand, and piers and docks, on the other; clearly mark the low-water line and be maintained regularly; reflect the proper relationship between rocks and the official tidal datums; and, where established, delimit roadsteads where they extend beyond the normal limits of the territorial sea. More precise and deeper bathymetric surveys, moreover, may be required if a depth criterion is maintained for seabed national limits. The Survey, with its present limited means and demanding mission, can not be expected to meet the new challenge without additional means. An augmented National Ocean Survey is imperative to perform these vital tasks within an expanded mission.

LEGAL CONSIDERATIONS IN COASTAL MAPPING - SHORELINE BOUNDARIES

Dr. Lewis M. Alexander
Department of Geography
University of Rhode Island
Kingston, R. I.   02881

BIOGRAPHICAL SKETCH

Lewis M. Alexander is Professor of Geography and Chairman of the
Department at the University of Rhode Island. He also is Director
of the Law of the Sea Institute and of the University's Master of
Marine Affairs Program. He specializes in marine geography, po-
litical geography, and law of the sea matters. He received his
A.B. from Middlebury College, and his M.A. and Ph.D. from Clark
University. He was a Weather Forecaster during World War II, and
served on the faculties of Hunter College and the State University
of New York at Binghamton before coming to Rhode Island. In 1967-
68 he was Deputy Director of the President's Commission on Marine
Science, Engineering and Resources. He is a consultant to the
Office of the Geographer, Department of State, and has been principal investigator for several studies for the Office of Naval Research.

ABSTRACT

The exact positioning of offshore boundaries is a problem of both
international and domestic interest. The basic guidelines for
determining the baselines along the coast from which territorial
and contiguous zone limits are measured were laid down in the
1958 Geneva Conventions to which the United States is a party.
Yet the delimitation articles of these Conventions contain a
number of imprecisions, particularly with regard to (1) the breadth
of the territorial sea (2) straight baseline regimes, (3) the exploitability criterion, (4) historic waters, and (5) special
circumstances. An ad hoc Marine Boundary Review Commission might
be created by the federal government, containing both government
and non-government representatives, to assess the Geneva articles
on delimitation, along with other relevant data, and make recommendations on what the responses the United States should make to offshore claims by foreign countries which exceed a literal interpretation of the Geneva provisions. A concurrent Review Commission
should analyze the problems of domestic offshore boundaries and
recommend procedures for handling their delimitations.

The problems of offshore boundary delimitation are in one sense
gaining in importance as the potential value of seabed and subsoil
resources become increasingly evident; yet, in another sense, the
problems are becoming less as the distance offshore at which the
outer limits of coastal State competence are fixed becomes progressively greater. The choice of basepoints along the coast from
which offshore limits are established is of considerable significance if these limits are within a few miles of the coast, or if -
as in the case of median lines on the seabed - their exact positioning depends on the choice of specific basepoints some distance away.
But if we are dealing with arcs of circles many miles in radius, or
if the outer boundary of an offshore region be fixed within some
general physiographic zone, then the exact choice of specific basepoints becomes of limited importance.

The basic guidelines for selection of basepoints from which offshore boundaries are measured are laid down in the 1958 Geneva Conventions to which the United States is a party. Despite what the U. S. and other adherents to the Conventions may do domestically these guidelines take precedence over alternative arrangements so far as international offshore boundaries are concerned. They represent a unique set of accommodations with the variety of coastline conditions existing throughout the world, and are to my mind one of the truly remarkable compendia of international rules and regulations based on things as they are, rather than as they might be. But there are at least two principal drawbacks to the Geneva articles so far as the U. S. is concerned. First, there are delimitation problems which they deal with only obliquely, if at all; second, there are cases in which these articles are inadequate to handle detailed delimitations, such as are required for certain United States purposes.

In five general categories of boundary delimitation the Geneva articles are far from precise. These are the provisions with respect to (1) the breadth of the territorial sea; (2) straight baseline regimes; (3) the exploitability criterion; (4) historic waters; and (5) special circumstances.

At both the 1958 and the 1960 Conferences on the Law of the Sea the delegates were unable to reach agreement on a uniform breadth for the territorial sea, although the 1958 Territorial Sea Convention implies that the maximum breadth should be twelve nautical miles. So far as the outer boundary of the territorial sea is concerned it reflects far less the sinuosities along the coast, or the choice of alternative basepoints close to one another, at the twelve-mile distance than at three miles. For countries claiming more than twelve miles minor coastal irregularities have even less significance. Should 200-mile limits eventually be adopted either for territorial waters or for exclusive resource zones many of the details of baseline delimitation contained within the Territorial Sea Convention would become academic. The arcs of circles method for outer boundary determination might then be replaced by some other method, such as the use of straight baselines joining fixed geographic coordinates located some 200 miles from the coast.

With respect to the regime of straight baselines the language of the Territorial Sea Convention is open to a variety of interpretations. Article 4 permits the use of a straight baseline system "in localities where the coastline is deeply indented and cut into, or if there is a fringe of islands along the coast in its immediate vicinity." But how indented must a coastline be, or how fringed with offshore islands, in order to qualify for this special regime? Also, if the necessary conditions exist along all or a part of a country's coast what restrictions are there on the delimitation of individual baselines?

The only authoritative review of a particular delimitation process was that by the International Court of Justice in the 1951 Anglo-Norwegian Fisheries Case. Here, the Court repeatedly referred to the unique geographic and historical nature of the Norwegian situation, thereby complicating the process of translating the delimitation conditions existing there to other countries' straight baseline proposals. Certain mathematical criteria for straight baseline systems have been suggested by Hodgson and Alexander in an article which is being published as an "Occasional Paper" by the Law of the Sea Institute. Among the topics

covered are the maximum length of individual baselines, the definition of a "fjord" and the procedure for determining the "general
nature" of a particular coast. But outside of this effort, very
little has been done since 1958 in searching for exact criteria for
these baseline systems. Over sixty States now have adopted straight
baseline regimes along all or a part of their coasts, yet the United
States continues to adhere to a policy of non-adoption of a special
straight baseline regime for its own use. At the same time the
U. S. Government has never established any criteria for recognizing
or not recognizing the delimitation procedures of other countries
which have adopted such a regime.

A third case of imprecision in the Geneva Conventions is the exploitability clause. Article 1 of the Continental Shelf Convention
defines the shelf as including the submarine areas adjacent to the
coast, outside the area of the territorial sea, to a depth of 200
meters or beyond that limit "to where the depth of the superjacent
waters admits of the exploitability of the natural resources of the
said areas." But what constitutes "exploitability"? This is a
question many experts have been addressing over the past years with
the result that a wide spectrum of possible interpretations have
emerged. The International Court of Justice, in the 1969 North Sea
Continental Shelf Cases decision held that Article 1 has acquired
the status of customary international law. Yet to date no nation
has claimed jurisdiction over the seabed and subsoil beyond the
200-meter isobath on the grounds of exploitability.

Under the impetus of the impending Third Law of the Sea Conference
a number of proposals have been advanced for replacing the exploitability criterion with a new type of regime for determining the outer
limit of the legally-defined shelf. One of these, suggested by the
United States, would provide for a "Trusteeship Area" lying seaward
of the 200-meter isobath, within which an international authority
would own the resources of the ocean floor, but only the nationals
of the coastal State, or its lessees, would be permitted to exploit
the seabed and subsoil resources. A portion of the revenues derived
would go to an international fund. One unique feature of the proposed Trusteeship Area is that its outer boundary, located somewhere
along the upper part of the continental rise, would be determined by
the degree of declination in slope as the ocean floor gradually
levels out along the rise.

Still another case of imprecision involves historic waters. Article
7 of the Territorial Sea Convention treats of historic waters without
elaboration as to what the qualifying conditions for such a designation are. Presumably national claims to historic waters can exceed
claims based on the physical criteria laid down by the Territorial
Sea Convention in terms of the extent of waters involved. Thus an
historic bay can have a closing line across its mouth greater than
twenty-four miles in extent and/or can be claimed as internal waters
even if its configuration does not meet the requirements of a "natural" bay as laid down in Article 7.

In order to justify its claim to a water area as historic a country
must presumably have treated the waters in question as internal for
a considerable period of time (even if for most of these years the
country was a dependency of another nation). Historic waters are

generally of two types: (1) bays or other semi-inclosed water bodies; or (2) waters between offshore islands or separating an offshore island chain from the mainland. No general rules have been laid down for the extent of water areas which may be claimed as historic, nor for the bases on which other countries may challenge an historic water claim. Indeed it is not yet clear on whom is the burden of proof for legitimatizing such a claim - the interested State, or the international community. Characteristically, the United States has made no claim to waters as being historic which could not otherwise be closed off as internal; nor has it made any decisions as to which historic claims by other countries it will recognize, and which it will not.

There are other claims extant which are not specifically historical, but which nevertheless lie outside the aegis of the Geneva Conventions. The most important of these are the Soviet claims to the seas along its Arctic coast - the Kara, Laptev, East Siberian and Chukchi, as well as the Sea of Okhotsk - as "closed seas" without specifications as what these designations are based on, nor what the status itself actually implies so far as rights of other countries are concerned.

A final imprecision in the Geneva agreements is the use of the term "special circumstances" in Article 6 of the Continental Shelf Convention as one justification for the delimitation of particular boundaries between adjacent States. This provision was expanded by the International Court of Justice in its North Sea Continental Shelf Cases decision, and has now become a rather general basis for extended offshore claims not only to the seabed and subsoil, but to the water column as well. For the most part, claims to special circumstances are based on one of four types of conditions. First, there may be claims to certain areas on the grounds of historic usage, a topic which has already been covered above. Second, there may be assertions of the existence of a unique environment which demands special treatment, as Canada claimed for the Arctic at the time of the passage of the Arctic Waters Pollution Prevention Act. Third, a country may feel that it has a unique dependence on the sea, and is thereby entitled to special privileges. A prime example here is Iceland, where fish and fish products comprise the bulk of the country's exports, and where a new 50-mile exclusive fisheries limit goes into effect in September. Finally, a country may contend that its physical configuration justifies special consideration. The case of archipelago countries provide an example. Are these countries entitled to close off all inter-island waters as internal, or should some mathematical limits be placed on such activities? As in the case of straight baseline regimes few suggestions have been made for limiting the extent of closed waters within archipelagos. The United States Government has no policies with regard to this matter, but again suggestions for such limits are contained in the Law of the Sea Institute "Occasional Paper" which was noted earlier.

The implication in this discussion is that the international community, some fourteen years after the original Conventions were adopted, might do well to reconsider the separate delimitation articles and, in the light of recent experience, seek to tighten up their provisions in order to eliminate some of the uncertainties noted above. In point of fact, however, the prevailing mood among many of the countries of the world is the reverse of this; that is, they appear anxious to loosen up, rather than tighten, the provisions for offshore delimitations. Only about one-third of the independent States of the international community have ratified or acceded to the Territorial Sea Convention, and roughly the

same number have adhered to the Convention on the Continental Shelf.
Given this situation, why worry about the minutiae of boundary delimitations as laid down in the Conventions?

One answer is that the United States, in its dealings with other
countries, tends to rely heavily on the tenents of international
law. This is particularly true where offshore boundary locations
may affect the ownership of oil and gas deposits, or the freedom of
movement of ships in restricted areas. With increasing use of the
sea and its resources it is important that the U. S. work out its
own official interpretations of these imprecise rules and regulations
in order that it may adopt a firm and consistent position with respect
to other governments in times of contest.

To this end I would recommend that the federal government establish an
ad hoc Marine Boundary Review Commission, charged with the responsibility of assessing the Geneva articles on delimitation, along with
other relevant data, and compiling a series of recommendations to the
Government on what responses the United States should make to existing
or projected offshore claims by other countries which go beyond a
literal interpretation of the Geneva provisions. Such a Commission
should have representation from sources outside the federal government,
and should have a specific time frame within which to operate. There
should also be arrangements which ensure, as much as possible, that the
Commission's recommedations are followed in a reasonable time by some
form of positive or negative action on the part of the Government. For
too many years, I feel, that the United States failed to come to grips
with the definitional problems of the Geneva provisions, with the result that a standardized set of delimitation procedures, which we are
clearly in favor of, become with the passage of time less and less
likely to be evolved.

Let us turn now from the international to the national aspects of
boundary delimitation. The three most important types of domestic
offshore boundaries are first, the limits between state and federal
jurisdiction on the continental shelf; second, the boundaries of offshore leasing tracts; and third, the seaward extension of land boundaries between adjacent states of the United States. To these, might of
course be added property boundaries at the water's edge. In these
situations the question arises are the provisions of the Geneva Conventions the optimum criteria for boundary determination?

The Territorial Sea Convention is based on the principle of an ambulatory shoreline; as the mean low water line moves so too does the
baseline from which the breadth of the territorial sea is measured.
For the United States much of the shoreline is relatively stable over
long periods of time, but there are some areas in which there is a
continual process of erosion and/or deposition. This is particularly
true in the delta region of Louisiana where the shoreline is everywhere
receding except in the vicinity of Atchafalaya Bay. Considerable
shoreline changes were also wrought not far from here by the 1969
hurricane. What stability in this area can be achieved for the determination of offshore limits?

There are other problems. In addition to the cases cited earlier,
there are examples of Geneva Convention articles where the specific-
ities are subject to various interpretations. For example, Article 7
of the Territorial Sea Convention speaks of the "natural entrance

points" of a bay between which straight closing lines up to twenty-four miles in length may be drawn. Anyone familiar with charts of the U. S. shoreline recognizes that many bays would appear to have more than one "natural entrance point." What criteria then should be used for selecting the appropriate ones? Or take Article 13 of the same Convention which reads, "If a river flows directly into the sea the baseline shall be a straight line across the mouth of the river between points on the low-tide line of its banks" - a provision that may lead to widely-different interpretations in the case of specific river mouths. And what should be done with respect to man-made structures along the shoreline, such as jetties or filled-in land? Need the United States in its internal dealings follow the same set of criteria for boundary delimitation as it would in relation to foreign countries?

In the 1965 California decision the Supreme Court ruled that there should be a single coastline for both the administration of the Submerged Lands Act and for the conduct of our international relations, although it was recognized that the international coastline might be changed by future changes in the law that would not affect the Submerged Lands Act boundary. In other words there can be no difference between the coastline as used for our territorial sea and exclusive fisheries limits, and that employed for determining the boundary between state and federal jurisdiction on the continental shelf. But for boundaries of leasing tracts, and for determining the limits between the offshore areas of individual states, different criteria might be used.

One alternative to the Geneva articles is to "freeze" the shoreline at a specific point in time, agreed to by the individual states (in the case of delimiting inter-state boundaries) or between the state and the federal governments in the case of offshore leasing arrangements. Should the shoreline subsequently change the legal baseline would nevertheless remain fixed. This process could be carried out either by following the mean low water line as it exists at a particular time, or by using fixed geographic coordinates connected by straight baselines which conform to the general direction of the coast.

In the case of leasing tracts, where boundaries must be precisely determined in metes and bounds, an alternative method would be to set the outer boundary of the leasing area by fixed geographic coordinates between which straight line limits would be drawn. The coordinates would be established through agreement between the state and federal governments, and would have some form of relationship with the physical shoreline as it existed at some point in time. Should the low water line subsequently change, only the innermost portion of the leased area would then be affected.

The use of different offshore boundaries for different purposes by the United States is not necessarily a new idea, but it is one to which I feel inadequate attention has been given by government officials. It may well be that at the international level, highly complex boundary arrangements may not appeal to many of the newer countries of the world, whose perceived interests in the ocean involve broader-gauged concepts. But there is no reason why such complexities could not be worked out satisfactorily with respect to relevant domestic activities.

Again, I would suggest that problems of domestic boundary delimitation be referred to an ad hoc Marine Boundary Review Commission for recommendations. Its membership need not be the same as that which would handle international boundary issues, but the two units could work concurrently, and there should be a certain overlap in memberships.

It is sometimes difficult to understand why so many of the problems of offshore boundary delimitation have received only passing attention within recent years by decision-making agencies within the government. The problems associated with these delimitations are growing in complexity with the passage of time, yet relatively few concerted efforts have been made since the First Geneva Law of the Sea Conference to establish precise U. S. policies on these boundary issues. Several years ago the Stratton Commission recommended that increased attention be given to these issues, but apparently without any subsequent action having been taken. I think it is time these offshore boundary problems receive the attention which is due them.

LEGAL PROBLEMS ENCOUNTERED
IN LOUISIANA COASTAL MAPPING

Mr. Marc J. Hershman
Research Director
Sea Grant Legal Program
Louisiana State University
Law Center
Baton Rouge, La. 70803

BIOGRAPHICAL SKETCH

Marc J. Hershman is research associate for coastal resources
law at the L.S.U. Law Center specializing in coastal zone
management and environmental legal problems. Hershman received his B.A. and J.D. degrees from Temple University in
Philadelphia, Pennsylvania where he also practiced law for
a short period. He did graduate work at the University of
Miami's ocean law program for graduate lawyers. In addition
to his research and teaching responsibilities in the Sea
Grant Legal Program at L.S.U., he is the Executive Director
of the Louisiana Advisory Commission on Coastal and Marine
Resources, an alternate delegate from Louisiana to the Coastal
States Organization, editor of a bi-monthly newsletter entitled "Louisiana Coastal Law" and a member of numerous special committees and task forces involving management of
Louisiana's coastal resources. He is currently involved in
the legal aspects of projects such as the superport off
Louisiana's coast, the Atchafalaya Basin in Louisiana, the
utilization of Louisiana's marshlands, and many other issues
of this nature.

ABSTRACT

The question of boundary location continually arises in
Louisiana's coastal zone: the tidelands dispute between
Louisiana and the U.S. continues; accretion in the Atchafalaya Basin and in the Gulf of Mexico continues to add
new lands to the state; marshlands erode at a rapid pace
in Louisiana's coastal zone; continuous dredging and ca-
nalling in the coastal area creates boundary issues; management of shrimp and oyster fisheries is based upon boundaries; and, new proposals for building lands in Lake
Pontchartrain and barrier islands in the Gulf of Mexico
raise boundary issues.

The land-water interface in Louisiana's coastal area is
dynamic and continually changing. Such dynamic conditions
suggest a need for a dynamic measure for boundaries for
timely and rapid identification of boundary delineations.
Developing concepts of coastal zone management on a regional
basis suggests that new boundary areas designated on principles of ecology may be needed. Coastal zone planning will
be proceeding at many levels each of which needs precise definition. Demands for coastal mapping and charting services
will continue to grow indicating a need for more coordination
among mapping services provided by the U.S. Government.

THE NEW JERSEY WETLANDS MAPPING PROGRAM

Edward B. Feinberg
New Jersey Department of Environmental Protection
P. O. Box 1390
Trenton, New Jersey 08625

BIOGRAPHICAL SKETCH

Edward B. Feinberg is an environmental scientist on the staff of the Commissioner, of the New Jersey Department of Environmental Protection. He received his B.S. from the Massachusetts Institute of Technology, his M.S. from New York University, and is working toward his Ph.D. at New York University. Feinberg served as a geophysicist with the USAF for three years. At NJDEP, he is responsible for developing new programs which apply remote sensing to problems of environmental protection. For the last year and one half, Feinberg has been assistant director of the New Jersey Wetlands Mapping Project.

ABSTRACT

New Jersey's Wetlands Act of 1970 empowers the Department of Environmental Protection to regulate use of privately held wetlands. Before any regulation can be promulgated, the act requires

(a) The establishment of a precise boundary differentiating wetlands from adjacent fast lands;

(b) That wetlands be mapped and inventoried and the maps filed in county recording offices;

(c) That all wetlands owners be notified of mandatory public hearings;

(d) That all wetlands owners be notified of the promulgation of regulations affecting them.

New Jersey has developed a mapping methodology and has determined map scale and accuracy specifications which comply with stringent statutory requirements and can withstand the challenge of litigation. The requirements of coastal wetland mapping will vary from State to State. Usually these requirements will be governed by the magnitude of the burden placed upon an administrative agency by enabling legislation. Mapping can be costly, but the cost of lost wetlands resources will be much greater if preservation measures are defeated because of mapping insufficiencies.

THE ROLE OF STATE GOVERNMENT IN COASTAL MANAGEMENT
MAPPING - FLORIDA, A CASE HISTORY

Bruce Johnson
Coordinator - Staff Director
Florida Coastal Coordinating Council
Larson Building, Room 682
Tallahassee, Florida 32304

(Coauthors - Fred Barloga, Research Coordinator
and Louis Burney, Planning Coordinator,
Coastal Coordinating Council staff)

BIOGRAPHICAL SKETCH

Mr. Johnson holds a Master of Science degree in Geology, minor
in Land Use Geography from Southern Methodist University. He
is a graduate of the Naval Amphibious Intelligence School and
the Naval Mine Warfare School and served as a minesweeping
officer in the Pacific Theater in World War II. After the war,
he was employed a number of years as a civilian coastal analyst,
later coordinator, with the Amphibious Unit of the Office of
Naval Intelligence doing coastal studies around the fringe of
the Eurasian land mass from Europe through the Middle East to
Korea. As part of this work, Mr. Johnson authored or edited
coastal studies on fourteen countries which were published as
chapters in the National Intelligence Surveys Program. He later
was a coastal consultant for the Office of Naval Research and
the Arctic Institute of North America in Spitsbergen in the
Norwegian Arctic, and for the government of Pakistan where he
trained and established an amphibious intelligence unit for the
Pakistan Navy.

Mr. Johnson was a resident for many years of the Isle of Pines,
Cuba before the Castro revolution, where he developed a winter
season hunting and fishing business for sportsmen. More
recently, he served as administrative assistant to the Chairman of the Physical Sciences Division of the Institute of Marine
Sciences, University of Miami, and then was employed as Oceanographic Coordinator, later Executive Director of the Florida
Commission on Marine Sciences and Technology. His present
position is Coordinator and Staff Director of the Florida Coastal
Coordinating Council, where he serves as Florida's alternate
delegate to the Coastal States Organization. He was a member
of the Governor's Task Force on Resource Management which recommended the new Florida Environmental Land & Water Management
Act passed by the 1972 Legislature.

ABSTRACT

Coastal management mapping techniques illustrating new planning
and zoning concepts designed to influence the direction of new
development in the coastal zone of Florida are presented as an
illustration of the role of state government in coastal mapping.
The planning of Florida's coastal zone management program has
been assigned, under present statutes, to the Florida Coastal
Coordinating Council. A pilot study area for the coastal zone
management plan was selected in Escambia-Santa Rosa counties in
the western Panhandle centered on Pensacola. The inland extent
of the coastal zone has been delineated and mapped by means of
Census Enumeration Districts selected on the basis of terrestrial

areas influencing the adjacent waters. In Escarosa, this zone
varies from 2.5 to 16.5 miles inland from estuarine waters. The
seaward extent of the zone includes the territorial sea and is
9 n. miles from the M.L.W. line of the Gulf of Mexico shoreline.

A suggested state zoning system is proposed and illustrated on
specially constructed maps for land and water areas utilizing
the three basic categories of "Preservation" (no further development), "Conservation" (limited development permitted), and
"Development" (suitable for intensive development). "Preservation" areas would protect ecologic units of sensitive flora and
fauna as well as areas of dunes, marshes and swamps. "Conservation" areas would include hurricane and flood plain zones useable
for parks, open space, greenbelts, and other non-intensive uses.
"Development" areas would include those lands with soils and
topography suitable (or suitable with minor corrections) for
intensive development. The geographic extent of each category
in the pilot area has been mapped using aerial photography, soil
surveys, topographic maps, and spot field checks. Totals for
land zoning categories in Escarosa are: Preservation - 6.5%;
Conservation - 30.5%; and Development - 63%. Environmental
aspects and uses for each Preservation and Conservation category
are enumerated. Although detailed zoning in Development areas
is recommended to be left primarily to local and county authorities, "key facilities" and shoreline use zoning would be subject
to criteria recommended by the Coastal Coordinating Council and
hopefully enacted by the Legislature.

INTRODUCTION

The Florida Coastal Coordinating Council, which was created by
the 1970 Florida Legislature, unites in one body the directors
of the three state departments with primary concern for the
coastal environment, namely, the Department of Natural Resources,
Department of Pollution Control and the Trustees of the Internal
Improvement Trust Fund. The Executive Director of the Department
of Natural Resources serves as chairman. The Council, which has
its own staff, has four primary assignments: (1) develop a comprehensive coastal zone management plan for Florida, (2) coordinate
state coastal zone research, (3) coordinate federal, state and
local agencies with responsibilities in the coastal zone, and
(4) act as a clearinghouse for coastal zone information.

The key words in these charges are research, coordination and
plan, and the latter implies adequate back-up maps displaying
new types of coastal information as well as standard types of
coastal maps. Accomplishment of these tasks will allow the state
to make crucial policy decisions based on facts, in advance,
rather than reacting to individual problems after they occur.
It is important to note that, even though the Council is placed
under the Department of Natural Resources, it is inter-departmental
in its functioning. This allows maximum input from those agencies
having a direct interest in the coastal zone, yet prevents domi-
nation by any one interest group. It is also important to note
that the Council's efforts involve a continuous program, rather
than being stop-gap in character.

DELINEATION OF THE FLORIDA COASTAL ZONE

One of the first problems encountered by the Council was to
decide on a working definition of Florida's coastal zone. As
defined in the enabling state bill, "coastal zone means that

area of land and water from the seaward territorial limits to the
most inland extent of maritime influences." Speaking in very
general terms, this definition seems fairly reasonable. But
speaking in terms of coastal zone management, such an area defies
delineation. If maritime influences on the atmosphere are considered, this area would include all of Florida. If considerations are restricted to the most inland extent of salt water flow,
then management efforts are far too narrow in scope. It is
obvious that, for working purposes, the most favorable boundary
location lies somewhere between these two extremes. Ideally,
from an ecological standpoint, this border should be defined in
physical terms. However, research soon revealed that a region
defined in terms of drainage basins, flood zones, ancient shorelines, saltwater-freshwater interface, or any other strictly
physical consideration does not have compatible socio-economic
data. Such data is an absolute necessity if man's activities are
to be considered in the management program. Also, definitions
based on physical features usually require time-consuming and
expensive surveys to locate the boundaries on the ground.

Lengthy research revealed that the most practical method for
defining the coastal zone is to use physical features in combination with boundaries of areas for which socio-economic data is
readily available. On this basis, then, it was decided to use
physical characteristics in combination with boundaries of
selected Census Enumeration Districts. Defined in this way,
Florida's coastal zone has an inland boundary varying from two
to twenty-five miles from the coastline, with the seaward boundary being the limit of Florida's territorial sea. (Figure 1).

The use of such a definition allows planners to utilize over 400
data items such as population totals and distribution, housing
and income patterns, etc. No other system of defining the
coastal zone has as much flexibility or allows such ease in
utilizing available data and computer support.

PILOT STUDY AREA - "ESCAROSA"

The Council has selected Escambia and Santa Rosa counties of
western Florida as a pilot study area in which to work out the
format and methodology to be followed in developing a coastal
zone management plan for the entire Florida coastal zone. For
convenience, we collectively refer to this area as Escarosa.

This particular area was selected because it contains prime
examples of hydrography, coastal physiography and coastal econom-
ics which are common to the entire length of the Florida coastline. It has barrier beaches, lagoons, marshlands, bays and
estuaries, as well as a significant port and metropolitan area
(Pensacola), a progressive university (University of West Florida),
and increasing pressure for conflicting multiple-uses of the
shoreline brought about by an expanding population and expanding chemical industrial uses. Moreover, Escarosa has a regional
planning program (Escambia-Santa Rosa Regional Planning Council)
and has been the subject of two Federal-State Water Quality
Conferences. Existing information has been utilized wherever
available but new research on previously unknown factors is now
underway. Results of this new research, which will include
oceanography of the territorial sea, aesthetic enhancement of
the region, a coastal law inventory, environmental zoning,
marine ecology of the estuaries, etc. will be included in the
completed Escarosa master plan.

FLORIDA'S COASTAL ZONE

Note: Coastal zone boundaries are based on
selected census enumeration districts.

FLORIDA COASTAL COORDINATING COUNCIL

Figure I

RECOMMENDED COASTAL ZONING CATEGORIES

In recent years, man's understanding and appreciation of environmental sciences has increased to the point of realization that certain shoreline areas must be preserved in their natural state if marine resources and the quality of life in Florida are to be maintained, and if possible, enhanced. Working on this premise, and mindful of the legislative charge to develop a coastal management plan allowing for both preservation and development, the Coastal Coordinating Council has developed three basic zoning categories for land and water use.

. Preservation - no development

. Conservation - limited development

. Development - intensive deveopment

These zoning categories are illustrated for the Escarosa area in Figures 2 through 5. It is felt that this scheme is general enough to allow local government to perform adequately, yet specific enough to encourage wise use of our coastal resources.

In arriving at these conclusions, the Council staff conducted an exhaustive study of many parameters, including existing maps of soils, vegetation, topography, beach erosion, ground water conditions, shoreline land use, recreational resources, marine ecology, etc. Aerial photography, soil surveys, topographic maps, spot field checks and other source material were utilized for the Escarosa area. Criteria and recommended policy for each zoning category follow. (These criteria are elaborated on in large matrix tables available upon request from the Coastal Coordinating Council.)

Preservation:

Preservation areas are recommended to be protected from any further development except in extreme cases of overriding public interest authorized by the Cabinet or the Legislature. The preservation concept includes considerations of ecologically sensitive flora and fauna as well as fragile topographic features such as beaches, marshes and dunes. Included are historical and archaeological sites and any unique, environmental features peculiar to the region such as selected springs, caves, waterfalls, and reefs. The water areas are classified for shellfish propagation (Class II), which is the most stringent marine water classification.

This resulting "preservation" environment would offer enhanced aesthetic values, recreational opportunities, and substantial hurricane protection to coastal residents and visitors. It is further recommended that this be a state-level zoning responsibility because of the often intensive development pressures brought to bear at the local level. <u>Approximately 6.5 per cent of the land area of the Escarosa coastal zone is classified as "preservation"</u>.

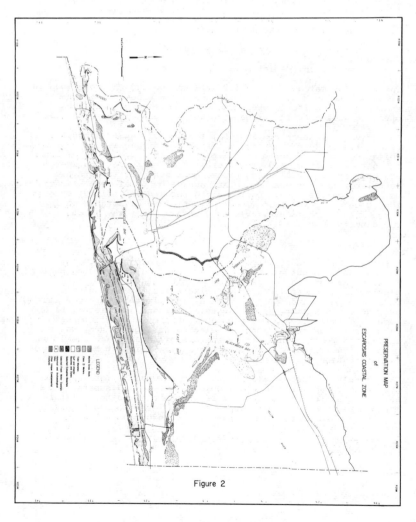

PRESERVATION MAP
of
ESCARISAS COASTAL ZONE

Figure 2

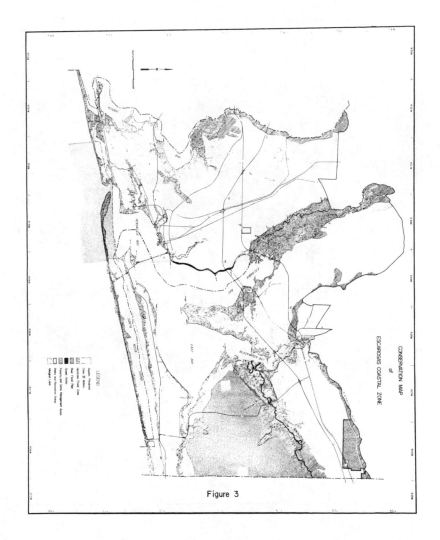

CONSERVATION MAP
of
ESCAROSAS COASTAL ZONE

Figure 3

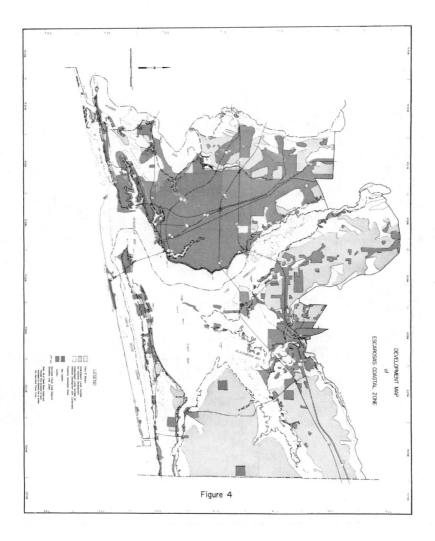

DEVELOPMENT MAP
of
ESCAROSAS COASTAL ZONE

Figure 4

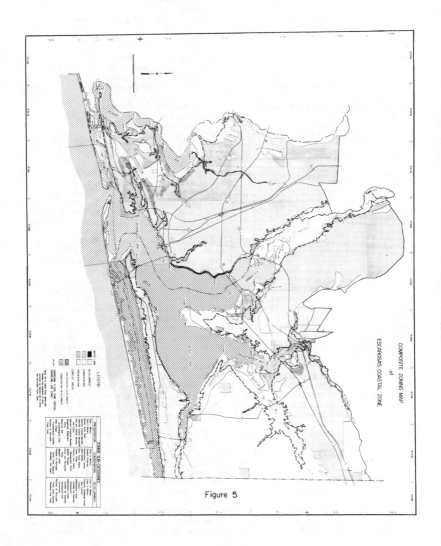

Figure 5

47

Subcategory	Priority Use
Class I Waters	Source of potable water
Class II Waters	Shellfish propagation
Marine Grass Beds	Commercial and sport fish propagation
Selected Coastal Marshes	Commercial and sport fish propagation
Selected Coastal Mangroves	Commercial and sport fish propagation
Gulf & Atlantic Beaches and Dunes	Shore erosion protection, recreation
Estuarine Beaches	Shore erosion protection, recreation
Wilderness Areas	Ecological protection
Selected Fresh Water Swamps	Ecological protection and flood water storage
Historical and Archaeological Sites	Cultural enhancement
Other Unique Environmental Features	Aesthetic enhancement, recreation

See Figure 2, "Preservation" Map of Escarosa.

Conservation:

Conservation areas are recommended to be used for extensive land uses as opposed to intensive uses. The conservation concept includes lands inherently unsuited to high density, intensive development because of physical limitations of the soil and/or high flooding probability. They are not considered critical to ecological balance but do provide buffer zones for preservation areas and represent a retention of use options for future generations. The lands with soil limitations, herein called "marginal lands", could in the future be used for development but based on present technology and engineering, would require a considerable expenditure of capital.

Conservation lands can be utilized for open space recreation, greenbelts, forestry, game management, and wildlife refuges. These lands can be utilized for certain types of agriculture and grazing if such uses do not require draining or pumping. Development should be limited to low density uses, bearing in mind that ground floor elevations of new construction situated in flood prone areas must be above the 100-year flood level to qualify for federal flood insurance. Scenic easements are recommended for the immediate foreground of locations with outstanding views of the landscape. Construction of marinas and other shoreline recreational facilities would be permitted provided environmental safeguards are complied with. Special guidelines and criteria will apply in the Shoreline Use Zone extending from the M.H.W. line to the inland limits of the Hurricane Flood Zone.

The water areas are Class III as delineated by the Department of Pollution Control and designated for fish and wildlife propagation with pollution levels compatible with body-contact water sports. The water areas also include special uses such as aquatic preserves and aquaculture leases which are not included in preservation areas because they permit limited shoreline development and can utilize Class III waters.

The conservation zoning category is recommended to be primarily a state-level responsibility, since the majority of the subcategories are established by state or federal action. County

and local zoning participation would be encouraged for limited
development controls, parks (other than state owned), scenic
vistas, and marginal lands. <u>Approximately 30.5 per cent of
the land area of the Escarosa coastal zone is classified as
"conservation"</u>.

Subcategory	Priority Use
Class III Waters	Fish and wildlife propagation, water-contact sports
Aquatic Preserves	Fish and wildlife propagation
Aquaculture Leases	Fish farming
Spoil Islands	Aesthetics, recreation
Hurricane Flood Zone (Special Shoreline Use Zone)	Priority shoreline use given to activities requiring waterfront locations; areas behind the shore are recommended for non-intensive use
River Flood Plains	Non-development (open space, greenbelts, timber, agriculture
Scenic Vistas	Aesthetics
Forestry and Game Management Areas	Hunting and timber production
Wildlife Refuges	Wildlife enhancement
Parks	Recreation
Marginal Lands	Open space, greenbelts, grazing, timber

See Figure 3, "Conservation" Map of Escarosa.

Development:

Development zoning includes (1) lands already developed; (2) undeveloped lands now vacant or used for other purposes, including
forestry and agriculture, which are intrinsically suitable for
intensive development; and (3) undeveloped lands with some
physical limitations - drainage problems, poor permeability,
salt water intrusion - which can be corrected by drainage techniques, central sewage systems or central water supplies. In
general, these lands are not considered to be environmentally
fragile. However, there are areas presently developed that
would have been recommended for "conservation" and "preservation"
zoning had they not already been developed. Such areas are
classified as "conflict" areas on Figures 4 and 5. Special
guidelines and criteria will apply in the Shoreline Use Zone
extending from M.H.W. to the inland limits of the 100-year
Hurricane Flood Zone.

Zoning for specific uses inside "development" areas is recommended to be primarily county or municipal responsibilities.
However, the Coastal Coordinating Council will develop shoreline-
use criteria for "development" areas as guidelines for local
zoning authorities. The state will also develop guidelines for
construction of "key facilities"; i.e., those facilities of
such size and importance that they exert regional influence
beyond the localities involved. Examples of such "key facilities" would be major airports, large housing subdivisions,
interstate highway interchanges, etc. <u>Approximately 63 per cent
of the land area of the Escarosa coastal zone is classified as
"development"</u>.

Subcategory	Priority Use
Class IV Waters	Agricultural and industrial water supply
Class V Waters	Navigation, utility and industrial use
Undeveloped Lands Suitable for Intensive Development	Development (if needed)
Undeveloped Lands Suitable for Intensive Development with Corrections	Development (if needed and if economically feasible to correct)
Presently Developed Lands: Conflict Areas	Those uses allowed in "conservation" areas
Non-Conflict Areas	Development
Hurricane Flood Zone (Special Shoreline Use Zone)	Priority shoreline use given to activities requiring waterfront locations; areas behind the shore are recommended for non-intensive use

See Figure 4, "Development" Map of Escarosa, and Figure 5, Composite Zoning Map of Escarosa.

SHORELINE MANAGEMENT

It can be anticipated that the state will take a direct interest in "development" areas immediately on the shoreline and including all of the 100-year hurricane flood zone. It is obvious that something more than just local controls are needed but what direction they might take requires considerably more research, analysis and discussion before a logical and reasonable plan can be recommended.

With limited shoreline and increasing competitive demands, agencies having advisory or controlling powers over shoreline development must consider priorities of land use. Those activities that can only function through use of waterfront property or access to it must have first priority for inclusion in shoreline areas designated for development. Of second priority are those activities that can function inland but a shoreline location significantly enhances the land use on an economic or aesthetic basis. Any waterfront use, of course, must still make every effort to minimize environmental impact. Land uses not requiring a coastal location, or that are not economically or aesthetically enhanced to a significant degree should not be allowed waterfront usage since there are sufficient areas inland. Multiple-uses of a locale are to be encouraged.

A considered priority of shoreline uses can be summarized as follows:

1. Preservation
2. Conservation (including Recreation)
3. Development
   a. Military (where necessary to assure the security of the area and country)
   b. Transportation (when waterfront location is mandatory)
   c. Utilities (when waterfront location is mandatory. Transportation and Utilities are fundamental to the development of any area.)

3. Development (cont'd)
   d. Water Related Industry
   e. Water Related Commercial
   f. Residential
   g. Commercial enhanced by waterfront
   h. Industry enhanced by waterfront

COASTAL MAPPING REQUIREMENTS

The foregoing recommended coastal zoning system must, by
necessity, be based on the very best and latest information,
preferably illustrated on maps. A combination physical map
showing both land topography and marine hydrography would be
a most useful base map, but because of the well-known
"amphibious gap", such maps do not generally exist and must
be constructed. A federal program to do this for the coastal
states would seem to me to be one way to assist the states'
coastal management programs.

The importance of the latest and best scale soil survey maps
are another federal responsibility that cannot be overstressed.
The soil characteristics are the key to most of our land use
recommendations, particularly regarding which coastal areas
are most suitable for new construction and high density use.
Maps illustrating flood-prone areas, for both river flooding
and coastal storm wave surges are also essential to coastal
planning and are now the subject of federal mapping programs.
Where these do not exist, the soils maps give indications of
alluvial soils subject to periodic inundations and storm wave
surges can be estimated from historical records if detailed,
small-contour interval topographic maps are available.

Inventory maps of marine areas are of special importance to
evaluate dredge and fill applications. The location and extent
of marine grass beds, oyster bars, the various types of bottom
sediments, and the distribution of salt marsh and mangrove
vegetation are of vital significance to us in Florida in
coastal management decisions. Maps illustrating the distribution of all types of living marine organisms, particularly
bottom dwelling types, are most useful.

The single most important map we need is one showing the
location of the mean high water line because under present
state laws, this line generally determines the boundary
between offshore state-owned submerged lands and private
upland owners. NOAA now has a program underway in Florida
in cooperation with the State Department of Natural Resources
to do this mapping.

On the landward side, we need hydrologic maps such as those
showing the present extent of salt water intrusion. Detailed
vegetation maps are also required as are large-scale maps of
historical and archaeological sites and maps inventorying
what we call "Other Unique Environmental Features", which are
of limited geographic extent but are of such unusual regional
significance as to merit "preservation" zoning.

Maps illustrating cultural features of many types are generally
available, but special purpose maps constructed to emphasize
important coastal management considerations add much depth and
understanding to coastal planning. For example, the Coastal
Zone Resources Corporation of Wilmington, North Carolina has

constructed for us a set of maps portraying a method of locating
and evaluating the areas of high aesthetic value in the coastal
zone. These areas, once identified, are then subject to more
detailed planning at the state level than areas of lesser
attraction.

Computer mapping techniques (Symaps) have also proved useful to
us by showing the geographical distribution of the 400 socio-
economic data bits gathered by the 1970 Census. Once programmed,
a computer will produce in a few seconds a usable map showing,
for example, the distribution by Census Enumeration Districts
of house trailers in the coastal zone on a scale of one to ten
for density. The same can be done for substandard housing,
income patterns, residential density, etc.

Land use and land ownership maps are the key to future coastal
management administration. The State of Florida has published
a land use and ownership Atlas of the coastal zone at the scale
of ½" equals 1 mile. (Copies can be obtained from the Coastal
Coordinating Council free of charge.) This Atlas is useful for
general regional planning but to properly implement a complete
coastal management system, maps at a much larger scale will be
needed and these will have to be periodically up-dated with the
latest information as changes in use and ownership occur.

CONCLUSION

We feel the most urgent role of state government in coastal
management mapping would be the immediate identification of
those coastal zone areas that should be preserved and conserved
from future development, followed by the delineation of those
areas most suitable for intensive, high-density use. The mere
identification of preservation, conservation and development
zones by an appropriate state agency, even without supporting
legislation, can have a favorable effect.

Traditionally, areas of Florida's coastal zone are being preserved as the exception rather than the rule. It is not
infrequent that extensive plans are made, monies expended, and
in some cases, construction begun before opposition to a development is apparent. The results are conflict and confrontation
with further expenditure of energy and dollars on both sides.
Such an approach is unfortunate, impractical and needless.

Without exception, each state agency and many representatives
of private industry have expressed the same thought. "Tell me
what areas are not to be disturbed early enough so that we may
plan to avoid them. We wish to avoid controversial areas,
where possible, and not expend monies and energy needlessly."

It is considered that the most immediate and meaningful contribution the Florida Coastal Coordinating Council can make is to
coordinate the documentation of "preservation" and "conservation"
areas for the entire coastal zone of the state and support
actions that will make development of these areas the exception
rather than the rule. This results in development agencies,
industry, and individuals being aware of the state's position
and knowing the path of least resistance.

EFFECTS OF URBAN AND INDUSTRIAL GROWTH
ON COASTAL ZONE RESOURCES

Richard A. Waller
Office of Environmental Quality
Bureau of Sport Fisheries and Wildlife
Department of the Interior
Washington, D. C. 20240

BIOGRAPHICAL SKETCH

Richard A. Waller is a Fish and Wildlife Administrator with the Bureau
of Sport Fisheries and Wildlife in Washington, D.C. He specializes in
environmental analyses of coastal zone development projects. Waller
received his B.S. and M.S. degrees from Florida State University. For
several years he was involved with various undersea research activities,
serving as an aquanaut and program director in the TEKTITE--Scientists-
in-the-Sea projects.

ABSTRACT

The combined effects of man's development activities has created a significant impact on the estuarine environment. Large areas of highly productive estuaries and marshlands have been destroyed and extensive stretches
of coastal wet lands have been adversely effected by pollution and physical
modification. Rapid urban and industrial growth in coastal population centers
is resulting in increasingly large volumes of waste discharges to the estuarine
environment at the same time that reclamation and development projects are
physically reducing the available acreage.

Effective management techniques are necessary to check the destruction of
coastal resources. Management techniques will require an increased
knowledge of the estuarine ecosystem and its assimilative capacity before
steps can be taken to govern developmental impacts. Remote sensing offers
one of the most promising methods for monitoring and assessment of the
estuarine environment. It does not seem likely that the conventional field
survey approach can keep pace with present informational needs. Remote
sensing from aircraft and satellites, however, can supply real time data
for detecting point source and immediate effects of pollution, as well as
elapsed time overlays for determining more subtle changes having a potential
for damage.

THE NATIONAL SHORELINE STUDY

Neill E. Parker, P.E.
Office of the Chief of Engineers
U.S. Army Corps of Engineers
Washington, D.C. 20314

BIOGRAPHICAL SKETCH

Mr. Parker is a civil engineer specializing in staff planning for
harbors and shore protection works. He is now in the Planning Division
of the Civil Works Directorate. Before transferring to the Office of
the Chief of Engineers, he was engaged in planning and designing water
resources projects in the Los Angeles District of the Corps of Engineers. He holds a Bachelor of Engineering degree from the University
of Southern California and is registered in the State of California.
He is a Fellow of the American Society of Civil Engineers and a
member of the Society of American Military Engineers.

ABSTRACT

In the River and Harbor Act of 1968, the Congress gave the Chief of
Engineers special responsibilities for appraising, investigating, and
studying the condition of the Nation's shorelines and for developing
suitable means for protecting, restoring, and managing them so as to
minimize erosion induced damage. To discharge these responsibilities,
the Corps of Engineers inventoried 84,000 miles of shorelines. The
results of these inventories are reported in nine regional inventory
reports and are summarized in "Report on the National Shoreline
Study." Additional reports, "Shore Protection Guidelines" and "Shore
Management Guidelines", address protection and management techniques.

The National Shoreline Study finds 20,500 miles of the ocean and Great
Lakes shores of the United States, Puerto Rico, and the Virgin Islands
undergoing significant erosion. The study further finds that action
to halt significant erosion appears justified along 2,700 miles of
shore. The cost of constructing suitable protective works for these
shores is estimated to be $1.8 billion. The study suggests that
priority attention should be given to 190 miles of shores where continued erosion is most likely to endanger life and public safety within the next 5 years. The cost of constructing protective works along
these shores is estimated to be $240 million. About two-thirds of
the areas where erosion is a serious problem are privately owned and
not eligible for Federal assistance under present law. The study
also finds that management to minimize adverse effects of erosion
appears appropriate for 17,800 miles of shores undergoing significant
erosion where action to halt the erosion may not be justified.

THE IMPENDING SUBMERGENCE
OF THE COASTAL ZONE

Dr. Michael H. Levin and Christopher S. Cronan
Center for Ecological Research in Planning and Design
Department of Landscape Architecture and Regional Planning
University of Pennsylvania
Philadelphia, Pennsylvania 19104

BIOGRAPHICAL SKETCH

Michael H. Levin is an Assistant Professor at the University of Pennsylvania where he specializes in plant ecology and wetlands ecology. He received his B.S. from the University of Vermont and the M.S. and Ph.D. in botany from Rutgers University. He held positions at the University of Notre Dame and the University of Manitoba before coming to the University of Pennsylvania in 1968. His present research is on structure and function of wetlands ecosystems.

Christopher S. Cronan is a third year undergraduate majoring in ecology at the University of Pennsylvania.

ABSTRACT

The salt marshes of the coastal zone are prairies where the predominant influence controlling the major distribution of plants is fluctuation in relative sea level. The wetlands include salt marshes, stabilized and unstabilized fluvio-marine deposits.

The production of organic materials within the coastal zone is consumed by shellfish, fish, fowl, furbearers, and man. The area provides a permanent or temporary home for these largely omnivorous animals. The tendency of man to alter the character of the wetlands runs counter to the natural processes and, as a result, disaster or gradual deterioration occurs.

This paper deals with three aspects of wetlands: geologic processes involved, alteration of the wetlands of Ocean County, New Jersey, and the proposed total destruction of a site within Ocean County. Taken together they illustrate how, within a fraction of a second of geologic time, a wilderness that is a natural resource of national value may be destroyed. The results of numerous destructive acts gain significance in ways not easy to foresee. The ultimate objective of ecological research in the coastal zone is to conserve, preserve, manage, and restore this embattled arena where land meets sea.

CHANGES IN RELATIVE SEA LEVEL

Evidence presented by Milliman and Emery (1968) suggests that sea level 30,000 to 35,000 years B.P. was near to the present level. Locking of water within glaciers accounted for a lowering of sea level to -130m, 16,000 years B.P. (Milliman and Emery, 1968) or -123m, 19,000 years B.P. (Emery and Garrison, 1967). During the period of low sea

level terrestrial vegetation covered the region that is now
the continental shelf (Emery et al, 1967) as determined from
the fact that similar pollen sequences have been obtained
from freshwater peat deposits recovered from the continental
shelf and those peats from fresh water bodies that are presently above sea level. During the periods of low sea levels
it is believed that the continental shelves became extensions
of the land with the result that coastal plains were much
wider than at present. Following the establishment of forest
and grassland vegetation, terrestrial animals and man were
able to inhabit the newly emerged coastal plain. This
occupation was temporary, for as sea level rose it drove
before it or submerged the animals and submerged the plants
which are now found as remains. This Holocene transgression
which began some 14,000 years B.P. continued rapidly to
some 7,000 years B.P. (Milliman and Emery, 1968) when it
slowed gradually and reached the low rate that began approximately 4,000 years B.P. (Emery and Garrison, 1967). The
shells of long dead oysters (Crassostrea virginica)have
been recovered from 71 locations in the Atlantic Ocean at
depths between 14 and 82m (Merrill, Emery and Rubin, 1965)
and these oysters are assumed to have inhabited lagoons or
estuaries on what is now the continental shelf. These
animals were submerged when sea level rose at the close of
the glacial epoch which reached its climax approximately
18,000 years B.P. (Merrill, Emery, and Rubin, 1965).

Observations and radiocarbon dates from Alaska (Brown, and
Sellman, 1964; Hume, 1965) suggest marine transgression
between 4,500 years B.P. to 800 years B.P.

On the Gulf Coast, the evidence for sea level rise generally
supports the concept that rates have been somewhat less than
those for the Atlantic.

For the eastern coast of the United States, Redfield (1965)
demonstrates that the earliest peat in the salt marsh at
Barnstable, Massachusetts may be as old as 4,000 years or
more at depths of 23 feet below present Mean High Water.
Stuiver and Daddario (1963) report radio-carbon dates for
peats deposited between the Brigantine City Barrier and the
mainland to indicate a rate of submergence of 3m/1,000 years
between 6,000 and 2,600 years B.P. and that during the last
2,600 years the submergence was reduced to 1.2 to 1.4 m/
1,000 years. (cf. Daddario, 1961; Scholl Craighead, and
Stuiver, 1969).

Although there are complicating factors including the possibility of differential warping of the Atlantic Coast
(Newman and Rusnak, 1965) and variations in river inflow
(Meade and Emery, 1971) the mean annual rate of sea level
rise approximates 33cm /1 00 years, (Meade and Emery, 1971),
to 21.24cm/100yrs relative sea level rise.(Kraft, 1971).
Kraft points out that the relative rate of sea level rise
may include compaction, tectonic subsidence, as well as
eustatic rise. Redfield (1967) accepts an increase in the
eustatic change of sea level at 0.76×10^{-3}m/year during the
past 4,000 years for Bermuda, southern Florida, North
Carolina, and Louisiana, but that the rate in the northeastern
United States has proceeded at a much greater rate, indicating
local subsidence. A rate of 1.87 x

10^{-3}m/year is suggested by Redfield (In press) for relative sea level rise at the Barnstable Marsh.

These data carry the clear message that relative sea level has risen to the present and that man as an inhabitant of the barrier islands, wetlands, and regions of potential flooding has, what appears to be, a limited future in the coastal zone as a consequence of long term geologic processes.

DESTRUCTION OF TIDAL WETLANDS IN OCEAN COUNTY, NEW JERSEY

Introduction. As the leisure time that Americans have at their disposal increases, greater use is made of popular recreational areas to accomodate larger numbers of people. In the Barnegat-Manahawkin-Little Egg Harbor-Great Bay area of Ocean County, New Jersey, this results in the disturbance and destruction of tidal wetlands. Because proximity to open water has been considered essential for residential housing development, these wetlands have been degraded, increasing the loss of wetlands in recent years. There is a definite need to determine and to document the extent of this disturbance before management can be accomplished. Development of quantitative information is necessary in order to provide a basis for response from conservationists.

This report illustrates the extent of destruction to the Ocean County wetlands between the years 1951 and 1971. It was estimated (Ferrigno, 1968) that in the years 1953-1968 +19.1% of the Ocean County wetlands were lost, primarily to housing development. Channel dredging during this period accounted for 73.2 hectares and housing, roads, lagoon and marina construction were reported to account for 2,452 hectares.

Before proceeding, it is important that the area of tidal wetland be defined. Field observations and experience with aerial photographic interpretation suggest that tidal wetlands can be identified on black and white aerial photographs in contrast to upland areas. Hence, it is the boundary defined by differences in black and white contrast that has been accepted as a preliminary boundary between tidal wetlands and the upland. The bay edge of the marsh, easily identifiable on the aerial photographs, defines the limit of measurement for both the mainland and the barrier beach. The results for the fourteen year period, 1951-1965, are derived from controlled planimetry of 1:24,000 scale air photo mosaics. In comparison, the 1965-1971 results are based on planimetry of areas transferred by eye between air photo mosaics of 1:62,500 and 1:24,000 scale. Finally, the pre-1951 estimate represents an attempt to detect on the 1951 photo mosaic areas which were tidal marsh prior to 1951.

In referring to tidal marsh, a grassland physiognomic type is implied that is characteristically maintained by periodic inundation with brackish or saline tidal water.

It is recognized that the use of false color infrared and
color photography will allow a more precise description of
tidal wetlands. These were not available when the research
began.

Methods. The first step in this study was to determine the
percent error in the measuring instrument, a K & E compens-
ating polar planimeter. Using the 100 cm^2 calibrating
device, the error calculation was made by comparing the
actual planimeter reading, after ten revolutions, with the
expected 1000 cm^2 value. Three measurements were taken and
the mean value was used as error intrinsic in the planimeter.
(Table 1.)

Two measurements for error -- distortion resulting from both
improper alignment of photos in the mosaic and paper expansion and contraction -- were incorporated into the experimental procedure. Prior to measurement, each air photo
mosaic was examined for north-south and east-west distortion.
(Table 1.) Distances between specific landmarks on lines
running north-south and east-west on the air photo mosaics
were compared with measured distances on the corresponding
U.S.G.S. topographic maps. (U.S.G.S. - 1947, 1951, 1952,
1953, 1954). The distortions were recorded, with percentages
of error indicating the amount to be subtracted from observed air photo distances to obtain adjusted values.

Variations in humidity and temperature necessitated compen-
sation for expansion and contraction of photographic paper.
This error determination was accomplished through the use
of a 900 ha standard square, 12.5 cm on a side, which was
pencilled onto a photo mosaic at the initiation of the work.
(Table 1.) Each day, the standard square was planimetered,
with the aid of a straight edge, and the area was recorded.
A mode was selected from the five standard square measurements, a percentage of error due to paper variation was
assigned to each day, and the percentages of error were
applied to measurements of the tidal wetlands.

The base value for tidal wetland area was obtained by plani-
metering appropriate areas on the 1951 air photo mosaic.
(Aero Services 1951, Numbers 1-3). The procedure was to
planimeter contiguous areas of wetland on the photo mosaic
contact prints, to pencil the boundaries of the planimetered
areas onto Bruhning prints of the mosaics, and then to
record the areal measurements.

As each area was planimetered, the instrument was again set
to zero, with the guide dot placed on a conspicuous landmark
along the perimeter of the area to be measured next. The
guide traced a clockwise path around the boundary of the
particular segment of wetland. In this fashion, the 1951
tidal wetland area was planimetered. Areas of post-1951
disturbed wetlands were located by careful simultaneous
examination of both the 1951 and 1965 air photo mosaics.
Once defined, the disturbances were planimetered on the
1965 air photo mosaic in the same manner that was applied
for the 1951 tidal marsh planimetry. Hence, the measurement
of disturbance proceeded with the understanding that wetlands

Table 1. Determination of instrument error and distortion of
aerial photograph mosaics.

Planimeter instrument error------------------------- -0.24%

Photo Mosaic Number	Linear Distance Deviation From U.S.G.S. Topographic Base Map		Area of a Standard Square, 12.5 cm on a Side.
	East-West(%)	North-South(%)	cm^2
1 North, 1951	-0.8	+0.1	158.0
2 Mid-Region, 1951	+3.0	-0.8	156.6
3 South, 1951	-3.6	+4.7	157.3
4 North, 1965	+2.4	+0.65	157.3
5 Mid-Region, 1965	+0.3	+1.9	157.3
6 South, 1965	+2.0	+2.0	157.3

would not be newly planimetered on maps subsequent to 1951.
Tidal wetland area would be considered constant over the
twenty year time interval, except for areas lost to man-
made disturbance. Natural erosion and aggradation to the
wetlands was not included in the calculations.

An estimate for disturbance occuring between 1965-1971 was
obtained through the use of unpublished 1:62,500 scale 1971
air photo mosaics, (M. Hurd Aerial Surveys, Inc. 1971). The
map scale necessitated the transfer of the recent disturbance
areas to the 1:24,000 scale base photo mosaic before these
were measured. Measurements were then carried out using a
grid marked in cm^2.

Measurements were also made of areas which appeared to have
been wetland at some time prior to 1951 with the cm^2 grid
and were designated as "pre-1951 wetland". Finally, bay
areas on the air photo mosaics were planimetered.

Results. Planimetry of the 1951 air photo mosaic (Aero
Services, 1951, Numbers 1-3) of Ocean County, N.J., revealed
the areal extent of tidal wetlands to be 14,472 ha (Table 2).
This value represents the 1951 area delineated on Figure 1.

With the same 1951 photo mosaic, it was possible to estimate
the area covered by pre-1951 disturbance to tidal wetlands.
The value of 573.6 ha obtained corresponds to the area
designated as pre-1951 tidal wetlands.

Disturbances, as of 1965, to the 1951 tidal wetland area
were noted and planimetered on the 1965 air photo mosaic
(Aero Services 1965, Numbers 4,5,6). These disturbed areas
are designated on Figure 1. Measurements indicate that
2,342 ha of 1951 tidal marsh area had been degraded by the
year 1965. (Table 3.)

Through use of the air photo mosaics (M. Hurd Aerial 1971,
Numbers 2,3,4), it was possible to obtain an estimate of
tidal wetland disturbance occuring between the years 1965-
1971. Figure 1 indicates these most-recent disturbances
which have a measured areal extent of 535.1 ha. Planimetry
of bays produced an areal value of 28, 633 ha.

Error in the planimeter and that due to expansion and
contraction of the photographic paper are values which were
applied to produce the values in the results.(Table 3.)
Because of the lack of topographic relief in the area being
measured, a decision was made not to attempt to adjust the
planimetry measurements for error due to elevation. For
reference, however, the north-south and east-west linear
error values are provided in Table 1 as examples of discrepancies observed between the U.S.G.S. maps and the
aerial photograph mosaics.

Conclusions. The planimetry results lend themselves to a
quantitative description of changing tidal wetlands   area
since 1951 in Ocean County.

Significant marshland alteration, i.e. reduction, occurred

Figure 1.

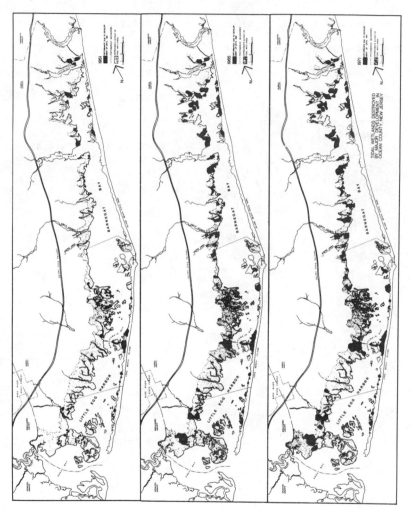

Table 2. Extent of tidal marsh, 1951.

	Planimeter reading Sub-totals (cm^2)	Sub-totals adjusted for paper distortion (cm^2)	Value in ha
Photo Mosaic 1	520.4	522.1	
Photo Mosaic 2	1,171.6	1,176.2	
Photo Mosaic 3	879.9	879.9	
Total		2,578.2	
Corrected for planimeter error		2,584.4	14,472

in the twenty years following 1951. Planimeter results
indicate that between the years 1951 and 1965, the 14,470 ha
extent of tidal marsh was reduced by 2,342 ha. (Table 3.)
Thus, in the space of fourteen years, major disturbance due
to residential development, dredging, and filling and diking
claimed 16.2% of tidal wetlands present in 1951.

The measured net intrusion upon the tidal wetland in the
twenty year period is a value derived from the combination
of the 1951-1965 disturbance values with the 1965-1971
disturbance estimate. With the addition of the 535 ha of
most recently disturbed (1965-1971) wetland area to the
earlier disturbance value of 2,342 ha, the tidal marsh areal
loss over twenty years becomes 19.8%. Considering the
results of the error calculations, such a value may be
regarded as being accurate to ±5% of the actual areal loss.

An approximate gross calculation of tidal wetland destruction may be formulated with the aid of the pre-1951 disturbance value. The incorporation of that value produces a
value of 22.8%, a sizeable loss of the "original tidal wetlands". Correction could not be made for wetlands destruction resulting from activities not evident on the photo
mosaics. Road construction, degradation, minor disturbance,
etc., represent an additional unknown percentage, perhaps
between 5% and 10%.

It is worth noting that the pattern of disturbance was not
evenly distributed over the 70.3 km (42.8 mile) length shoreline extending between the northern and southern boundaries
of Ocean County. In terms of percentage of 1951 wetlands,
the northernmost sector of the county (Aero Services, 1965.
Number 4) demonstrated the largest wetlands loss with a
value of nearly 45%. The larger wetland areas, located in
the other sectors of the county (Aero Services 1965, Numbers
5, 6), exhibited much less reduction, with respective losses
of 8.4% and 9.5%.

Discussion. The phenomena of destruction, degradation, and
disturbance in tidal wetlands have become the subject of
public concern in recent years. This is reflected in
Ocean County by the fact that disturbance between 1965 and
1971 has amounted to a reduced +3½%, as compared to the
16.2% over the period 1951-1965.

It should be noted that the results of this study describe
wetland areas that have been directly built upon or otherwise altered. Another aspect of wetland disturbance that
should not be overlooked is the fact that residential
development has in numerous cases extended directly to the
marsh border, encircling the land and eliminating any buffer
between the residential and natural areas.

In summary, at least 22.8% of the Ocean County tidal wetlands
has been sacrificed. The "death of the marsh" described by
John Teal (Teal and Teal, 1969) is documented. In all
probability the reported percentage is low, because the
scale of the aerial photographic prints employed was not
suitable for the accounting of the numerous wetlands which
have been degraded.

Table 3. Loss of tidal wetlands in Ocean County, New Jersey, 1951-1965.

	Wetlands area 1951 (ha)	Wetlands area 1965 (ha)	Wetlands area lost 1951-1965 (ha)	% 1951 wetlands lost by 1965	
				% by sector	% by county
Photo Mosaic 1 (North, 1951)	2,894.4			45.3	
Photo Mosaic 2 (Mid-region, 1951)	6,657.1			8.4	
Photo Mosaic 3 (South, 1951)	4,920.5			9.5	
Photo Mosaic 4 (North, 1965)		1,582.9	1,311.5		9.1
Photo Mosaic 5 (Mid-region 1965)		6,095.0	562.1		3.9
Photo Mosaic 6 (South, 1965)		4,452.1	468.4		3.2
Totals	14,472	12,130	2,342		16.2%

66

VEGETATION OF AN ESTUARINE WETLAND,
BRICK TOWNSHIP, OCEAN COUNTY,
NEW JERSEY

Introduction. This wetland fronts on both the northern part
of Barnegat Bay and the Metedeconk River (Lat. 40° 03' N,
Long. 74° 04' W) (Fig. 2.) As here defined. it includes, but
is not restricted to, approximately 60 ha within the Township
of Brick,also described as Lots 23, 24, 25, 38-50 inclusive
shown in Block 68 of the most recent tax map. If appropriate
dredging permits are approved, these lands will be subdivided into 451 lots to be used primarily as summer residential housing.

Lands within the site are no higher than 5' above mean sea
level with the exception of recent dredge-fill mounds and
these unstabilized deposits are approximately 15' in height.
Much of the land lies at 1' to 2' above mean sea level as
evidenced by vegetation present on the site.

The Ocean County Engineering Department reported the follow-
in high water (Table 4.) reached during the storm of 25
November 1950 (Stockman, W.D., personal correspondence,
1971).

Stockman also pointed out that preliminary studies over a
6-year period indicate that there is probability of even
greater flooding. (Table 5.). Although these data were
developed from an extremely short period of record (6 years),
tides of +6.6' above mean sea level could occur. These
observations are generally consistent with results previously
reported. Therefore, it is probable that successive storm
tides will show increases in the future.

The physical characteristics of the site illustrate a
geology basically derived from estuarine deposits.with sands,
silts, and clays. The first two predominate in the near
surface materials to depths of at least 20 feet. These
sediments were deposited where the waters of the Metedeconk
meet the waters of Barnegat Bay. Lagoon deposits of eel-
grass clays were not observed in the dredge materials and
this supports the concept that the deposits are more riverine in nature.

Peat deposits are thin, ranging from approximately 2 feet in
depth at the forest edge to very shallow (under 1 foot)
where Spartina alterniflora is well developed at river's
edge. All evidence points to a relatively recent development of the tidal wetlands.

Three roads had been constructed at an earlier time. These
consist of gravel road beds placed directly upon the tidal
marsh. The firm sands beneath the shallow peat have
prevented settling. At the terminus of each branch of the
road a raised area of fill was deposited in circular
fashion with a diameter of approximately 300 feet. Roads,
shoulders, and circular fill have been invaded by shrubs
and herbaceous plants.

Eggs of the diamondback terrapin were discovered frequently

Table 4. High water levels in Barnegat Bay, November 25, 1950. (Courtesy Ocean County Engineering Department).

Location	Elevation
	Ft. - m.s.l.d.*
Lavallette	5.88
Station 24 + 0 on Bay Shore, Silverton Road	5.7
Main Street Bridge, Toms River	5.6**
Midstreams Bridge	5.8

*   mean sea level datum
**   elevation verified by June, 1970 survey of high water mark at Dock Street, Toms River.

Table 5. Preliminary tidal frequencies at Bay Shore, New
Jersey and their occurrence intervals. Six year period of
occurrence. (Courtesy U.S. Army Corps of Engineers).

Frequency	Elevation Ft. - m.s.l.d.*
1-year	+3.3
10-year	4.4
50-year	5.7
100-year	6.6

* mean sea level datum

in nests in the road beds. Six clapper rails were observed
in the eastern part of the Marsh on 28 July and two broods
of mallards (8 and 6 young) were observed in the tidal
channel at the western end of the marsh. Flocks of black
ducks, baldpate, brant and teal utilize the area in late
winter and early spring.

The objective of the present investigation is to (1) determine major vegetation types, (2) to describe successional
trends, (3) to recommend management of the ecosystem in
the event that further disruption ceases and the site is
restored.

Even with the disturbances previously noted, remaining
portions of the wetlands are in good condition and are
valuable inclusions to the tidal ecosystem complex of the
New Jersey Coast. This wetland, overlying estuarine sands,
is unique in many respects and has potential as a research
area as well as a natural area.

Methods. The site was first visited in late April, 1971,
and later during three days in July, 1971. On one of these
visits, photographs were obtained using high speed
ektachrome (Kodak ASA 160) and false color infrared (Kodak
ASA 80). Both types of imagery were obtained on 16 July,
1971 and subsequently used to ascertain distribution of
vegetation types determined by ground reconnaissance of the
site.

Nomenclature of plants follows Fernald (1950) in Gray's
Manual of Botany.

Results and Discussion. Imagery obtained by aerial photographs was mapped to a scale of 1"=200' using a 1965
photograph (Aero Service, ASJ 1486 Exp. 171) as the base.
An overlay was constructed illustrating the extent of the
dredging as of 16 July, 1971, and the approximate extent of
the vegetation types as of that date.

Vegetation types:

The major vegetation types are placed in 5 categories
(Fig. 2, Table 6.): marshes, shrub thickets, herb and shrub
thickets, forest, and those species found along roads and
embankments.

Marshes. Spartina alterniflora (tall) marshes are found on
those low portions of the site. These marshes are flooded
in excess of 360 times per year. (Chapman, 1960.) The
stands of S. alterniflora are dense and vigorous. However,
S. alterniflora is not found as extensive border along
the numerous man-made ditches to as great an extent as has
been observed further south slong the New Jersey Coast.
The lack of S. alterniflora along these ditches is probably
determined by the sandy soil materials raised above the
zone where successful germination and establishment occurs.

Pannes with scattered S. alterniflora (short) are numerous.
These pannes are of the hard-bottom type and appear to
represent developmental stages arising from other marsh

Table 6.   Vegetation Types of 'Mantoloking West'

Marshes

1. _Spartina_ _alterniflora_ (tall)
2. _Spartina_ _alterniflora_ (short) pannes
3. _Spartina_ _patens_, some with _Distichlis_ _spicata_
and _Limonium_ sp.; most non-numbered areas
3*. Includes non-living 3

Shrub Thickets

4. _Baccharis_ _halimifolia_, _Iva_ _frutescens_
5. _Myrica_ _pensylvanica_, _Baccharis_ _halimifolia_, _Iva_
frutescens
6. _Prunus_ _maritima_, _Baccharis_ _halimifolia_, _Iva_ _frutescens_,
Ilex _glabra_, _Ilex_ _opaca_, _Amelanchier_ _canadensis_,
Rhododendron _nudiflorum_, _Pinus_ _sylvestris_, _et_ _al_.

Herb and Shrub Thickets

7. _Phragmites_ _australis_, _Iva_ _frutescens_, _Myrica_
pensylvanica, _et_ _al_.

Forest

8. _Acer_ _rubrum_, _Amelanchier_ _canadensis_, _Ilex_ _opaca_, _Nyssa_
sylvatica, _Rhododendron_ _nudiflorum_, _Smilax_ _rotundifolia_,
_et_ _al_.

Roads and Embankments

9. _Baccharis_ _halimifolia_, _Iva_ _frutescens_, _Phragmites_
australis, _Rosa_ sp., _Panicum_ _virgatum_, _Andropogon_
virginicus, _Myrica_ _pensylvanica_, _Prunus_ _maritima_, _Myrica_
asplenifolia, _Vaccinium_ _corymbosum_, _Viburnum_ _dentatum_,
Parthenocissus _quinquefolia_, _Baptisia_ _tinctoria_, _et_ _al_.

Figure 2. Vegetation types of 'Mantoloking West'.

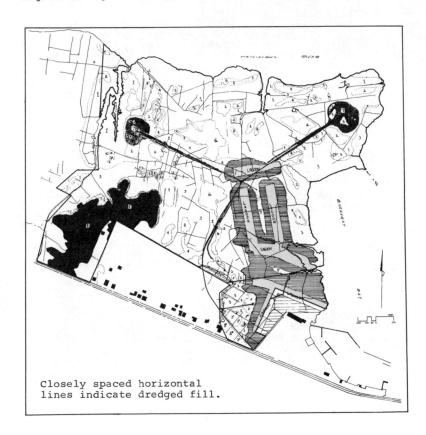

Closely spaced horizontal
lines indicate dredged fill.

types, particularly <u>Spartina</u> <u>patens</u>. They are wet at the surface with a poorly defined black anaerobic zone. Since these pannes illustrate advanced stages of development, it is assumed that they result predominantly from interruption of tidal flow caused by ponding of brackish water over <u>S.</u> <u>patens</u>.

<u>Spartina</u> <u>patens</u> in some areas is mixed with <u>Distichlis</u> <u>spicata</u> and <u>Limonium</u> <u>sp.</u> This is the most extensive of the marsh types. Both the erect form and the decumbent or 'cowlick' form of <u>S.</u> <u>patens</u> are present. This marsh type is found where frequency of tidal inundation is less than 360 times per year. (Chapman, 1960). In areas where drainage has been impeded gradually, <u>S.</u> <u>patens</u> is replaced by <u>S.</u> <u>alterniflora</u>. Where tidal flow has been impeded over a short period of time and detritus is not removed, rapid drying of the marsh leads to death of <u>S.</u> <u>patens</u>. There is no thinning of the populations, and the plants dry in place. This rapid drying leads to oxidation of the soil surface with a resultant drop in pH. No living plants, of any species, were observed in these areas, and death has probably occured within the past year

Shrub thickets. These occur throughout the site. Where banks have been deposited from dredge-fill along ditches, <u>Baccharis</u> <u>halimifolia</u> and <u>Iva</u> <u>frutescens</u> are prominent. The abundance of <u>Baccharis</u> is probably a reflection of the sandy nature of the dredged substrate. <u>Myrica</u> <u>pensylvanica</u> is a psammophyte and its presence argues for sand near or at the soil surface. Along the Metedeconk River, <u>Prunus</u> <u>maritima</u> forms extensive stands and these are established on sandy materials, presumably representing high water phases with sediment load and organic load deposited. The function of these shrub thickets in successive storms is probably to comb the detritus and sediment from flowing waters. As a result of this enrichment, the stands are dense and well developed.

Herb and shrub thickets have developed on the raised circular deposits terminating the gravel roads. <u>Phragmites</u> <u>australis</u> mixed with <u>I.</u> <u>frutescens</u> and <u>B.</u> <u>halimifolia</u> predominate along with an admixture of <u>M.</u> <u>pensylvanica</u>. <u>Phragmites</u> <u>australis</u> may have become established in road fill by vegetative parts or developed from seed.

The presence of <u>Phragmites</u> in a narrow band along the forest edges, indicates drying of this part of the site. This is local drying and is probably a recent result of impeded or diverted tidal flow accompanying construction of the road, drainage ditches or both. A second hypothesis for its occurence could relate to fresh water runoff during spring and summer.

Forest. The major forest adjoining Adamston-Mantoloking Road is comprised of <u>Acer</u> <u>rubrum</u> with an admixture of <u>Amelanchier</u> <u>canadensis</u>, <u>Ilex</u> <u>opaca</u>, <u>Nyssa</u> <u>sylvatica</u>, <u>Rhododendron</u> <u>nudiflorum</u>, and small amount of cat-brier, <u>Smilax</u> <u>rotundifolia</u>. This is part of the forest type which extends along the coast of New Jersey where forest meets marsh.

Certain herb-shrub thickets contain <u>A</u>. <u>rubrum</u> seedlings and saplings along with large dead <u>Prunus</u> sp. and abundant <u>Rhus radicans</u>. This has been interpreted as representing a trend toward ponding of water.

Roads and Embankments. These have become stabilized by species of shrub and herb with succession proceeding to trees in places along their length.

Proposed Successional Trends

Plant succession is a process of change promoted by changing environmental factors as well as the effects of plant populations upon those which succeed them. Without further research it is difficult to separate one from the other in a majority of examples. An interpretation is possible, however, without necessarily indicating all possible causes. Therefore, the proposed plant successions is indicated in Figure 3. represent estimates based upon observance.

The three marsh types represent a developmental series as well as patterns which exist in space. As the marsh builds to successively higher levels, <u>S</u>. <u>alterniflora</u> (tall) is replaced by <u>S</u>. <u>patens</u> and an admixture of <u>D</u>. <u>spicata</u> may become established. Prolonged tidal flooding may lead to <u>S</u>. <u>alterniflora</u> (short) pannes. Dry years may allow eventual return to a <u>Spartina</u> <u>patens</u> marsh.

Further drying and/or the deposit of sandy material upon any of the marsh types will lead to the development of shrub vegetation. The species normally found upon dredged sands along drainage ditches consist of <u>I</u>. <u>frutescens</u> and <u>B</u>. <u>halimifolia</u>. However, these species will be in reversed order of dominance where sands are the primary substrate. Both <u>M</u>. <u>pensylvanica</u> and <u>P</u>. <u>maritima</u> are interpreted as entering these shrub stands either early in development or at a later stage. They appear to thrive with accumulation of litter.

Ponding of fresh water may lead to death of shrubs and small trees and the result is that <u>Rhus toxicodendron</u> and <u>A</u>. <u>rubrum</u> become established.

Drying of the soil in the shrub thickets may lead to the development of <u>Phragmites</u> stands, particularly those adjoining forest.

In closing this discussion, there are two major successional trends. The first is towards drying of portions of the site. This is evident where shrub vegetation is in a stage of development. A second trend leads to the creation of pannes and the death of shrub thickets. This involves ponding of tidal flow and of rainfall.

Management of the Ecosystem Complex

Disruption of the site by dredging and piling fill on the vegetation has proceeded for at least several months. Approximately 1/5 of the site has been affected by this

Figure 3.

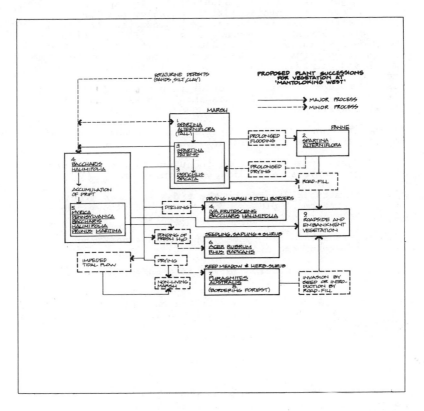

destruction. However, if these operations were to cease and the fill material returned to the excavations and levelled to mean high water, it would be possible for salt marsh vegetation to be reestablished. An experimental program could be initiated first to allow _Spartina_ to become established in the way it has done for thousands of years, naturally. Second, energy could be expended to provide a suitable seed bed and to sow the seeds. Finally, plugs of _Spartina_ could be removed from other parts of the marsh and planted. The results should lead to re-development of _Spartina_ marsh and, of course, associated species should return as well. In order to promote flooding and drainage, a series of ditches should be emplaced according to an overall plan to be developed for the altered areas.

There are cogent reasons why these management recommendations should be implemented.

1. A restored salt marsh in the upper part of Barnegat Bay would serve as a significant natural area.

2. Salt marshes flooded by the tides serve as free tertiary treatment plants, for the plants remove nutrients from the waters that wash over the marsh.

3. Detritus released by decaying marsh vegetation provides food for marine organisms.

4. The marsh vegetation serves as a buffer during severe storms and prevents erosion of soils.

5. Each marsh is a valuable link along the entire Atlantic Coast. The minimum acreage required to support the species of animals valued by man is unknown, and therefore, it is important to conserve as much as possible now.

IN CONCLUSION

Wetlands are assumed to be vital ecosystems in the nutrient cycles which begin with the accumulation of inorganic substances and organic compounds in green plants. A portion of the growth of these green plants (producer organisms) is ingested by animals (consumer organisms) at feeding or trophic levels. Death of both plants and animals eventually liberates the elements and, providing no blocks occur in the cycles, they can repeat cycles almost indefinitely.

The nutrients are intimately related to the energy required by all living organisms to make more of themselves. Two fundamental laws of physics apply here; first, that energy is neither created nor destroyed but can be transformed from one form into another, and second, that processes involving energy transformation will not occur spontaneously unless there is a degradation of energy from a non-random to a random form. These laws govern maximum numbers, although not necessarily species richness or equitability, of plants and animals which can be supported within an ecosystem.

Ecologists recognize coastal wetlands to be among the most highly productive ecosystems on earth because they are the sources of nutrients which nourish fish, clams, and crustacea. The food potential of managed wetlands will become a concern as the human population depletes food produced on land by agricultural pursuits. It is probable, however, that major modifications of the north temperate coastal zone wetlands will not occur initially.

The continuing pressure by land developers has already destroyed and will continue to physically damage wetlands. With the physical damage comes ecological devastation as the waters within wetlands receive sewage and chemicals. The impact of these pollutants becomes evident at higher levels in the food web. It has been recognized that certain of these such as the chlorinated hydrocarbons can be concentrated by living organisms to levels where reproduction and survival are imperiled. Under these circumstances extinction could result before we have a complete understanding of the effects of pollutants in both energy and nutrient cycles. The basis for management of any animal population can be reduced, ultimately to an understanding of energy and nutrient cycles, and in animal populations the evolution strategy of behavior and sexual reproduction.

New Jersey wetlands include coastal marshes which are considered major nutrient producing areas for the coast fisheries and nursery and wintering ground for fishes. These marshes are also part of migration, wintering and, to a lesser degree, breeding grounds for waterfowl and other birds on the great Atlantic Flyway. The largest concentrations of the common brant goose, at times close to 200,000, winter in these wetlands.

An increasing number of conservationists, sportsmen, as well as the general public, have become concerned with the future of wetlands. Such lands are already on the verge of extinction in states where they were vulnerable. Connecticut, with its originally numerous but small marshes, has few surviving. The Long Island Bays have declined to a fraction of their original quality and commercial development has already claimed much of the total amount of original marshes.

New Jersey's major coastal wetlands begin south of Point Pleasant. In the 15 year period from 1953 to 1968, it has been estimated that 34,703 acres of coastal wetlands, from Tom's River around Cape May to Salem County (16.3% of New Jersey's total) have been lost to filling or diking.

A state supported conservation policy under the Green Acres Program allowed the public acquisition of wetlands to a point where development projects begin to appear less attractive. This public acquisition of wetlands is for multiple use or to restrict development.

Both public and private ownership can protect the value of wetlands but who can tell when the time will be right for the rapid sale to land developers or the misuse of a privately owned marsh? When this occurs, another part of the wetlands ecosystem is removed once and for all time from the public domain.

The ecologist realizes that the animal life that utilizes these marshes does not recognize the boundaries of a refuge, a state, or a nation. An unused marsh or bay during most of the year, may become a vital feeding ground when all else is frozen, or it may be a traditional and essential tarry area on a migration route. Each marsh is an inseparable link in the ecosystem along the Atlantic Coast. A fishing party, clam dig, and fall sunrise with waterfowl, will all become experiences of the past when the marsh is land-filled or polluted. Public officials need to learn about wetlands. State legislators, federal lawmakers, and labor officials endorse public works or private enterprise which, if incorrectly conceived and improperly manipulated, will damage the value of public and private wetlands alike for countless years. It is essential that sound information be made available to these leaders to guide their decisions and to evaluate the consequences of projects which would affect wetlands.

We must enlarge our understanding of wetlands ecology by engaging in research, promoting the inventory, preservation, conservation, and management of the coastal wetlands ecosystem complex, extending public awareness of this resource, and contributing to the education of men and women in ecology and the land planning professions through the study of systems ecology. Most important, we must instill an ethic for this land.

The key to successful conservation of wetlands is in the understanding that wetlands are __natural__ systems, greatly influenced by the use of surrounding or nearby land. They are renewable resources in which multiple use can be encouraged if there is prompt and sound planning. If this does not occur, then the wetlands of the Atlantic Coast will be submerged beneath mounds of dredged materials.

Aldo Leopold, the person who had the greatest effect upon conservation, wrote,

> "Twenty centuries of 'progress' have brought the average citizen a vote, a national anthem, a Ford, a bank account, and a high opinion of himself, but not the capacity to live in high density without befouling and denuding his environment, nor a conviction that such capacity, rather than such density, is the true test of whether he is civilized."

This eloquent and timeless plea was never more true than it is today.

ACKNOWLEDGEMENTS

The authors express their appreciation to Michael Pawlukiewicz, Jerome Shapins, Carter Van Dyke, Joseph E. Murray, and the Ocean County Chapter of the Izaak Walton League.

APPENDIX I.

Scientific and common names of plants named in report.

Acer rubrum	red maple
Amelanchier canadensis	shadbush
Andropogon virginicus	broom-sedge
Baccharis halimifolia	sea-myrtle
Baptisia tinctoria	wild indigo
Distichlis spicata	spike grass
Ilex glabra	inkberry
Ilex opaca	American holly
Iva frutescens	marsh elder
Limonium sp.	sea elder
Myrica asplenifolia	sweet fern
Myrica pensylvanica	bay berry
Nyssa sylvatica	black gum
Panicum virgatum	switchgrass
Parthenocissus quinquefolia	virginia creeper
Phragmites australis	reed
Pinus sylvestris	scotch pine
Prunus maritima	beach plum
Rhododendron nudiflorum	pinxter flower
Rosa sp.	rose
Smilax rotundifolia	cat-brier
Spartina alternifolia	salt-water cord-grass
Spartina patens	salt-meadow grass
Vaccinium corymbosum	high-bush blueberry
Virburnum dentatum	southern arrow-wood

LITERATURE CITED

Aero Service Corp. 1951. Index of photographic survey of
Ocean County, N.J. Scale 1:24,000. Index Numbers 289:
8,9,12,13. (North,1)Division of Litton Industries.
Philadelphia, Pa.

_____. Index Numbers 289:6,9,12,18, 46. (Mid-
region,2)

_____. Index Numbers 289:6,12,18,23,46. (South,3)

_____. 1965. Index of photographic survey of
Ocean County, N.J. Scale 1:24,000. Index Numbers 1486
8,9,10,11,12. (North,4).

_____. Index Numbers 1486:6,7,8,9,10,11 (Mid-
region,5)

_____. Index Numbers 1486: 4,5,6,7,8 (South,6)

Brown, J. and P.V. Sellman. 1966. Radiocarbon dating of
coastal peat, Barrow, Alaska. Science 153:299-300.

Chapman, V.J. 1960. Salt marshes and salt deserts of the
world. Interscience Publishers, Inc., New York. +392 p.

Daddario, J.J. 1961. A lagoon deposit profile near Atlantic
City, New Jersey. Bull. N.J. Acad. Science 6:7-14.

Emery, K.O. and L.E. Garrison, 1967. Sea levels 7,000 to
20,000 years ago. Science 157: 684-687.

Emery, K.O., R.L. Wigley, A.S. Bartlett, M. Rubin, E.S.
Barghoorn. 1967, Fresh water peat on the continental
shelf. Science 158:1301-1306.

Fernald, M.L. 1950. Gray's manual of botany. 8th Ed.,
American Book Co., New York. +1632 p.

Ferrigno, F. 1968. Marsh losses to filling and diking, N.J.
Division of fish and game. + 4p. (Xerox).

Hume, J.D. 1965. Sea level changes during the last 2,000
years at Point Barrow, Alaska. Science 150:1165-1166.

Hurd, M. 1971. Photo index mosaic, Ocean County, N.J. Scale
1:62,500. Index Numbers 2,3,4.

Kraft, J.C. 1971. Sedimentary facies patterns and geologic
history of a Holocene marine transgression. Geol. Soc.
America Bull. 82:2131-2158.

Meade, R.H. and K.O. Emery. 1971. Sea level as affected by
river runoff, eastern United States. Science 173: 425-
427.

Merrill, A.S., K.O. Emery, and M. Rubin. 1965. Ancient oyster
shells on the Atlantic continental shelf. Science 147:
398-400.

Milliman, J.D. and K.O. Emery. 1968. Sea levels during the past 35,000 years. Science 173:1121-1123.

Newman, W.S. and G.A. Rusnak, 1965. Holocene submergence of the eastern shore of Virginia. Science 148:1464-1466.

Redfield, A.C. 1965. Ontogeny of a salt marsh estuary. Science 147: 50-55.

Redfield, A.C. 1967. Postglacial change in the western north Atlantic Ocean. Science 157: 687-691.

Redfield, D.W. 1972. The development of a New England salt marsh. Ecol. Monogr. In press.

Scholl, D.W., F.C. Craighead, Sr., and M. Stuiver. 1969. Florida submergence curve revised: its relation to coastal sedimentation rates. Science 163:562-564.

Stockman, W.D. 1971. Personal correspondence, 4 August, 1971.

Stuiver, M. and J.J. Daddario. 1963. Submergence of the New Jersey coast. Science 142:951.

Teal, J. and M. 1969. Life and death of the salt marsh. Little, Brown and Company. Boston +278.

United States Department of the Interior, Geologic Survey, 1947-1954, Topographic quadrangles. Barnegat Light, 1953; Beach Haven, 1951; Forked River, 1953; Lakewood, 1947-54; Long Beach NE, 1951; New Gretna, 1951; Point Pleasant, 1953; Seaside Park, 1953; Ship Bottom, 1952; Toms River, 1953; Tuckerton, 1952; West Creek, 1951. N.J. Scale 1:24,000: Washington, D.C.

AN AUTOMATED SYSTEM
FOR
DETERMINING ESTUARINE BATHYMETRY[1]

George F. Smoot, Research Hydrologist
U.S. Geological Survey
Washington, D. C. 20242

Verne R. Schneider, Hydraulic Engineer
U.S. Geological Survey
Bay St. Louis, Mississippi 39520

Kenneth R. Daughtrey, Aerospace Technologist
National Aeronautics and Space Administration
Mississippi Test Facility
Bay St. Louis, Mississippi 39520

BIOGRAPHICAL SKETCH

George F. Smoot is a graduate of Auburn University, Auburn, Alabama. Since joining the U.S. Geological Survey in 1948, he has had extensive experience in the area of water resources, having served with the Survey in various capacities in Alabama, Alaska, and Ohio before coming to Washington, D. C., as Coordinator of Instrumentation Research for the Water Resources Division.

At present, he is a member of the American Society of Civil Engineers; a member of the Hydrometry Committee, International Association of Scientific Hydrology; and Chairman of the Working Group for Flow Measuring Instruments and Equipment, International Organization for Standardization.

ABSTRACT

An automated bathymetric profiling system capable of surveying estuarine bathymetry quickly, at low cost, and with a high degree of areal coverage has recently been developed. The bathymetric profiler meets a very critical need by providing a practical means of collecting and processing the voluminous and detailed data needed for many estuarine water-quality investigations.

The system includes a ranging device, a depth sounder, a digital tape recorder, a precision clock and a digital logic package to control the system operation. Components have been compactly packaged so that they can be easily transported and the system can be operated from a small boat. It is capable of operating over a maximum range of 100 km, (kilometers), radio line-of-sight, with a probable range

---

[1] Publication authorized by Director, U.S. Geological Survey

range accuracy of 1 meter. The standard shipboard record
includes time, two ranges, and depth, and the shore-based
water-level stations provide the data necessary for the
tide-correction adjustments. A computer contouring program
utilizes the data to provide a contour map of the estuarine
basin.

INTRODUCTION

The U.S. Geological Survey has recently acquired a bathymetric profiling system capable of measuring estuarine
geometry quickly, at low cost, and with a high degree of
areal coverage. Development of this capability was part of
the research required to carry out several projects, in
cooperation with local agencies, related to tidal flow in
broad estuaries and coastal embayments. The successful
completion of these projects depended on the use of multi-
dimensional mathematical models which simulate time-
dependent flows, dispersion, and chemical reactions in a
tidal water body. Use of the models, in turn, required
enormous quantities of diverse data with which to pa-
rameterize and operate the models.

With regard to collection of data suitable for use with
the models, the principal need was position-fixing equipment
to determine rapidly, accurately, and automatically, the
location of a boat collecting prototype data while operating
several miles from visible shore references. It was clear
that measurements with which to describe water basin bathymetry and water quality (including temperature and salinity)
would need to be accurately referenced with both time and
geographical location in order to calibrate and verify a
simulation model.

The basic field data necessary for the testing, calibration,
and use of a mathematical model of the movement of water and
water-borne wastes in an estuary includes those parameters
defining the fresh-water inflows, the tidal stage, and the
geometry of the bay. Equipment and techniques have been
available for some time to measure fresh-water inflows and
tidal stage. However, for many years the data required to
map the bottom profiles and contours of rivers, reservoirs
and estuaries had to be acquired manually. None of the
techniques available was completely satisfactory because of
various problems ranging from accurate position determination to data handling. The bathymetric profiler developed
for these projects meets a very critical need by providing
an automatic data-acquisition system capable of collecting
and processing the voluminous and detailed data needed for
many estuarine investigations.

BATHYMETRIC PROFILER

The primary objective in developing the bathymetric profiler
was to collect data on the geometry of estuarine basins.
The system was designed to measure and record, automatically
and accurately, water depth, time of day, and position.
Provision was made to record these data in a digital format
compatible with existing automatic-data processing equipment.
Components are compact and easily transported, and the
system can be operated from a small boat. Because the water
is shallow in many estuaries, it was necessary that the
system be suitable for operation in a small boat (fig. 1).

Figure 1 - Small Boat on Trailer

The resulting system, known as the bathymetric profiler,
consists of five major elements:

(1)   Depth finder
(2)   Position finder
(3)   Clock
(4)   Data formatter
(5)   Incremental digital tape recorder

This modular, low-powered, highly mobile system is in six
containers. Two aluminum containers are used to house the
shipboard-based equipment, and four fiberglass containers
are used to house the land-based parts of the position-
finding equipment (responders and antennae). The two shipboard units (fig. 2) contain most of the functional elements

Figure 2 - Shipboard Units

of the system. Unit 1 houses all of the depth-finding
equipment and an interface panel, and unit 2 contains the
clock, the tape recorder, the data formatter, the interrogator portion of the position-finding equipment, and an
input/output interface panel. Each cabinet weighs about
150 pounds, and is fitted with side-panel handles for
portability. Both have been sealed to protect the
instrumentation from salt spray and to allow for internal
air conditioning. The system has been designed for
installation in an outboard boat 21 feet long, which is
about the minimum size in which the system can be operated
satisfactorily. However, as previously mentioned, the
system is modular and can be easily transferred to other
boats. A 25-Kw generator provides the instrument system
and the air conditioner with continuous power.

A diagrammatic sketch of the major elements of the bathymetric profiler is shown in fig. 3. As indicated in the
diagram, the data formatter is the central element of the
system. It receives inputs from the clock, position
finder, and depth finder, and presents them to the tape
unit for recording. The equipment outside the dotted line
is land-based, and that inside is shipboard-based. A
functional description of each element follows.

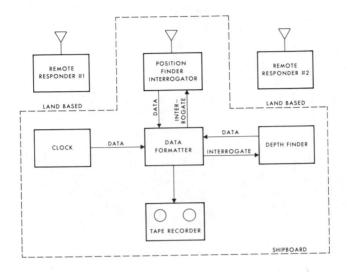

Figure 3 - Diagrammatic Sketch of Bathymetric Profiler

Depth finder

The depth finder employs ultrasonic waves for water-depth measurement. A short acoustic pulse is emitted by one of two transducers in a vertical conical pattern toward the bottom. For a hard bottom a 30-kHz transducer is employed, and for a soft bottom a 210-kHz transducer is used. Part of the sound energy is reflected and returns as an echo to the transducer. The time delay between the emission of the acoustic pulse and the return of its echo is proportional to the water depth. If desired the two transducers can be operated simultaneously, and both soundings can be graphically recorded; however, only the signal from one of them can be digitally recorded during a measurement.

The depth finder consists of three units in addition to the transducers: a control unit, a graphic recorder, and a digitizer. The control unit compensates for variations in the velocity of sound in water and for the ship's draft. It transmits and receives the acoustic pulses and controls the graphic recorder. The graphic recorder accepts the data from the control unit and displays them on moving paper. In this manner the bottom profiles can be observed as they are being measured. The digitizer unit converts the analog data from the control unit into a digital, 20-bit, binary coded decimal format. The digital outputs provide depth data to the profiling system, and the chart serves as a back-up record. Although the depth sounder is capable of operating graphically over several sliding ranges, the fixed-range digital capability is from 0 to 99.95 meters, with a resolution of 5 centimeters.

Position finder

The position finder consists of an interrogator unit and two responders. It utilizes UHF electromagnetic waves to determine range to a probable accuracy of less than 1 meter. The system is based on the principle that RF modulation applied to an electromagnetic wave that is propogated through space exhibits a phase shift that is proportional to the distance travelled and to the modulating frequency.

The position finder provides a series of simultaneous, dual-range measurements from a mobile shipboard location to each of a pair of fixed, shore-based responders. It computes the two different ranges by measuring the total phase delay between a reference signal and a signal which has traveled from the interrogator unit to the two responder units. The two resulting range data are presented to the data formatter in a digital, 20-bit, binary-coded decimal form. With the baseline distance between the two responders known, boat position is determined from the two ranges by triangulation (fig. 4). The system is capable of operating over a maximum range of 100 km, radio line-of-sight, although in most applications it will not normally be required to operate over a range greater than 15 to 20 km.

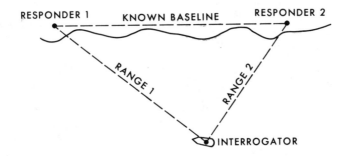

Figure 4 - Position Determination

Clock

In order to correlate tidal information with the water depth and position data, time of day must be known. The clock used for this purpose is a solid-state digital unit with nixie-tube display and electrical outputs. Thus, time of day is provided both visually and as a 24-bit, binary-coded decimal (BCD) output. Real time is furnished in hours, minutes, and seconds, using an internal, crystal-controlled time base. Not only is time of day recorded on magnetic tape but the 1-second timing pulses from the clock are used for synchronization of the various bathymetric profiler elements.

Data formatter

As shown in fig. 3, the data formatter is the central component of the bathymetric profiler. It provides the functional hardware and electronics necessary to coordinate the activities of the various component instruments into an integrated data-collection effort.

Data-recording cycles are initiated, automatically, at programmed intervals of 1, 2, 4, or 8 seconds, using the digital clock as a time base. At the start of each recording cycle, an interrogation signal is transmitted to the depth- and position-finding instruments. When these measurements are completed, as indicated by appropriate signals from the two instruments, the data formatter sequentially transfers the digital-clock time, depth, range-one data and range-two data, in that order, by way of a temporary storage register, to the digital magnetic-tape recorder. Three auxiliary input channels are provided and may be activated to provide additional data-input capabilities, as required.

Switches are provided on the front panel to enter data manually, set the record size, insert inter-record gaps, check the data inputs, and start and stop the automatic procedures.

Incremental tape recorder

The digital magnetic-tape recorder is a ½-inch, 7-track unit which records digital data incrementally in IBM-compatible format. Packing density is 200 bytes per inch (BPI). The recorder is presented with data from the data formatter and records the data on the tape. Also, inter-record gaps are inserted upon command from the data formatter.

SHORE SYSTEM (RESPONDER PLACEMENT)

Two responder units, their antennae, and batteries are included in the shore-based elements of the bathymetric profiler system (figs. 5 and 6). The responder units must be located over two known geographical points in order to establish a triangulation baseline. The responder antennae have a horizontal beam width of $\pm 30^\circ$ from the center, and it is important, therefore, that the antennae be aimed properly in order to provide coverage of the area to be mapped (fig. 7).

It is usually necessary to reposition the responders a
number of times in order to get complete coverage.
Communications between the responder operator and the survey
vessel can be accomplished by use of a voice-mode circuit
built into the unit. A headset and microphone are provided
for this purpose. A responder identifier is inserted on the
boat system magnetic tape and each time a responder is re-
located it is assigned a new identifier. Later, in the data-
reduction process, punched cards are used to provide input
data for station name, station number, responder identifier,
and responder coordinates. At that time ranges are converted
to coordinates in the designated grid system based on the
known responder coordinates.

Figure 5 - Responder

Figure 6 - Responder

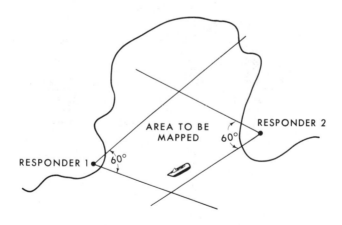

Figure 7 - Area Coverage of Responders

SHORE SYSTEM (WATER-LEVEL STATIONS)

Shore-based water-level stations provide the data for the tide-correction adjustments that must be computed throughout the area of study. The information is used to adjust the depths collected to mean sea level. Water level is recorded on 16-channel punched paper tape at a preselected interval of 5, 15, or 30 minutes throughout the period of measurement. Later, in the data-reduction process, this information is transferred to magnetic tape by an off-line translator. The assumption is made that the water-surface elevation is the same at all points along a station cross section. Adjustments are computed lineally for all points lying between any two consecutive cross-section stations. Punched cards can be used to provide data on station name, station number, and station coordinates.

DATA REDUCTION

The first step in data reduction is to edit the boat system tape to eliminate write errors, machine errors, and any other spurious data. At this point, the operator's log is especially valuable in eliminating spurious data caused by machine malfunctions (rundown batteries, faulty setups, and so forth). Many of the machine write errors can be corrected. The edited data is blocked uniformly and written onto magnetic tape for further processing. The tidal-stage record is also edited and translated onto 7-track tape in preparation for co-processing with the boat-system information.

Next the ranges are converted to coordinates in the designated grid system based on the known responder coordinates. The grid system is designated by assigning the appropriate coordinates to the responder and water level stations. The system is operated and responders located so that data are taken only on one side of the base line. This eliminates the possibility of redundant data.

The depth data at the point in space and time are corrected to the working datum, for example, mean sea level. First the true water level is interpolated from the two adjacent water level stations. Next the measure depth is subtracted from the interpolated water-surface elevation to determine bottom elevation. Any corrections for the auxiliary parameters would be made at this point and stored with the data set.

The established edited data set can be processed in a variety of ways, depending on how the information is to be used. As an illustration, the boat track can be traced by plotting every n^{th} point and writing the depth alongside. The data can be fed to a gridding and contouring program to establish a map of the estuary; or by logging over an existing map, areas of change can be detected. In the gridding program the random data set is adjusted and interpolations applied to determine the depth at a grid point. The fineness of the grid network is established by the user and depends in part on the spacing of the available data. The contouring

program accepts the data output from the gridding program
directly. The user controls the contouring interval, spacing
of lines, type of lines, insertion of barriers, and so forth,
to produce a usable contour plot.

SUMMARY

The limited initial test surveys using the bathymetric
profiling system have been successful. All of the equipment
has functioned properly and the surveys were completed without any major difficulties. Thus far the equipment has been
used primarily to check or update existing maps and data.
More comprehensive and sophisticated data-collection efforts
are planned for the near future.

OPERATIONAL WETLANDS MAPPING USING
MULTIBAND AERIAL PHOTOGRAPHY

Dr. Frank J. Wobber
Dr. Richard R. Anderson
Earth Satellite Corporation

BIOGRAPHICAL SKETCH

Frank J. Wobber is Director of Geosciences and Environmental
Applications Division at Earth Satellite Corporation,
Washington, D.C. He received his M.S. in Geology from the
University of Illinois and Ph.D. from the University of
Wales, United Kingdom. He was the recipient of two
Fulbright Scholarships. Dr. Wobber specializes in the
practical application of remote sensing techniques to
problems of environmental protection and natural resources
and analysis of small scale imagery obtained from aircraft
or spacecraft. He is currently directing wetlands mapping
projects for EarthSat.

Richard R. Anderson is an Associate Professor and Chairman
of the Department of Biology, the American University where
he specializes in aquatic plant ecology with emphasis on
applications of remote sensing to the ecology of submerged
and wetlands vegetation. Dr. Anderson received his B.A.
from Lewis and Clark College and M.S. and Ph.D. from the
University of Maryland. He is a Principal Associate of the
Earth Satellite Corporation. He has acted as an advisor to
the state of Maryland and the Council on Environmental
Quality regarding wetlands legislation and has worked in
the wetlands of numerous east coast states. For the last
three years he has been a Principal Investigator of the
NASA/USGS funded Remote Sensing Applications in Hydrology
with focus on the Chesapeake Bay and tributaries.

ABSTRACT

Recently, increased concern over the loss of wetlands has
resulted in state and Federal action to protect these
important natural resources. Many states including Connecticut, Massachusetts, Maryland, South Carolina, and New
Jersey have begun wetlands mapping programs using a variety
of aerial and field techniques.

Proposed federal legislation and many state laws require
the "mapping" and "inventorying" of wetlands resources as
a first step in the protective process. Having once established which lands are "wetlands" regulatory bodies may
then evaluate requests for permits to alter the wetlands
and may, for example, plan recreational and economic development, designate areas for acquisition, and assess man's
impact on the ecology of the wetlands.

The essential requirements of existing and anticipated
laws, so far as mapping is concerned, include determination
of (a) the landward extent of wetlands (upper wetlands
boundary), and (b) mean high water, or high tide line; the
inventory of wetlands vegetation is a stated or implied
element of many laws. Aerial photomaps often provide the

least expensive means of making a wetlands' inventory.
Where map accuracy is not a statutory requirement, aerial
photographs themselves can be used to adequately delineate the wetlands boundaries, support permit programs, and
assist in wetlands protection. The basic objectives
of all aerial photo interpretative procedures for wetlands
mapping can be focused on the development of products which
meet the requirements of specific laws or regulations. A
basic requirement of all mapping is that the process can
be verified and supported by qualified experts when and if
the maps are submitted as evidence in the courts.

The authors unconscious bias -- if it exists -- has been
shaped by a close working relationship with officials in
the State of New Jersey during the on-going wetlands mapping
project. Recently passed laws, such as the New Jersey
Wetlands Act, indicate an awareness of the need to manage
wetlands areas. The Wetlands Act requires the mapping and
inventorying of wetlands along the marine coastal zone and
tidally-influenced estuaries of the State to assure that
this important natural resource will be properly managed.
The State judged that aerial photography was the most cost
effective and timely method by which the wetlands might
be mapped. Traditional ground surveys, or extensive tide
gauging, in addition to being prohibitively expensive,
might take so long to complete that much of the remaining
wetlands would be destroyed before the laws to protect them
can be enforced.

A prime requirement of the New Jersey program is that map
products have validity which will withstand the challenge
of litigation. Natural color and color infrared aerial
photography at a scale of 1:12,000 is being used and nearly
100 square miles of wetlands have thus far been mapped.
Final map products are being prepared which contain: (a)
the upper wetlands boundary; (b) the line of biological
mean high water; and, (c) the delineation of major plant
species associations.

The New Jersey statewide wetlands mapping effort is one of
the few operational wetlands projects now being conducted.
The authors believe that the methods developed, ecological
data collected, and products prepared, must -- by virtue
of their acceptance, utility and proven wetlands management value at several levels of state government -- have
far reaching effects on future coastal wetlands mapping
programs.

The purpose of this paper is to briefly examine available
aerial methods based on the operational statewide mapping
project the authors are conducting in New Jersey, and the
experience the authors have gained by utilizing aerial
remote sensing methods of wetlands in the states of Maryland, Virginia, North and South Carolina, and New York.
From this experience, the authors will recommend an operational wetlands mapping system, for several time frames,
which is responsive to state needs. It is understood that
no single system can be fully responsive to the varied
ecological, legal, administrative and aesthetic objectives

96

of all state governments. That products are required which
are specifically responsive to state interests and financial resources, is understood; our objectives are not to
debate the detail or format of these products, but rather
to utilize multidisciplinary experience in making a technical judgment with respect to aerial remote sensing
procedures for wetlands mapping.

COASTAL MAPPING WITH REMOTE SENSORS

Robert J. Reimold, Assistant Professor
John L. Gallagher, Research Associate
The University of Georgia
Marine Institute
Sapelo Island, Georgia 31327

Donald E. Thompson, A.I.A.
MAPCOtec, INC.
P. O. Box 310
Daytona Beach, Florida 32015

BIOGRAPHICAL SKETCH

Robert J. Reimold is an Assistant Professor of Zoology at the University of Georgia and is stationed at the Marine Institute on Sapelo Island, Georgia. He received his B.A. from Thiel College and his M.A. and Ph.D. from the University of Delaware. His work concentrated on the marine sciences. His recent publications deal with mathematical modeling, remote sensing of primary production, radionuclide flux in the salt marsh, pesticides and bioenergetics.

John L. Gallagher is a Research Associate at the University of Georgia Marine Institute on Sapelo Island, Georgia. He received his B.S. and M.S. in Agronomy and his Ph.D. in Biological Sciences from the University of Delaware. His study concentrated on algal ecology and plant physiology. He is currently working on projects dealing with the application of remote sensing to plant ecology and the environmental physiology of marsh plants.

Donald E. Thompson is manager of the Thermal Survey Division, MAPCOtec, INC., Daytona Beach, Florida. Thompson received a B.S. in General Studies and a second B.S. in Architectural Engineering from the University of Illinois. He also received his M.S. in Architectural Engineering from the University of Illinois. His current interests center on development of new uses for remote sensing technology.

ABSTRACT

Kodak Aerochrome Infrared 2443, Ektachrome MS Aerographic 2448, Infrared Aerographic 2424 and a Bendix Thermal Mapper were used to obtain images of marshland areas in coastal Georgia. In conjunction with ground truth observations, images in scales ranging from 1:2,500 to 1:40,000 were made from fixed wing aircraft. Stereopairs were visually interpreted with a Kern PG 2 Stereo plotter and single frames were examined on a coordinograph table. The living plant dry weight biomass figures, from the ground truth observations at the time of flowering, were combined with the photo interpretations to compute agronomic yield estimates for the marsh (602 g m^{-2} year^{-1} for a 46 hectare Spartina alterniflora marsh area). This paper summarizes the techniques employed and the information obtained in a new approach to mapping coastal resources via remote sensing.

INTRODUCTION

In the estuarine environment, contemporary research has focused on quantification of biological, chemical, and physical events. The most important questions appear to relate to how, when, and where. The increased pressure on the coastal zone scientists to answer these types of questions has resulted in a great need for quantitative coastal zone mapping. Such questions as: where shall the Corps of Engineers place dredging spoil?, where shall the proposed interstate highway cross the salt marsh?, and where shall the new industry locate its water purification ponds?, must be answered immediately. Other concerns related to the lines of mean high tide, mean low tide, and mean sea level have a far reaching impact in today's coastal decision making processes. Consequently, there is an urgent need for basic information leading to the general knowledge of coastal zone utilization.

The central focus of the research reported herein relates to remote sensing and the measurement of quantitative features of the coastal zone. Special attention is directed toward different types of sensors and their economic and photoquantitative applicability.

METHODS AND MATERIALS

The geographic location of this research was coastal Georgia. Figure 1 depicts the Duplin Estuary on the western edge of Sapelo Island, Georgia. This discrete estuarine watershed was chosen because, to date, it is one of the most intensively quantitatively studied estuarine ecosystems known (titles of the more than one hundred papers related to this estuary will be supplied by the authors, upon request).

Photographs (in a 9½" x 9½" square format) using Kodak Aerochrome Infrared 2443 film, Kodak Ektachrome MS Aerographic 2448 film, and Infrared Aerographic 2424 film were acquired using a Zeiss RMK/A15-23 camera. Stereo coverage of the study area with a minimum of 60% end overlap at scales of 1:2500; 1:5000; 1:10,000; 1:20,000; and 1:40,000. Imagery was conducted with a Bendix Thermal Mapper, Model LN-3. This was employed with a mercury cadmium telluride head which, with proper filter combinations, permitted inspection of the 2.0μ to 3.5μ; 3.7μ to 5.5μ; 8.0μ to 12.5μ; and 2.0μ to 13.0μ windows. In addition, an indium antimonide head was used on the thermal mapper to inspect the 2.0μ to 3.5μ window.

Prior to photography and imagery, ground truth stations were established in the marsh using one quarter divisions of the 1000 meter Mercator Universal Grid Ticks on an east-west, and north-south orientation. These resultant 250 meter grids were marked at the point of intersection with a one meter, white circular plywood disk. The disk forms a collar around a two inch square by fourteen foot post (inset 5 feet into the marsh substrate), and is free to float with the rise and fall of the tide.

Photography and imagery were conducted during June, August, and September 1971, and February and May 1972. Ground truth measurements were made simultaneously with each aerial mission.

Ground truth assessment of variation in primary production of the salt marsh angiosperms was conducted according to the techniques established by International Biological Program on measurement of primary grassland production (Milner and Hughes, 1970). Square meter samples of vegetation were harvested at ground level and returned to the laboratory for further measurements. Transect, random plot, and uniform sample locations were all tested. A minimum of thirty, one square meter samples were collected from each photographic mission.

Laboratory quantification of the grass samples included sorting each sample into different species, dead and living matter, and one half

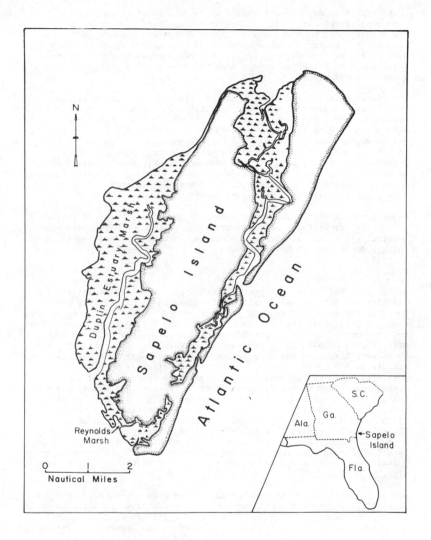

Figure 1. Location of the Duplin study area on the west side
of Sapelo Island, Georgia.

meter size classes. Assessment of the number of stems in each of these
size classes was also made. Also pigment analysis was conducted using
the technique of Odum, et al. (1958) to determine chlorophyll "A" concentration. Minerals analyses were conducted according to the techniques of Jones and Warner (1969). Caloric equivalent determinations
using the Parr Adiabatic Oxygen Bomb Calorimeter were conducted on
selected subsamples.

Photointerpretation and quantification were conducted using various
techniques. Vegetation maps were created with the use of a Kern PG-2
stereo plotter. The precise areas of the outlined regions was determined with an H. Dell Foster coordinatograph table coupled to a graphic
quantizer, electronic scaler, and digital planimeter. Quantification
of imagery was conducted using a Datacolor System Model 701 color
densitometer coupled to a digital planimeter. Microdensitometry of
selected positive transparencies was also employed by utilizing a Joyce
Loebl microdensitometer with a four color isodensitracer and an Optro-
nics International, Inc. Photoscan System.

Other ground truth measurements conducted on selected samples included:
1) spectral reflectance measurements using a Beckman DK-2A spectropho-
tometer; and 2) emissivity and reflectance measurements in the field
using a Barnes PRT-10 Radiometer.

RESULTS

Aerial Infrared Color Photography immediately revealed the ability to
discriminate between major salt marsh vegetative species. The two predominant angiosperms, Spartina alterniflora and Juncus roemerianus, were
easily distinguished by the human eye from the 1:2500 scale color infrared photography up to and including the 1:40,000 scale photography.
Minor floral components of the salt marsh were also discovered to be
photoidentifiable on the color infrared photography. From positive
transparencies of this media, vegetation zonation was delineated and
quantified. A typical area representing a monospecies stand of Spartina alterniflora is depicted in Figure 2. Here this singular species
was separated into four distinct, discernable color patterns on the
color infrared positive transparency. These four divisions represented:
1) tall, robust plants up to three meters tall portrayed as bright red;
2) medium height, high density robust plants displayed as light red;
3) medium height, low density plants depicted as blue-red; and 4) low
density, short plants less than one half meter height exhibited as blue.
Quantification of this area revealed a total of 46.63 hectares of Spartina.

Similar quantification of another marsh site with stands of Spartina
alterniflora, Juncus roemerianus and other marsh flora is depicted in
the vegetation map, Figure 3. Here the same differentiation in color
patterns within the Spartina was contrasted to the brownish rendition
of the Juncus (again from the color infrared positive transparencies).
Here, too, the total area for each of the zones was computed. Due to
limitations of the publisher, color prints of these positive transparencies are not incorporated herein.

The results of the thermal imagery at the various energy windows is
depicted in Figures 4 and 5. The 2.0 μ to 3.5 μ window using the mercury cadmium telluride detector, and the indium antimonide detector
gave similar results. These permit the greatest differentiation of
land vs. water, and Spartina vs. Juncus. In these figures (4 and 5),
the extreme right edge of the scene is woods. In the center (top to

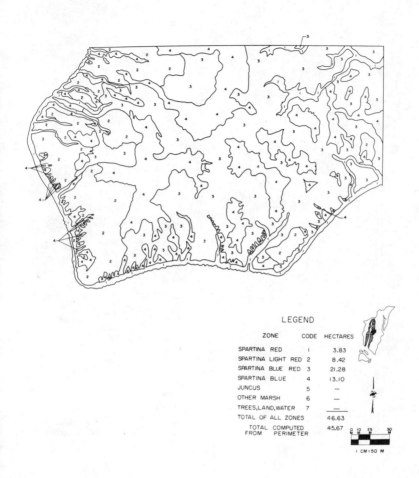

Figure 2.   Marsh grass zones in south study area defined by
visual interpretation of color infrared photography.

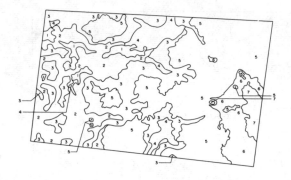

LEGEND

ZONE	CODE	HECTARES
SPARTINA RED	1	.43
SPARTINA LIGHT RED	2	2.93
SPARTINA BLUE RED	3	3.68
SPARTINA BLUE	4	.89
JUNCUS	5	6.55
OTHER MARSH	6	1.24
TREES, LAND, WATER	7	.40
TOTAL OF ALL ZONES		16.12
TOTAL COMPUTED FROM PERIMETER		16.45

1 CM = 50 M

Figure 3. Marsh grass zones in north study area defined by
visual interpretation of color infrared photography.

104

Indium Antimonide Detector

2.0 - 3.5 microns

Mercury Cadmium Telluride
Detector

3.7 - 5.5 microns

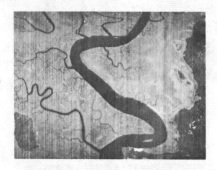

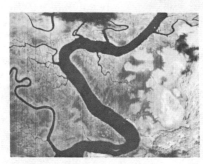

Mercury Cadmium Telluride
Detector

2.0 - 3.5 microns

Figure 4.   Imagery of north study area with Bendix LN-3 Thermal Mapper.

Mercury Cadmium Telluride
Detector

2.0 - 13.0 microns

Mercury Cadmium Telluride
Detector

8.0 - 12.5 microns

Figure 5.   Imagery of north study area with Bendix LN-3 Thermal Mapper.

bottom) proceeding from right to left, is a sand hammock, and then lighter tone areas further to the left, depicting the extent of the _Juncus_. Further to the left are darker gray areas depicting the _Spartina_, and finally the wide black, meandering line representing the Duplin River.

Analysis of color photography yielded color patterns similar to those found on the color infrared photography but more subtle and less easy to distinguish. The black and white infrared photography yielded clear delineation of land, water boundaries, but did not enable one to easily differentiate vegetative types. Figure 6 depicts the same marsh area portrayed in Figures 4 and 5, but Figure 6 represents the result of black and white infrared photography.

The results of ground truth measurements are summarized in Tables 1 and 2. Although chlorophyll "A" content of _Juncus_ was consistently higher than that found in the _Spartina_, there was no correlation between increased chlorophyll content and increased infrared reflectivity as portrayed in the color infrared photography. The biomass of the _Spartina_ was as high as 1618 g m^{-2} dry weight while that for _Juncus_ was 905 g m^{-2} dry weight. Significant differences in caloric content and several minerals also are exhibited in differences between _Juncus_ and _Spartina_.

An indication of why there are distinct differences between _Juncus_ and _Spartina_ is suggested by consideration of the spectral reflectance of the two genera. Figure 7 depicts the differences in spectral reflectance between _Juncus_ and _Spartina_ as exhibited in the 0.5 μ to 2.5 μ wavelength band. In the near infrared and visible band (0.5 μ to 0.9 μ) the _Spartina_ has a greater reflectance than does the _Juncus_. This accounts for the greater infrared reflectance as depicted on the color infrared photography. Between 2.0 μ and 2.5 μ , the _Juncus_ has a greater reflectance and consequently is depicted as the lighter tone (greater reflectance) as displayed on the thermal imagery (2.0 μ to 3.5 μ bandwidth) shown in Figures 4 and 5.

A result of the machine interpretation of thermal imagery not anticipated was the ability to determine the tidal flooding pattern. Using thermal imagery in the 8.0 μ to 12.5 μ bandwidth, taken at low tide, color enhancement reveals the tidal flooding patterns with successive increments of tidal rise. Preliminary examination of successive photography taken over a flooding tidal period appears to verify this new method for conducting preliminary hydrographic studies in the intertidal zone.

DISCUSSION

The data represented herein related to remote sensing technology and coastal parameters document its feasibility. The goals of most concerns interested in the coastal zone relates to some utilization of the resource with a minimum impact of adverse effects. The ultimate concern appears to relate to improving the economy and quality of the coastal community. Since the eastern United States coastal zone is closely interwoven and dependent upon vast stands of marsh plants such as _Spartina_, _Juncus_ and other genera, it is impossible to implement any method of coastal exploitation without first considering the coastal resources, their geographic distribution and abundance. Although these marsh plants are not usually considered as a living resource, it is important to realize that _Spartina alterniflora_ is one of the most productive resources we know. Odum (1971) has shown that the _Spartina_ marsh is among the most productive ecosystems in the world.

Figure 6. Black and white infrared photograph of the north study area.

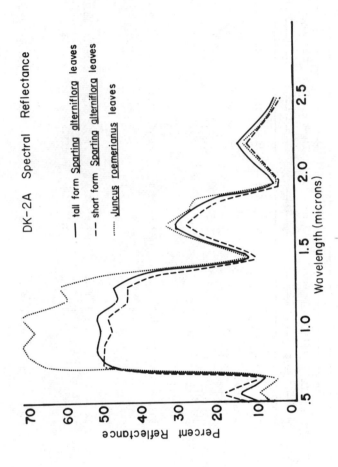

Figure 7. Reflectance spectra for leaves of _Juncus roemerianus_ and two forms of _Spartina alterniflora_.

Table 1. Ground Truth data from the second mission (18 August 1971) on the Duplin Estuary Marsh
$\overline{Y}$ = mean, CV = coefficient of variation, n = sample number

					Production Classification							
								Spartina				
Data	Juncus		Distichlis stand		red		light red		blue-red		blue	
	n = 4		n = 4		n = 3		n = 5		n = 6		n = 8	
	$\overline{Y}$	CV	$\overline{Y}$	CV	$\overline{Y}$	CV	$\overline{Y}$	CV	$\overline{Y}$	CV	$\overline{Y}$	CV
DENSITY Stems m^{-2}	859	7.8			76	9.0	87	41.0	106	45.2	147	30.7
Height Class (Percent abundance)												
0.01 - 0.50 m	12.2				24.7		22.4		39.4		80.6	
0.51 - 1.00 m	55.9				9.2		54.1		57.7		16.2	
1.01 - 1.50 m	31.8				11.1		23.5		2.9		3.2	
> 1.51 m					54.9							
LIVING MATTER Dry Weight (g m^{-2})	905.3	34.6	239.0	57.1	1618.9	25.8	480.8	13.3	416.2	29.2	291.4	32.3
Dry Weight (percent)	45.2		36.1		26.1		34.2		34.8		35.8	
DEAD MATTER Dry Weight (g m^{-2})	321.4	43.8	123.2	80.1	247.9	75.0	234.3	61.8	187.3	46.1	67.1	72.4
Dry Weight (percent)	62.6		57.2		41.5		55.5		54.5		54.9	
CHLOROPHYLL "A" (mg g^{-1} of fresh weight)	0.685	11.3	0.138	48.0	0.449	23.1	0.352	21.2	0.344	32.9	0.340	25.8

Table 2. Comparison of caloric and mineral contents of
Juncus roemerianus and _Spartina alterniflora_

	Juncus roemerianus	Spartina alterniflora
Caloric content (calories g^{-1} dry weight)	4220	3759
Mineral content (% dry weight)		
N	0.96	0.86
P	0.15	0.16
K	0.98	1.17
Ca	0.09	0.15
Mg	0.11	0.22
(PPM dry weight)		
Mn	63	57
Fe	446	1000
B	22	13
Cu	7	4
Zn	19	11
Al	802	1990
Mo	4	8
Sc	6	18

It serves as a living resource for fish, crustaceans and mollusca. It serves as a physical factor to stabilize the marshes and provides suitable habitat and protection for many animals that spend part of their life cycles in the estuary. The grass also modifies the chemical composition of the estuarine water, and after death, becomes the source of much of the energy for the marine food web.

The effects of coastal zone perturbations initiated by man are reflected in the quality and quantity of the marsh grass. These manipulations also influence its regenerative powers. It becomes obvious that we must know the answers to where, when, and how these perturbations are effecting our coastal zone.

The interpretations of physiographic features seen in the photographic and nonphotographic images, the creation of vegetation maps, and the measurement of various parameters of plant vigor and primary production over large areas of the coastal zone is already becoming useful to many different interest groups. The results of this work have been used by the U. S. Army Corps of Engineers, State Highway Departments, State Water Quality Control Boards, and other state and federal agencies, for decision making purposes. This type of coastal mapping of natural resources represents a first in natural resource inventory in the estuarine coastal zone.

LITERATURE CITED

Jones, J. B. and M. H. Warner. 1969. Analysis of plant ash solutions by spark-emission spectroscopy. In Developments in applied spectroscopy. Plenum Press. Vol. 7A, p. 152-160.

Milner, C. and R. E. Hughes. 1970. Methods for the Measurement of Primary Production of Grasslands. IBP Handbook No. 6. International Biological Programme. London, England. 70 pp.

Odum, H. T., W. McConnell and W. Abbott. 1958. The chlorophyll "A" of communities. Publ. of the Inst. of Mar. Sci. 5:66-96.

Odum, E. P. 1971. Fundamentals of Ecology. 3rd Edition. W. B. Saunders. Philadelphia.

ACKNOWLEDGMENT

This research has been supported in part by National Science Foundation Grant GA 29446 to the University of Georgia.

QUASIOPERATIONAL CURRENT MAPPING BY THERMAL
INFRARED IN SOUTH KOREAN COASTAL REGIONS

Donald R. Wiesnet
Formerly, Research Hydrologist, NAVOCEANO
Currently, Senior Research Hydrologist
NOAA/National Environmental Satellite Service
Washington, D. C. 20031

BIOGRAPHICAL SKETCH

Donald R. Wiesnet is Senior Research Hydrologist at NOAA's National Environmental Satellite Service. He received his B.A. and M.A. from the S.U.N.Y. at Buffalo, and is a PhD. candidate at the University of Arizona. Wiesnet spent 14 years with the U. S. Geological Survey as a geologist and geohydrologist. Recently, he worked with the Coastal Oceanography Branch of NAVOCEANO for four years specializing in remote sensing of coastal zone phenomena in various places including the Mekong Delta area and Korea. In 1971, he transferred to NOAA/NESS. He published many papers on remote sensing, geology, geophysics, and geohydrology. He is a former member of the Water Resources Council's Committee on Hydrology. Currently, he is a principal investigator for two ERTS-A projects.

ABSTRACT

Quasioperational thermal infrared aircraft surveys have been successfully flown by Navy aircraft off South Korea. IR mosaics were converted into charts showing near-synoptic details of coastal currents. The IR scanner is useful to study tidal currents, water-mass boundaries, freshwater and thermal plumes, streamlines, convergent and divergent flows, eddies and shoals. The term "synoptic methods" is introduced to cover techniques of current charting by remote integrating sensors such as cameras, thermal IR scanners, and microwave imagers.

Concomitant and judicious use of IR imagery mosaics and conventional photographic mosaics will permit oceanographers to understand -- and therefore, ultimately to predict -- complex coastal currents, which are today rather imperfectly understood and at times, difficult to study.

INTRODUCTION

In late 1969 the U. S. Naval Oceanographic Office (NAVOCEANO) began planning oceanographic surveys of the harbors of Kunsan, Pusan, Ulsan, and Pohang, and adjacent offshore waters, in cooperation with the Republic of Korea (ROK) Hydrographic Office (Figure 1). The Nearshore Surveys Division (Code 9200) of the Naval Oceanographic Office inherited this enormous task and requested the aid of the Coastal Oceanography Branch in devising a plan to survey the areas quickly and efficiently. Airborne infrared imagery and aerial photography were proposed as a partial solution. The U. S. Navy's Heavy Photographic Squadron-61 (VAP-61) was tasked for support.

Using RA-3B jet reconnaissance aircraft, (Figure 2) this squadron flew more than 6,000 flight line miles in spring (March-April) and approximately the same distance in the fall (October-November) of 1970, over all four harbors. This survey is the largest infrared aircraft survey ever attempted. It was highly successful. (Slattery, 1971)

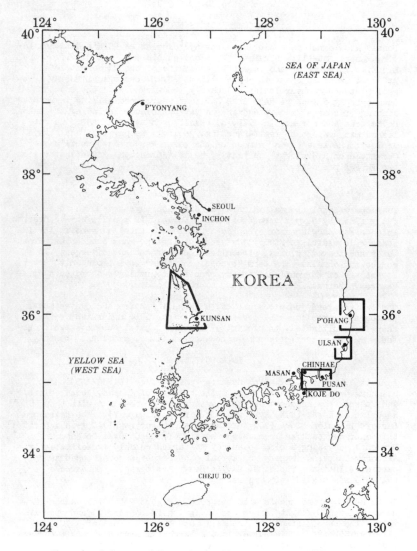

Figure 1.   Index map of Korea showing IR survey areas in 1970.

Figure 2. U. S. Navy RA-3B jet aircraft were used as survey
platforms in Korea.

The purpose of this paper is to describe a thermal infrared (IR) survey by operational units of the Navy using operational scanners to prepare near-synoptic coastal IR mosaics from which coastal current reconnaissance charts have been made. An additional purpose is to show surface features interpreted from the IR imagery that are believed to be unreported and undescribed in the literature.

INFRARED IMAGERY SYSTEM CHARACTERISTICS

Infrared imagery is the photo-like product of a thermal infrared line scanning system, which detects the non-visible infrared radiation given off by any material whose temperature exceeds absolute zero. The scanner discussed here is extremely sensitive to small thermal differences. The apparent radiation temperature of a substance is a function of both its temperature and its emissivity. Because water has a nearly uniform emissivity, it is an ideal target for detecting temperature changes, as the variations in the signal received are due almost entirely to thermal differences in accordance with the Stefan-Boltzman law.

IR systems are completely passive, that is, they require no illumination of the scene. Most IR imagery is collected in two atmospheric "windows," in the electromagnetic spectrum at 3-5 micrometers and 8-14 micrometers. At most other wave lengths the attenuation by the clear atmosphere is extreme. Aircraft IR imagery has a longitudinal scale, which depends on the forward motion of the aircraft and on the rate the recording film moves through the system; it also has a lateral scale, which is a function of the tangent of the angle from the nadir line. The lateral scale distortion is similar to that in a panoramic photograph. The scanner used in this investigation is the AN/AAR-35; basically it is an HRB Singer instrument modified by the Naval Air Development Center (Johnsville). Because the AN/AAR-35 has automatic gain control, only relative temperature variations can be determined. No attempt is made to map sea surface temperatures in this report.

APPROACH

Thermal energy in the 8-14 micrometer band is emitted from the top few millimeters of the water surface, a fact that makes this synoptic method most useful in studying surface currents. For example, in 1966, IR imagery of the Merrimack River Estuary, Massachusetts, was flown for the U. S. Geological Survey (Wiesnet and Cotton, 1967), and extensive surface truth was collected. Subsequent comparison of the imagery and surface truth disclosed that "the surface circulation pattern is clearly delineated by IR imagery" (Hartwell, 1970, p. 13).

The original purpose of the IR surveys over the Korean ports was to provide specific guidance to NAVOCEANO's Nearshore Survey Division for the installation of current meters on the basis of the IR reconnaissance. Aerial photography was also requested and is currently being worked on by Dr. Oscar Huh of NAVOCEANO (Huh and Wiesnet, 1971). The photography obtained was not coincident with the infrared imagery.

The chief variables in Korean coastal currents are (1) tide and (2) seasonal variations in offshore circulation, necessitating spring and fall surveys to record the predominant offshore circulation patterns. Despite a day/night capability, IR surveys must be carefully timed so that the "crossover effect" is avoided. This term refers to times when the temperature of the background equals the temperature of the "target." In this case, the background is the coastal water and the target is the upland "fresh" water discharging into the sea. High and low slack water also tends to be isothermal at the surface.

All flights were scheduled so that ebb or flood currents were well developed, except at Pohang, where no significant tide is observed. The scanner was configured to record in the 8-14 micrometer IR range. Daytime flights at 3,000 or 3370 feet were flown with 50% sidelap. The 3370-foot altitude was finally selected to provide an approximate scale in the mid-portion of the imagery of 1:50,000 to facilitate comparison with existing charts.

Clear, cold, dry Siberian air was sought for all flights; missions during which clouds occurred below the survey altitude were aborted.

GENERAL OCEANIC CIRCULATION NEAR KOREA

The three major water bodies whose circulation affects the coastal currents near Korea are the Yellow Sea on the West Coast, the Sea of Japan (or the East Sea as it is commonly called by the Koreans) on the East Coast, and the Korean Straits which not only connect these two bodies of water but also separate Korea from Japan (Figure 3).

The northern part of the Yellow Sea is rather shallow, the entire Yellow Sea having a mean depth of only 44 meters (Fairbridge, 1966). In spring and summer the Yellow Sea warm current branches off the northeastward-flowing Tsushima current and flows northward into the middle of the Yellow Sea at a speed of less than 0.5 knot. During the winter, cool coastal currents of less than 0.3 knot flow southward along the Korean West Coast in response to the northerly "monsoon" winds.

The Sea of Japan, with a mean depth of 1361 meters, is markedly different from the shallow Yellow Sea. Indeed, much of the Sea of Japan is more than three kilometers deep. Its major current is the Tsushima, which is fed not only by a branch of the Kuroshiro but also by coastal water from China and Korea. The Tsushima current enters the Sea of Japan via the Korean Straits. There, a branch called the East Korea Warm Current moves northward up the Korean Coast to Pohang, where it turns eastward and rejoins the main flow of the Tsushima. Flowing to the south along the Siberian and North Korean East Coast is the North Korea cold current (about 0.5 knot). The so-called Polar Front is the distinct boundary separating these cold and warm water masses.

The average speed of the Tsushima Current is less in winter than in summer, when it reaches a maximum of 1.5 knots in August.

METHODS OF CURRENT MEASUREMENT

In addition to the time-honored Lagrangian and Eulerian methods of current measurement must be added the new third, "Synoptic" methods. We define "synoptic current methods" as remote sensing techniques that record--from an airborne or space platform--one or more parameters of "large" areas of the sea surface known to be related to current speed or direction. Examples of such techniques are: aerial photography, microwave radiometry, radar, and thermal infrared imagery. Prior examples of synoptic current methods are photogrammetric measurements of Cameron, (1952, 1962), Forrester (1960), Keller (1963), and Duxbury (1967) among others.

EXAMPLES OF INFRARED IMAGERY OF THE SEA SURFACE

Water-mass boundaries -- Because the IR scanner detects differences in the thermal emission, scanners quickly detected the "Polar Front,"

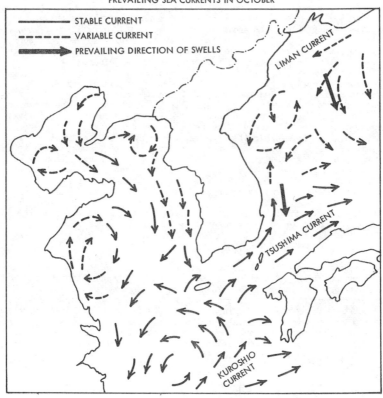

PREVAILING SEA CURRENTS IN OCTOBER

Figure 3. Surface current chart showing generalized current patterns off Korea in October.

(Figure 4) which Korean and Japanese oceanographers have long recognized
as the boundary between the warm East Korea current and the cool North
Korea current. These two currents have rather different source areas
and hence have very different salinity and temperature characteristics.
In Figure 4 the cooler (darker) coastal water moving southward and the
warm (light-toned) offshore water moving northward are separated by a
narrow zone of intermediate or mixed water in which an oil tanker may be
seen. Note the high radiant emission of the tanker (white).

The location of the "Polar Front" is important to the Korean fishing
industry, because the saury, a commercial fish, prefers the nutrient-
laden cooler water edge as a feeding ground. Figure 5 is a rough chart
prepared in Korea about two hours after the aircraft landed. It demonstrates the quick response that can be provided where practical applications, in this case the location of fishing grounds, are concerned.

Fresh water discharge into estuaries -- The port of Pohang lies on the
east coast of Korea on Youngil Man (Bay) (Figure 6). The Hyongsen Gang
(River) is shown discharging its cool water into Youngil Man (Bay)
(October 21, 1970, 0916 local time). Jet flow of cool (dark) fresh
water is clearly visible as is the conical spread (about a 40° cone) of
the free turbulent mixing zone, which can be seen extending out to
approximately one nautical mile. Scarpace and Green (1972, p. 6-7) have
mapped current speeds in thermal plumes by repeated overflights using
IR imagery.

Streamline currents -- If one examines Figure 6 carefully, streamline
current features indicating movement of water may be noted. Sinuous
"flow tubes" of maximum current below the surface are believed to be
causing surface temperature changes that are detectable. Figure 7 is
from the west coast; it shows the shallow Yellow Sea near Kunsan (see
Figure 1) and also shows streamline currents. Note the convergence of
the flow lines; an indication that the water is sinking or speeding up
in this area. The feathery pattern at the top of the figure has been
identified as a Langmuir cell pattern by O. K. Huh (personal communi-
cation).

Shoal areas -- Numerous warm (light-colored) shoals are visible in Figure 7. An elongated bar is also clearly delineated. The ability of the
IR scanner to discriminate shoals in turbid opaque water plus its day or
night capability are clear advantages over color photography, which is
limited to only a few hours a day of flying time owing to sun glitter
problems.

Shoal areas may be outlined and their changes, which are frequent, may
be charted by using IR imagery. The outlines of the uppermost portions
of the shoal areas, which are the most important to the navigator, are
unusually well delineated, especially when compared to bathymetric
charts. The details of the shoal areas are likewise important to the
small craft. Shoals are not shown in such detail on standard National
Ocean Survey or NAVOCEANO H. O. charts.

Eddies -- A remarkable visual example of island-wake eddies is shown
in Figure 8. The tiny island of Mak-to, which is southwest of Pusan in
the Korean Straits and about half a mile in its longest dimension,
produced upwelling and a series of alternating eddies or vortices extending as far as 8 km (4.3 miles) in the lee of the Island. Figure 9
shows the details of the currents inferred from the IR mosaic (Figure 8).
The author has not previously seen such dynamic turbulent flow eddies

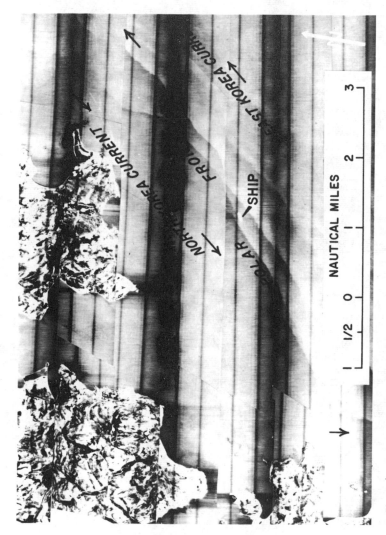

Figure 4. Infrared imagery mosaic showing the "Polar Front" off Ulsan Man (April 3, 1970).

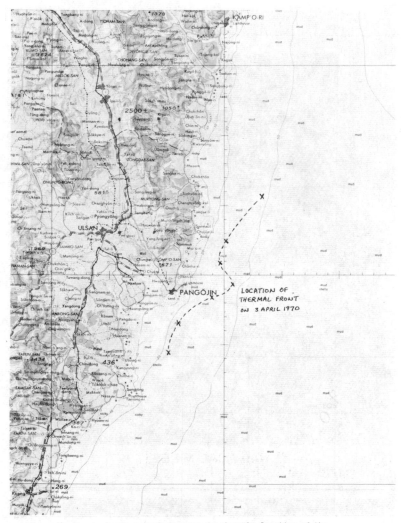

Figure 5. Rough chart prepared in Korea to show the location of the
Polar Front as an aid to ROK Fisheries Research and Development
Bureau.

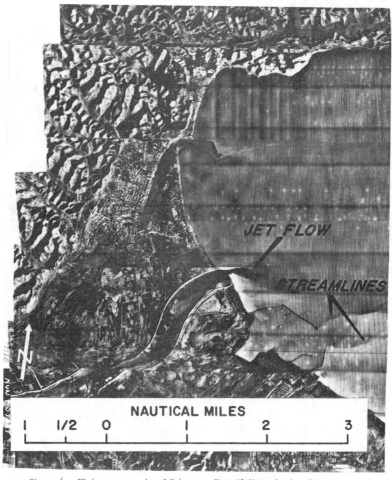

Figure 6. IR imagery mosaic of Pohang on Youngil Man, showing jet
flow from fresh water river discharge and streamlines.

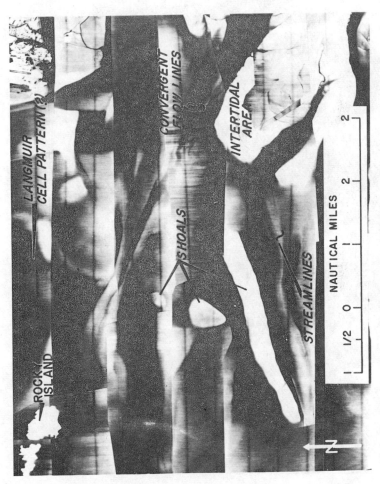

Figure 7. IR imagery mosaic of Kunsan area, showing streamlines, convergent flow lines and shoals.

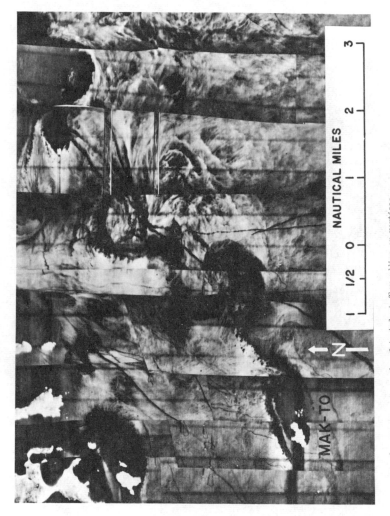

Figure 8. IR imagery mosaic of turbulent flow eddies or vortices resulting from an island wake.

124

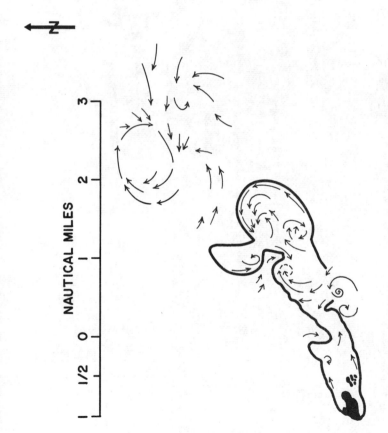

Figure 9. Diagram of circulation patterns inferred from imagery in Figure 13.

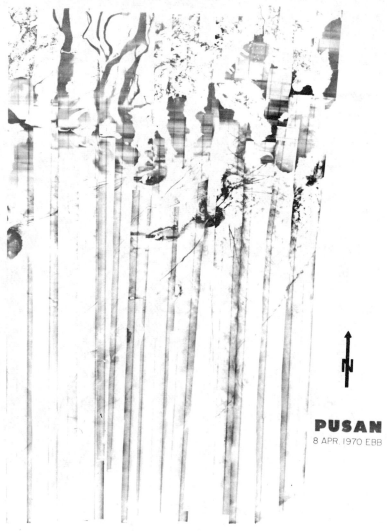

PUSAN
8 APR. 1970 EBB

Figure 10a. IR imagery mosaic for ebb conditions at Pusan, Korea,
8 April 1970.

PUSAN

8 APR. 1970 FLOOD

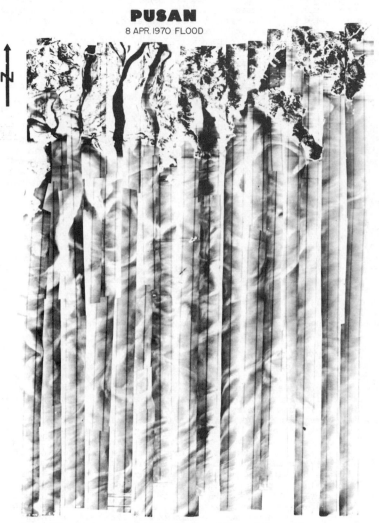

Figure 10b. IR imagery mosaic for flood conditions at Pusan, Korea,
8 April 1970.

associated with island wakes on any IR imagery. Rao, Strong, and Koffler (1971) have shown much larger scale eddies associated with the Gulf Stream from ITOS satellite IR imagery. Tank models of small eddies have been photographed in the laboratory but Figure 8 is an in situ IR image of a naturally occurring phenomenon. The use of IR imagery to study eddy formation and diffusion is readily apparent. A view of the entire Pusan mosaic for ebb and for flood conditions is shown on Figures 10a and 10b. Note the vast difference in the sea surface thermal patterns.

Rip currents -- Though rip currents are usually a small-scale phenomenon, the Korean survey did detect a rip-like current in the Yellow Sea north of Kusan (Figure 11); however, this current extends from the offshore Island of Anmyon Do to a point four nautical miles offshore. Interestingly enough, the flow follows a shallow trench (10-12 meters) and was flowing almost directly into the onshore wind. Tide is at ebb. In areas where rip currents are common, IR imagery and multispectral photography could provide a "visual" mechanism for empirically observing and recording the development and demise of these dangerous currents, which are directly responsible for scores of drownings each year.

RECONNAISSANCE COASTAL CURRENT CHARTS

Figure 12 is a reconnaissance coastal current chart for Pohang that shows thermal fronts, eddies, and coastal currents inferred from the IR mosaic (Figure 13). The two most significant details of the IR mosaics are the two large scale counterclockwise eddies, one directly seaward from Youngil Man and the other ENE of the peninsula. A large submarine escarpment extends northeast from the peninsula. In addition, the North Korea cold current and the northward flowing East Korea warm current meet in this area and move east into the Sea of Japan. The larger of the eddies shown on Figure 13 is about 10 km in diameter. The IR imagery reveals the details of mixing as these two opposite-flowing currents collide. Despite its grand appearance, there are many operational and cartographic details of these charts that can be improved. The preparation of IR mosaics is both an art and a science. Nevertheless, even the crude, uncontrolled mosaics that the author has prepared and used to chart synoptic currents in the Japan Sea and the Yellow Sea coastal areas represent a significant improvement in the oceanographer's continuing quest for a more thorough understanding of water motion and for betterment of the men who man the ships and those who use the seas.

CONCLUDING REMARKS

The IR current charting technique can produce synoptic current charts analogous to synoptic weather charts, thereby providing details of current and thermal patterns needed for ocean and harbor engineering. Regular monitoring of local areas can provide a wealth of data for statistical analysis under varying climatic conditions. The reconnaissance coastal current charts are useful in pollution studies, sediment transport studies, navigation, and marine engineering studies. As a new tool to study the sea surface, this technique makes synoptic charting of coastal currents practical. It is almost essential for the study of micro- and mesoscale phenomenon. It will permit theoreticians the joy (or dismay) of testing their models for estuarine and coastal areas. It can certainly compete with the techniques of the physical model makers who prepare elaborate and expensive scale models to study circulation patterns. In actual practice, both are useful; the IR technique being limited to observed surface phenomena, while analog and digital models can be programmed to react to input variations thus educing predictions based on hypothetical events.

NAUTICAL MILES

Figure 11. IR imagery mosaic of a riplike current in the Yellow Sea
north of Kunsan, April 1970.

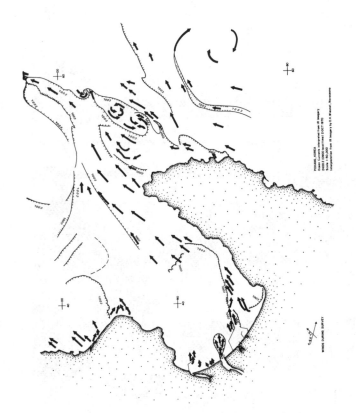

Figure 12. Reconnaissance coastal current chart of the Pohang area showing thermal fronts, form lines of currents, and eddies. The chart is based on Figure 13.

POHANG
21 OCT 70

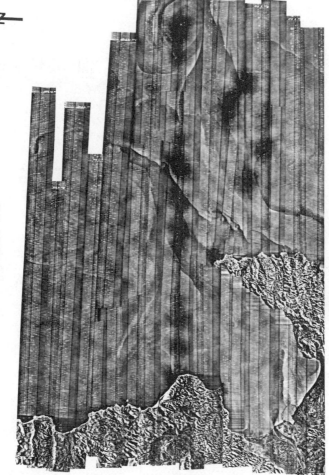

Figure 13. Infrared imagery mosaic of the Pohang coastal area for 21 October 1970. Imagery was collected from 0900 to 1200 local time. The eddy at the extreme right is about 10 n. mi. from the coast.

NOAA's National Ocean Survey (formerly the Coast and Geodetic Survey) has been experimenting with IR imagery along the South Carolina coast and at a recent survey in the Boston Harbor area. Analysis is incomplete but preliminary examination of the data indicate much useful information on circulation patterns will result.

In a negative vein, the presence of clouds, the attenuation of the IR signal through the intervening atmosphere, the problem of aircraft location and attitude, and the panoramic distortion are drawbacks of the IR system discussed here. However, these problems are merely details that can be or have been solved. Happily, higher resolution (0.5 n. mi.) IR sensors are scheduled for future environmental satellites, and under favorable weather conditions, environmental monitoring and synoptic charting of large scale coastal-zone currents should be possible by satellite.

REFERENCES

Cameron, H. L., 1952, The measurement of water current velocities by parallax methods, Photogram. Eng., Mar., vol. 18, pp. 99-104.

Cameron, H. L., 1962, Water current and movement measurement by time lapse air photography, Photogram, Eng., Mar., vol. 28, pp. 158-163.

Duxbury, A. C., 1967, Currents at the Columbia River mouth, Photogram. Eng., Mar., vol. 33, pp. 305-310.

Fairbridge, R. W., ed., 1966, The encyclopedia of oceanography, Reinhold Pub. Corp., New York, 1021 pp.

Forrester, W. D., 1960, Plotting of water current patterns by photogrammetry, Photogram. Eng., Dec., vol. 26, pp. 726-736.

Hartwell, A. D., 1970, Hydrography and Holocene sedimentation of the Merrimack River Estuary, Massachusetts, Contrib. No. 5-CRG, Dept. Geology, Univ. of Mass., Amherst, 166 pp.

Huh, O. K., and Wiesnet, D. R., 1971, Support of nearshore oceanographic environmental surveys by remote sensing, Proceed. 8th U.S.N. Symposium of Military Oceanography, Monterey, pp. 166-189.

Keller, M., 1963, Tidal current surveys by photogrammetric methods, Tech. Bull., no. 22, USC&GS, Oct. 1963, 20 pp.

Rao, P. K., Strong, A. E., and Koffler, R., 1971, Sea surface temperature mapping off the eastern United States using NASA's ITOS satellite, Proc. 7th International Symposium on Remote Sensing, Ann Arbor, Mich., pp. 683-691.

Scarpace, F. L., and Green, T., III, 1972, The use of a thermal line scanner in the remote sensing, Proceed. 8th U.S.N. Symposium of Military Oceanography, Monterey, pp. 166-189.

Slattery, F. L., 1971, Recent and future developments at NAVOCEANO, Proceed. 8th U.S.N. Symposium of Military Oceanography, Monterey.

Wiesnet, D. R., and Cotton, J. E., 1967, Use of infrared imagery in circulation studies of the Merrimack River Estuary, Mass., NASA Tech. Memorandum from U. S. Geol. Survey. NASA-78.

REQUIREMENTS FOR NATIONAL RESOURCE
DEFINITION IN THE COASTAL ZONE

William Spencer Davis
Chief, Estuarine and Oceanographic Section
Environmental Protection Agency
Washington, D.C. 20460

BIOGRAPHICAL SKETCH

The Estuarine and Oceanographic Section of the Environmental
Protection Agency provides technical assistance for marine
pollution control. William Spencer Davis was educated as a
Fishery Biologist at Virginia Polytechnic Institute and
State University. He has been employed by the U.S.
Department of the Interior as a field biologist investigating American shad and striped bass along the Atlantic
seaboard, as a biometrician in the coastal and inland areas
of the Pacific Northwest, and as a resource management
specialist for commercial fish in Washington, D.C. He
participated in the National Estuary Study conducted by the
Bureau of Sport Fisheries and Wildlife.

ABSTRACT

Existing information about the coastal zone is neither
available in a form nor adequacy to meet the needs of programs such as pollution control, emergency action, and
planning at the National level. To be maximally useful,
coastal zone information must be sufficiently detailed to be
meaningful at the local level and in a form that can be
accumulated simply and directly to furnish State and
National statistics. Modern cartography, computers, and
aerial photography constitute the techniques and technology
that can communicate the needed coastal zone information.
This symposium can be the catalyst that initiates the effort
to define the National coastal zone resource adequately.

INTRODUCTION

An integral part of pollution abatement and control in the
coastal zone is the identification, development,
demonstration, and implementation of ways human uses can be
made compatible with the coastal zone ecosystem. This
symposium offers a unique opportunity to discuss a tool that

can contribute appreciably to that goal. That tool is a comprehensive definition of the resources of the coastal zone in terms that are understandable and meaningful to all users. Such a definition does not exist even though all of the parts and the techniques are available to assemble it. I will discuss some present needs for this tool, its use at various levels of government, the way it can be assembled, and finally describe how I think this symposium can contribute to its development.

POLLUTION CONTROL PERSPECTIVE

Every human use of the coastal zone has the potential for modifying natural communities of organisms, the physical and chemical characteristics of the environment, and other human uses. If such modifications occur to the detriment of the environment or its inhabitants, they are attributed to pollution. That they can occur has been amply demonstrated. It is not necessary to destroy any more of this valuable and fragile resource to prove that it can be changed irreversibly. This does not mean, however, that it is necessary to eliminate the bulk of the human uses of the coastal zone. It does mean that we must make pollution control an integral part of existing and future uses of that area. Without going into detail about the reasons, I believe that pollution control in the coastal zone will be much more effective if emphasis is changed so that human uses and technology are studied and modified with an effort at least equal to that applied to studies of the environment to determine how much and what kinds of waste can be assimilated. It is extremely important to make human uses of the coastal zone compatible with the physical, chemical, and biological characteristics of that area. Without perspective, without the ability to visualize how local actions permitted or undertaken by all levels of government will impact the resource as a whole, protection of the coastal zone from pollution cannot be maximally effective.

KEY COMPONENTS OF THE COASTAL ZONE

It is difficult to obtain agreement among all users on a definition for the coastal zone because its use by humans is so varied. Rather than adding to the confusion by producing a very general statement that is meaningless, or, in contrast, excluding some users from consideration by proposing a specific definition, I shall point out some of the things that I think almost everyone can agree on concerning the coastal zone.

Coastal counties and cities receive assistance from State and Federal governments and are subject to constraints imposed by private landholders including industry and municipalities. They are on the scene as is no other level of government. They regulate or fail to do so, in the name of all the people in their jurisdiction. They constitute the next larger community beyond the family with its dwelling and individual freedoms. Thus, the landward portion of the coastal zone is occupied by individuals and small governments including slightly fewer than 400 coastal counties.

The Territorial Sea, which extends from land out to the three mile limit, is State controlled. In its control of that area each State is assisted by, or is a partner with, the Federal government and must be responsive to the needs of individuals, industries, and local governments in all parts of the State as well as those occupying adjacent lands.

The area seaward of the Territorial Sea, out to 12 miles, called the contiguous zone, is under the jurisdiction of the Federal government. In this area the Federal government must be responsive to the needs of all States with emphasis on solving and preventing problems associated with international waters.

The Federal government is, in many instances, the equivalent of a landholder in the Territorial Sea with regard to navigation, and actually owns land in coastal counties and cities to provide recreation areas and military reservations. States become landholders in counties and coastal cities and the latter hold land in their own jurisdictions. Therefore, each level of government not only controls activities of people in a different way, but also is affected as a coastal zone user by each of the other levels of government.

My reasons for going through this exercise are to remind you of the complexity of the institutions that control the coastal zone and call your attention to what I believe to be the locus of change in coastal zone modification. The time is long past when activities in one part of the coastal zone fail to affect activities in other parts. The role of each level of government can be generally expressed as follows:

- Ensure fair treatment of the general public within counties and cities, within States, and within the Nation.

- Undertake collection and evaluation of accurate information about the existing characteristics and uses of the coastal zone as they apply to counties and cities, States, and the Nation.

- Participate in responsible coordination and support among all involved parties both within and among the three levels of government.

The role of each level of government, although it can be described in the same general terms as the others, is different in that it is responsive to a different community. These roles are played out in specific actions, some examples of which are deciding whether a new housing project will be undertaken, setting and enforcing water quality standards, and making grants to build roads and sewage treatment facilities. There are times when one level of government infringes on another, just as there are times when an offer of participation by one level of government is rejected by another. The relationships between governments are dynamic. But basic decisions concerning the coastal zone have been made by all governments historically, and can be expected to continue so.

The decision makers in local, State, and Federal governments are usually thought of as generalists rather than specialists. The generalists have relied heavily upon the specialists for information about the coastal zone and its resources. Enormous amounts of material have been amassed by many different specialists to guide decisions about the coastal zone. The process, as it has operated to the present, has been for critically important areas to be studied by different specialists at different times, resulting in a number of reports. Frequent conflicts arise to the point where it is possible for the entire problem solving process to bog down while groups of specialists debate the merits of measurement techniques and data interpretation.

If a larger than local view is needed, such as a State or National relationship, it is necessary to evaluate a number of studies that have been made in different parts of the country and attempt to resolve different terminology and data to a common base before interpretations can be undertaken meaningfully. The usefulness of the accumulated information has depended largely on what the basic information was collected for and who collected it.

If information used to make management decisions can be considered a tool, then people who collect and present information for decision making can be considered to be tool makers. The complexity of the coastal zone casts the tool maker in the critically important role of supporting management decisions. Independent efforts by counties and cities to compile information will not satisfy State and National needs, nor will such effort by States satisfy National needs. Only National effort focused at the local level and based on a structured approach can conceivably satisfy the coastal zone information needs of county and city, State, and Federal governments.

COLLECTING AND PRESENTING INFORMATION

Where large amounts of many different kinds of information must be considered, as is the case in the coastal zone, computers greatly expand the capability for data manipulation and display in the form of tables, graphs, and plots; aerial photography greatly expands data collection capability; and modern cartography allows extremely accurate representation of an area. These techniques have been tested, are available, and could be very useful to tool makers and management decision makers who are attempting to develop the coastal zone wisely. It is time to use all of these techniques and capabilities collectively to produce a representation of both the land and water areas of the coastal zone that will be useful at the local level as well as the State and National levels for management decisions.

Let me give you some examples of how putting these techniques together has been used to process information for management decisions. The city of Los Angeles has created a

Community Analysis Bureau to collect, analyze, and interpret information concerning city functions, and then present it to decision makers such as city councilmen. The Bureau has accessed many data banks in different departments in the city for such varied parameters as crime statistics and assessments on real property. It would be an interminable job, if not a physical impossibility, to enter all of the data in those banks into one file, so the Bureau has used a commercially available multiple file information handling system to locate pertinent information, extract it, and manipulate it into the desired form. They have found that the usefulness of the output is enhanced appreciably by using computer plotting techniques which show concentrations of a characteristic on a base map of the city or a councilman's district. By use of this technique they can plot more than one characteristic on the same sheet to give perspective to what would otherwise simply be great quantities of numbers requiring special expertise for interpretation.

A second example is the Environmental Geologic Atlas of the Texas coastal zone that the Bureau of Economic Geology at the University of Texas is in the process of compiling. The Texas coast has been divided into seven study regions. The Galveston-Houston region has just been completed. Although the mappers have not used the computer extensively in the preparation of this material, they anticipate doing so in future work. For each of the seven study regions a multicolored base chart has been developed which is supported by text and tables. The key of the base map for the Galveston-Houston area consists of 80 separate categories. Eight additional colored maps showing the relationships between a few important characteristics have been developed also. One such chart, which I think is particularly valuable for interpretation of the coastal zone is entitled, "Active Processes". It gives a clear idea where changes due to such processes as weather, erosion, sedimentation, and the like, will probably modify the coastal region as it is depicted on maps and charts. For our purposes, the important consideration in the Texas effort is that a mapping technique is being applied by a small group of people along an entire State coastline in increments small enough to be useful to local decision makers, but in a form that is intended to be expanded to supply Statewide information.

The status of information about the coastal zone on the National level is structured around independent effort on the part of agencies and institutions. There are data banks, or information that could be included in data banks, in many Federal agencies such as the Environmental Protection Agency, the U.S. Army Corps of Engineers, and the Departments of Commerce, Interior, Agriculture, Health Education and Welfare, and Housing and Urban Development. These data banks contain tremendous amounts of information, but the exchange and correlation of information among them is often limited or prevented entirely by problems of agency priorities, programming, access, and descriptive terminology. If EPA computer systems can be used as an example, and I believe they are no more sophisticated than most others in the Federal government, then the present organization of information in data banks is only one of a number of possible organizations which can be produced, given time and a clear definition of what is required.

Mapping and charting in the coastal zone has been clearly divided between land and water areas. The U.S. Geological Survey (USGS) maps the land and the National Ocean Survey (NOS) charts the waters. The USGS is exploring the use of aerial photography to capture detailed land use information. NOS is producing charts on a prototype basis that show: land use by aerial photography, high tide lines, and areas inundated by hurricanes. From all of this effort, however, there is no single source from which to obtain a clear perspective of any characteristic of the coastal zone as it relates to another characteristic appearing on a different map source. The obvious place to look for such perspective is maps and charts, but the geophysical division of the coastal zone between USGS and NOS, the difference in scales (to obtain maximum detail from NOS charts in the Galveston Bay, Texas, area alone it is necessary to interpret about nine charts and four scales), and the use of symbols to depict characteristics that can be counted but not measured, all limit the interpretations that can be made readily by potential users.

NEW NEEDS FOR INFORMATION

The information that has been collected to date about the coastal zone generally has been in response to client requests. By clients I mean anyone from the Congress of the United States to small boat operators. Now, however, there is a new type of client emerging at the local, State, and National levels who interfaces with virtually every activity of man on land and in the water. Management and operation of pollution control programs, emergency preparedness programs, land use planning, and new cities development are some examples. In my view these new clients need:

- Detailed base maps showing land area in each coastal county and city and the adjacent Territorial Sea on a scale that will be useful in responding to emergencies and in planning.

- Detailed maps at a single scale for the entire coastal zone as baseline data so that information about counties and cities and the adjacent Territorial Sea can be summed to describe State coastal areas, and information about State coastal areas can be summed to describe the total National resource.

- Digitization* for maximum interpretation of base maps. This will make it possible to limit the characteristics depicted on any single map to those most pertinent while offering many other possibilities for combinations of data either as printed maps or overlays for base maps that might be important to a particular user.

*Digitization is a process in which line tracings on a chart are recorded as digits on computer punch cards or magnetic tape, which, with the proper program, can be used to reproduce the line originally traced. Map interpretations such as distances can be calculated, translations from one map scale to another can be made, and surface areas can be calculated by use of the digitized material and appropriate computer programs.

- Computer programs to allow the compilation of information from the charts as measurements, counts, and area by latitude and longitude; and to translate the scale of the base maps to other smaller scales.

- A dynamic mapping system so that any new complete and adequately qualified characteristic can be added to the system at random as it is described. It should not be necessary to wait for the collection of significant amounts of new information before starting this National mapping program.

I have deliberately avoided specifying the characteristics to be included in this proposed information system based on coastal zone maps. Those parameters must come from concerned users. The major problem as I see it is neither defining map characteristics, although that will require resolution, nor developing the techniques by which the project can be undertaken. EPA, for instance, already has an Automap program for the riverine systems of the United States in the Office of Water Programs that uses most, if not all, of the techniques described above. The big problems are to identify the agencies that will undertake the task, assist them in developing the necessary program, support them in requests for funding and manpower, and, where possible, participate directly. I think we can and should initiate this program at this symposium.

RECOMMENDED ACTION AT THIS SYMPOSIUM

In my view, the National Ocean Survey and the U.S. Geological Survey must cooperate to make possible a coastal zone information system based on standard large scale maps including detail on coastal counties and cities and the Territorial Sea. It must be funded from a single source, and not on a grant or cost sharing basis. If the cost of the operation must be recovered, it should be done after the fact and not be a prerequisite to the initiation of the effort. This symposium should be used as a source of informational needs of potential users. On that basis, a program should be developed by the principals with the assistance of at least the major user agencies. This would include justification, funding, levels of effort, manpower, equipment requirements, timetables, and designation of responsible agencies. The strategy for applying to the

Office of Management and Budget and the Congress for funding and manpower should be included, drawing heavily on all forms of support conceivable from potential user agencies including State and local governments, universities, industries, and the private sector. I recommend that the sponsors of this symposium initiate such an effort and make it part of the record of this meeting.

The coastal zone resource can be husbanded wisely through imaginative and cooperative local, State, and National action only by new commitment of funds and effort to obtain information about its characteristics and the uses which humans make of it. The importance of the coastal zone is abundantly demonstrated by the variety of human uses to which it is put and the intensity with which those uses are protected and pursued.

On the basis of independent efforts already initiated, I am convinced that the will to define the National coastal zone resource exists. That will, however, must be focused if it is to perform a service for the whole community of coastal zone users. This symposium can be the catalyst that starts the needed effort immediately.

FUTURE
BUREAU OF LAND MANAGEMENT
MAPPING NEEDS

Mr. Donald P. Truesdell
Division of Marine Minerals
Bureau of Land Management
Department of the Interior
Washington, D. C. 20240

BIOGRAPHICAL SKETCH

Donald P. Truesdell is an Environmental Specialist in the Branch of
Environmental Analysis, Division of Marine Minerals, Bureau of Land
Management and is involved in the analysis of the environmental impact
of mineral leasing on the Outer Continental Shelf (OCS). Truesdell has
a degree in Geology from the University of California at Los Angeles.
He has worked in the OCS minerals program for the last eight years
serving as the Assistant Manager of the New Orleans OCS Office and
currently is acting as Chief of the Branch of Environmental Analysis
in Washington, D. C.

ABSTRACT

Under the Secretary of the Interior, the Bureau of Land Management is
responsible for the leasing of all mineral rights on the Outer Continental Shelf (OCS) - that portion of the Continental Shelf which lies
beyond the jurisdiction of the individual states.

The Bureau of Land Management's comprehensive OCS minerals management
program has three major goals:

1. The orderly development of marine mineral resources to meet
    the energy needs of the nation;

2. The protection of the marine environment; and

3. The receipt of a fair return for leased mineral resources.

To assist in the accomplishment of these goals, especially that of
protecting the marine environment, the Bureau will need general and
detailed hydrographic, bathometric, biologic, isopach, sediment
distribution, temperature and salinity distribution maps covering
many areas of the OCS.

THE AUTOMATED ACQUISITION AND PROCESSING
OF MARINE DATA FOR COASTAL MAPPING

Mr. Robert G. Fish
Lt. Cdr. C. H. McClure
Lt. Cdr. J. L. Wallace
Marine Data Systems Project
National Ocean Survey
Rockville, Maryland 20852

BIOGRAPHICAL SKETCH

Robert G. Fish is a computer specialist and Chief of
the Electronic Data Processing Branch at the National
Ocean Survey (NOS) Atlantic Marine Center in Norfolk,
Virginia. He has been at the Atlantic Marine Center
since August 1970, and is responsible for the design
and implementation of the IBM 1130 Computer-Plotter
Software System used for processing of marine data.
Prior to joining the Atlantic Marine Center staff,
Mr. Fish was a mathematician assigned to the NOS Electronic Computing Division in Rockville, Maryland,
where he was responsible for designing portions of
the off-line software used in the HYDROPLOT/HYDROLOG
Systems. Mr. Fish attended the University of North
Carolina, where he received his B.A. degree and pursued graduate studies in Mathematics.

Charles H. McClure, a National Oceanic and Atmospheric
Administration (NOAA) commissioned officer, has served
with the NOS Marine Data Systems Project since its
formation in 1970. He has participated in the design
and implementation of the HYDROPLOT/HYDROLOG Systems.
In prior assignments, he has served with the NOS
Office of Systems Development and as computer officer
aboard the NOAA oceanographic research ship DISCOVERER.
Lieutenant Commander McClure received the B.S. and M.S.
degrees in electrical engineering from the University
of Kentucky and did graduate work in engineering at
Columbia University.

Jack L. Wallace, a NOAA commissioned officer, is serving
with the Marine Data Systems Project at NOS Rockville,
Maryland, Headquarters. He has served as computer officer aboard the NOAA Ship MT. MITCHELL, as operations
officer aboard the Ship WHITING, and as an officer aboard
the Ship HYDROGRAPHER. In shore assignments, he has held
the position of Chief of the Electronic Data Processing
Branch of the NOS Pacific Marine Center, and has authored
the manual describing the operational use of the HYDRO-
PLOT/HYDROLOG Systems. Lieutenant Commander Wallace received the B.S. degree in civil engineering from the University of Michigan in 1965.

ABSTRACT

The National Ocean Survey (NOS) of the National Oceanic
and Atmospheric Administration (NOAA) is responsible
for the production of charts of the coastal waters of
the United States and its possessions. The requirement
for these charts has increased tremendously during recent years, and NOS has applied automation equipment
and techniques to help meet the demand. HYDROPLOT and
HYDROLOG computer systems have been installed aboard
eleven NOAA vessels and have increased the speed and
efficiency with which hydrographic survey data can be
collected. A shore-based, computer-plotter system processes the automatically acquired data. Products of
the shore-based system include a verified smooth plot
of hydrographic data, a position overlay, and smoothed
data on hard-copy printout and magnetic tape.

INTRODUCTION

Since 1807, it has been the responsibility of the
National Ocean Survey and its predecessor, the Coast
and Geodetic Survey, to produce nautical charts of
the coastal waters of the U.S. and its possessions.
During this time, nautical charting requirements and the
tools and techniques available to both the hydrographer
and cartographer have changed. The increase in water-
borne commerce, the economic development in coastal
areas and the increase in popularity of recreational
boating have all contributed to the tremendous increase
in demand for timely nautical charts. This increased
demand coupled with increased production costs have provided the incentive to find faster and more economical
methods of gathering and processing data for marine
charting. With the coming of age of the digital computer,
automation seems to have offered a practical solution.
Modern systems using newly developed techniques and hardware are being used by NOS for the automated acquisition
and processing of marine data for coastal mapping.

In 1964, an IBM 1620 computer and an off-line Gerber
plotter were installed at the NOS Pacific Marine Center
(PMC) in Seattle, Washington, for the purpose of reducing
hydrographic surveys to corrected geographic positions
and soundings, and machine plotting these data. In July
of that year, PMC produced the first automatically processed and machine plotted hydrographic survey smooth
sheet from data logged aboard a NOAA vessel. The data
used in the first automated plot were acquired by the Ship
HYDROGRAPHER using a data logging system with no computational ability. The shipboard equipment automatically
logged data from electronic positioning equipment and
echo sounder, and provided printer and punched paper tape
output.

In 1967, a computer system was installed aboard the 164-foot coastal survey ship WHITING for test and evaluation purposes; this system proved to be quite successful and was to become the basis for the eleven HYDROPLOT/HYDROLOG systems now installed aboard National Oceanic and Atmospheric Administration survey vessels. Land based processing by automated methods had also been successful, and the PMC system had been developed to the point of producing necessary computations, plotting geographic position overlays, sounding overlays, excess sounding overlays, and producing the final plot.

In an effort to acquire hydrographic data at a higher speed, a data logging system using a Decca Digital Control Unit was installed in a 60-foot launch capable of operating at 22 knots. In 1969, after a year of successful operation with this logging system, a HYDRO-PLOT system was installed aboard the launch. By using the computer to control hydrography along straight, parallel lines rather than along hyperbolic arcs, a thirty percent productivity increase was realized.

By 1970, and probably before then, the PMC computer-plotter system had reached obsolescence. The IBM 1620 data processing system, a second-generation computer, was already obsolete by industry standards. Its speed could not even compare with the newer third-generation computers. It required 160 microseconds just to fetch an instruction from core and analyze it to establish the type of operation, compared with the 3.6 micro-second cycle time of many of the third-generation computers. In addition, the computer-plotter system was card oriented, which, in itself, led to many data storage, retrieval and handling problems. The data load began to exceed processing capabilities, resulting in a rapidly developing backlog of unprocessed data.

In 1970, the National Ocean Survey began the design and implementation of much more sophisticated data acquisition and processing systems. A computer-plotter system implemented at the Atlantic Marine Center (AMC) in Norfolk, Virginia, provided many improvements over the PMC system. Among these improvements were:

- A much faster third-generation computer for the central processing unit;

- Magnetic tape and disk employed for data storage and retrieval in lieu of a card oriented system;

- A line drawing plotter eliminating much of the manual plotting still required at PMC;

- High speed peripheral equipment interfaced where feasible;

- All software designed to eliminate as much human error as possible.

In 1971, NOS installed nine HYDROPLOT/HYDROLOG systems aboard three 231-foot Class II survey ships and two survey launches of each ship. A tenth HYDROPLOT system replaced the original WHITING system, which had become obsolete. These new systems were software compatible with the 60-foot launch HYDROPLOT system, and with the original WHITING system, thus they could effectively utilize software developed over the previous six years and experience gained with the earlier data acquisition systems.

Figure 1. The NOAA Ship MT. MITCHELL, typical of the Class II ships equipped with HYDROPLOT/HYDROLOG Systems.

AUTOMATED DATA ACQUISITION

HYDROPLOT/HYDROLOG System hardware

Figure 2 is a block diagram of the HYDROPLOT/HYDROLOG systems installed aboard NOAA vessels in 1971. HYDRO-PLOT systems include an incremental plotter and are installed aboard the NOAA Ships MT. MITCHELL, RAINIER and FAIRWEATHER, and aboard the Class III NOAA Ship WHITING. The HYDROLOG systems installed aboard six survey launches, ranging in length from 25-feet to 31-feet, are identical except that the plotter has been eliminated, primarily due to space and electrical power limitations. The computer is a Digital Equipment Corporation PDP-8/E with 12 bit word length and 8K of core memory.

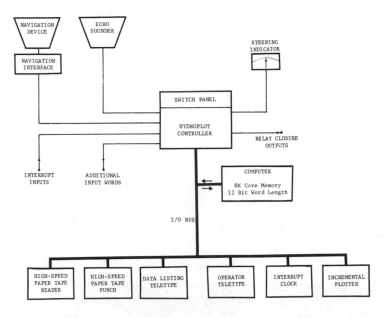

Figure 2.   HYDROPLOT System Block Diagram

All peripherals interfaced to the computer share a common input/output bus and include:

- An eight channel paper tape reader capable of a continuous read rate of 300 characters per second.

- A paper tape punch capable of 50 characters per second.

- Two Model ASR-33 Teletype units each of which can provide keyboard input to the computer, printer output from the computer, and paper tape read and punch functions. ASR-33 operations are limited to 10 characters per second.

- An interrupt clock, installed in the computer, provides the system with time information. All HYDROPLOT/HYDROLOG System clocks utilize a crystal time standard.

- A Houston Instrument COMPLOT DP-3-5 incremental roll plotter provides HYDROPLOT System graphic output. The DP-3-5 will accommodate 22 inch wide paper or drafting film and provides an

effectively unlimited plotting surface length.
Either conventional or pressurized ballpoint,
felt tip or Rapidograph type pens may be used.
Increment size is 0.005 inch   along either X
or Y axis, with a maximum speed of 300 increments per second.

The HYDROPLOT Controller is a special purpose input/output
interface designed to NOS specifications and manufactured
by Digital Equipment Corporation (DEC). The Controller
provides for the entry of data and parameters pertinent
to the hydrographic survey, and for some outputs. Both
depth and position information are input to the computer
through the Controller.

The echo sounder is a complete subsystem which produces an
analog recording of the depth, provides the operator with
a visual digital depth indication and provides the Controller with parallel, binary coded decimal (BCD) depth
data. Figure 3 shows the Ross digital echo sounder analog
recorder of the type used with the HYDROPLOT/HYDROLOG
Systems.

Figure 3.   Analog Recorder of a Ross Digital
Echo Sounder

The HYDROPLOT/HYDROLOG Systems were designed to accept position information from one of several types of positioning
systems used by NOS. A navigation interface designed by
NOS is used to convert the output of RAYDIST or HI-FIX re-
ceivers to parallel BCD information which can be handled

by the HYDROPLOT Controller. Any navigation or positioning system to which an incremental encoder can be attached
can also be used as an input to the navigation interface,
thus a considerable degree of versatility is provided.
Several of the newer types of positioning equipment will
interface directly with the Controller without the navigation interface.

The HYDROPLOT Controller is the heart of the HYDROPLOT/
HYDROLOG hardware, and as such, deserves more detailed
description. It provides the following five functions:

1. A digital multiplexer for up to 32-twelve bit
   data input words.

2. A twelve input interrupt system.

3. Four relay closure outputs.

4. An analog output used to drive a steering indicator.

5. Two pulse outputs.

All data from the echo sounder, positioning equipment, and
Controller panel switches enters the system under program
control via the 32-word input multiplexer. The operator
can select either of two echo sounders and either of two
positioning systems by means of switches on the Controller
panel. Forty-nine thumbwheel switches on the Controller
panel provide for input to the system of survey parameters
and infrequently changing data. The Controller provides
for the input of up to 33 BCD digits of information from ex-
ternal switches or equipment, to allow for future expansion.

A twelve input interrupt system provides for operator com-
munication with the computer and provides a means for
other equipment to communicate with the computer. Seven
momentary pushbuttons on the HYDROPLOT Controller panel
and five electrical connectors on the rear panel enter
the computer as interrupts. Interrupts are used for time
synchronization and similar functions that require immediate
special attention by the computer.

Four relays are controlled by the computer and are used to
put time marks on the echo sounder analog record and on
the positioning equipment sawtooth recorder when used.
Relay closures can also be used to generate audible or
visual alarms or time signals.

The Controller contains a digital-to-analog (D to A) con-
verter; the analog output drives a meter type left-right
steering indicator. By following the steering indicator
needle, the helmsman can keep the survey vessel on a
survey line determined by the computer.

Figure 4. HYDROLOG equipment installed aboard
a 25' Bertram Launch; cabinet, top
to bottom: Ross Echo Sounder Digitizer,
Navigation Interface, HYDROPLOT Controller, PDP-8/E Computer, High-Speed
Paper Tape Reader/Punch

The Controller provides two pulse outputs to inhibit depth
and position information from changing while being sampled
by the computer.

HYDROPLOT/HYDROLOG System software and operation

There are currently fifty-one computer programs used in
the HYDROPLOT/HYDROLOG System. These programs can be
divided into four basic groups; they are:

Group I   - Preliminary and utility programs.

Group II   - HYDROPLOT/HYDROLOG acquisition programs.

Group III - Off-line plot programs.

Group IV   - Pre-processing programs for shore-based
             facilities.

Group I consists of all utility programs used prior to
conducting actual hydrographic operations. This group
includes a program to construct X-Y and geodetic grids
on the Universal Transverse Mercator (UTM) projection.
The same program can also be used to produce range-range
and hyperbolic lattice plots, and will connect specified
points on the plot with a line segment. Also included

is a general purpose utility program which makes all the necessary conversions utilized in the UTM system. For example, this program will convert: lanes to X-Y to geographic position, or geographic position to X-Y to lanes, or a three-point fix may be converted to X-Y and from X-Y to geographic position and then to lanes, or vice-versa. Additional programs in this group include:

- A predicted tide generator

- A smooth tide corrector generator which fits a curve to hourly heights

- Geodetic inverse and position computation program

- A fifty state state-plane coordinate conversion and a traverse computations program

- Electronic control calibration program using sextant angles and the three-point fix as reference

Many of the original programs used aboard WHITING in 1967 required that individual program parameters be typed into the system on the Teletype keyboard each time the program was used. This often led to errors which were difficult to detect since the operator's entry was not usually suspect! As a result, one of the first changes made to the system was the addition of a parameter tape. The parameter tape enables the operator to type the program parameters only once, to put them on paper tape, to check them, and to use the tape as often as necessary. The tape is read into the system on the Teletype reader and appears on the Teletype printer as it is read into the system.

A sample parameter tape and explanation follows:

FEST=2ØØØØ

CLAT=4ØØØØØØ

CMER=76/1Ø/Ø

GRID=15

PLSCL=1ØØØØ

PLAT=36/54/4Ø

PLON=76/15/2Ø

MLAT=36/55/44.78

MLON=76/10/58.86

S1LAT=37/ØØ/Ø4.8

S1LON=76/18/19.Ø9

S2LAT=36/55/32.44

S2LON=76/Ø2/39.Ø3

Q=33ØØ.4

VESNO=293Ø

YR=7Ø

Where degrees, minutes, and seconds are used,
they are entered in the following manner:

3Ø   = 3Ø seconds

1/3Ø   = 1 minute, 3Ø seconds

1/Ø   = 1 minute, Ø seconds

1/1/3Ø   = 1 degree, 1 minute, 3Ø seconds

75/Ø/25 = 75 degrees, 0 minutes, 25 seconds

FEST = (False Easting) X-coordinate, in meters,
       assigned to the Central Meridian.   X-values
       are measured plus or minus from the Central
       Meridian. Thusly, the FEST must be greater
       than the distance (in meters) from the Cen-
       tral Meridian to the most westerly point
       used (i.e., control station, visual signal,
       sounding or grid line).

CLAT = (Control Latitude) Number of meters the
       lowest latitude to be covered by the survey(s)
       is from the equator. A whole number, in
       meters, below the working area is usually
       picked.

CMER = (Central Meridian) The value in degrees,
       minutes, and seconds of the central longitude
       for the work area.

GRID = The grid interval that will be used in the
       grid plot.

PLSCL = The plotter scale (1ØØØØ interpreted as 1 foot =
        1Ø,ØØØ feet).

PLAT = Latitude of the plotter origin.

PLON = Longitude of the plotter origin.

MLAT = Latitude of the Master Station (omitted in
       range-range).

MLON = Longitude of the Master Station (omitted in range-range).

S1LAT = Latitude of Slave 1 Station.

S1LON = Longitude of Slave 1 Station.

S2LAT = Latitude of Slave 2 Station.

S2LON = Longitude of Slave 2 Station.

Q = Frequency in kHz

VESNO = Four digit number, consisting of three-digit ship identification and one-digit vessel code.

YR = Year of survey.

Group II programs include the HYDROPLOT/HYDROLOG real-time data acquisition programs. The goal of the HYDRO-PLOT System is fourfold as follows:

1. to extend the shipboard capability for inshore hydrography by allowing computations not previously possible to be performed in real time;

2. to allow the automatic listing and coding of hydrographic survey information on machine-processable medium in real time, and, thereby, eliminate errors otherwise injected during manual, after-the-fact transformation of data to digital format;

3. to provide vessel guidance along straight lines during the conduct of hydrography thereby achieving increased operational efficiency, effectiveness and economy; and

4. to make more information available to the hydro-grapher at the time data is being collected by allowing decisions concerning the veracity and completeness of survey data to be made in the field while there is an opportunity to make corrections and collect additional data.

At the present time, position determination may be either three-station hyperbolic or two-station range-range electronic control. A program utilizing visual control with electronic digital readout sextants is being developed. Depth input may be either automatic entry from the digital echo sounder or by manual entry by the Controller thumb-wheel switches. Sounding units may be either feet or fathoms or both.

The HYDROPLOT program uses the UTM projection with a modified central meridian as a computational base. The system assumes the plotter to be a DP-3-5 or Calcomp 500 series. Because of the small plotting area offered by some of the plotters, skewed projections may be used; all plotted sheets may be skewed from 0 to 360 degrees, and individual characters may be rotated from 0 to 360 degrees. The hydrographer also has the option of expanding or reducing the size of plotted characters.

The program can use real time tide data received by digital radio telemetry link and entered through the HYDROPLOT Controller, or predicted tides punched in a binary code and read on the high speed paper tape reader, or no tidal information at all.

Output from the system consists of the real time position and sounding plot, paper tape punched in ASCII code with even parity, a printout corresponding to the data tape, a printout of operator messages on the second Teletype and left/right steering commands via a meter display. Although soundings may be entered in feet or fathoms and may be changed at the discretion of the hydrographer while running, the selection of feet, fathoms or meters as the plotting unit must be designated when the program is loaded. Figure 5 shows the output tape format.

Initially, the plotter pen is set at the lower left hand corner of the paper; when the computer clock is syncronized, the plotter pen moves to the vessel's position and begins tracking. From this time on, the pen continuously tracks the vessel even if no data is being recorded. If the vessel moves beyond the sheet limits, the plotter will track in one dimension if possible. When the vessel returns to the sheet, the pen will continue tracking. The vessel's plotted position and the steering meter are updated once each second.

The HYDROPLOT Controller is the means by which hydrographic information pertinent to the survey passes to and from the computer. The Controller is used to specify and update the following:

- Calibration corrections to electronic control
- Lane jump corrections
- Sounding interval
- Position number interval
- Draft correction
- Steering meter full scale sensitivity
- Sounding unit - (feet or fathoms)
- Suppression of lane jump detection routine
- Real or predicted tides
- Ross or Raytheon digital echo sounder

Time	Depth	Pos. No.	HI-FIX P1	P2
293Ø	7Ø	17Ø Ø Ø1 *		
Ø82920	-Ø46	-ØØ3	ØØØ51	ØØØØ51 **
Ø82922	ØØØ94	Ø5969	Ø16786	Ø22386
Ø82932	ØØ988		Ø1686Ø	Ø22385
Ø82942	ØØ984		Ø16933	Ø22384
Ø82952	ØØ981		Ø17ØØ7	Ø22383
Ø83ØØ2	ØØ978		Ø17Ø8Ø	Ø22382
Ø83Ø12	ØØ977		Ø17154	Ø22381
Ø83Ø22	ØØ974	Ø597Ø	Ø17228	Ø2238Ø
Ø83Ø32	ØØ973		Ø173Ø2	Ø22379
Ø83Ø42	ØØ97Ø		Ø17376	Ø22377

NOTE: * Day Word - from left to right - Vessel Identification, Year, Julian Day, Sounding Indicator, Velocity Table.

        ** Corrector Word - from left to right - Time, Tide Reducer, Draft Correction, HI-FIX Corrections.

Figure 5.   HYDROPLOT Master Data Format

        Output paper tape and printout use this format. Note that each sounding retains its own electronic control reading.

159

System interrupts are used for the following functions:

- to record a detached position;

- to temporarily break the present line;

- to start a new line; and

- to mark the echo sounder at a sounding interval.

The HYDROPLOT program utilizes an experimental routine, based on the allowable speed of the vessel, to detect electronic positioning equipment lane jumps. Once a possible jump is indicated, the hydrographer examines the positioning equipment, sawtooth recording, Teletype printout, plot and any other information available to him and enters a correction via the Controller if appropriate.

Another area being investigated is selection by software of soundings to be plotted. The HYDROPLOT approach is to record a sounding on a time interval and change it later, through correctors, if necessary. Other organizations have taken the approach of using sophisticated routines for selection of shoal soundings by meaning and filtering soundings without an independent measure of the sounding vessel's vertical motion. NOS is attempting to develop a practical method of determining the vessel's vertical motion and use this information to correct soundings before they are selected.

The HYDROLOG Systems, all of which are installed in small launches, are identical to the HYDROPLOT Systems except that the hardware configuration does not include a plotter. To compensate for the lack of information available to the hydrographer, additional software is provided which indicates to the hydrographer when he is inside or outside of a predetermined N-sided figure defining the survey limits. Figure 6 shows how the HYDROLOG System might be utilized.

The sounding vessel is maneuvered toward the beginning point on the first sounding line to be run. Depressing the "X" key of the console Teletype causes the X-Y coordinates of the vessel's position to be typed out. By plotting this position information on the previously prepared grid system (worksheet) covering the survey area, the hydrographer is able to guide the vessel as required.

When the sounding vessel crosses the first sounding line the steering meter will change from full scale left to full scale right. When this happens, the vessel is brought around to the right to the correct heading and maneuvered onto the sounding line by centering the steering meter. When the launch enters the survey area defined by the previously loaded area limits, the console Teletype prints out the message "INSIDE." The hydrographer then depresses the "Mark" interrupt on the HYDROPLOT Controller; this action activates the HYDROLOG data acquisition system.

When the vessel crosses the survey limit at the end of the sounding line, the console Teletype prints "OUT-SIDE." The hydrographer then breaks the sounding line (logging activity) by depressing the letter "B" on the console Teletype. This causes the X-Y coordinate of the starting point and heading of the next sounding line to be printed by the console Teletype; the system automatically begins to track the vessel's position with respect to the next sounding line which is parallel to the line just completed and at the previously speci-fied spacing distance. The steering meter immediately updates to the new line and indicates full scale left.

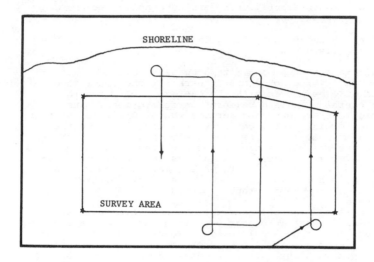

Figure 6. HYDROLOG System Survey Operation

The vessel's course is altered 90° to the left and the vessel is run approximately parallel to the adjacent sur-vey limit line. When the vessel crosses the extension of the next sounding line to be run, the meter swings from full scale left to full scale right. The vessel is then brought around 270° to the right and again maneuvered onto the sounding line by centering the steering meter.

When the vessel again crosses the survey limit line, the console Teletype prints "INSIDE" and logging process is again activated by depressing the "Mark" interrupt. The procedure is repeated until the day's sounding activity is completed. The paper tape recording generated by the HYDROLOG System during the day is edited and plotted aboard the host ship that night with the HYDROPLOT System operating in the off-line mode.

161

Group III, the Off-line Plot Programs provide for the hydrographer to massage position data, apply corrections to sounding and replot raw data prior to leaving the working area. Data to be plotted may be specified by geographic limits or position numbers, thus data of particular interest can be selected for plotting. Off-line plot programs are available to plot master tapes using position control of the following types:

- Hyperbolic electronic

- Range-range electronic

- Visual sextant fixes

- Hyper-visual, using one hyperbolic arc and one visual angle

- Range-visual, using one circular arc and one visual angle.

In addition to the master tape usually obtained in real-time, the hydrographer must generate a corrector tape which will be merged with the master. The corrector tape contains revised calibration corrections, lane jump corrections, new echo sounder transducer draft corrections, revised or inserted uncorrected soundings, and in the case of visual fixes, revised angles and object numbers. If he desires, the hydrographer may read in and store velocity corrections; he may also select a new tide tape in which case the tide data on the master tape is much shorter than the master tape, and by its use, frequent editing of the master tape is avoided.

The off-line plot programs are often used several times to assemble data into a graphic image useful in evaluating the quality of data collected by several launches under varying conditions. The information on the master tape is merged with the corrector tape. Soundings may be corrected for sound velocity in water, transducer draft, scanning errors and smooth tides. The resulting plot is a composite of all known information. If soundings don't agree at this point, they generally never will and there is no reason to leave the area until all discrepancies have been resolved.

Group IV programs consist of those programs used by Seattle based ships to pre-process data for processing on the IBM 1620 computer. The HYDROPLOT/HYDROLOG System has three tape readers and is considerably faster than the card producing 1620 computer. As a result, the data from the Master Tape, corrector tape, velocity and tide tapes is merged into one Master Tape. In addition the geographic positions are computed for each fix and appended to the Master Tape. Group IV programs are not used by Norfolk based ships as the IBM 1130 computer efficiently accomplishes these tasks.

SHORE-BASED AUTOMATED PROCESSING

The Atlantic Marine Center computer plotter system

By the end of 1970, the computer-plotter system shown in
Figure 7 had been implemented at the NOS Atlantic Marine
Center. The focal point of the new system is the central
processing unit consisting of 8,192 16-bit words of core
storage, soon to be expanded to 16,384 words, with a
cycle time of 3.6 microseconds.

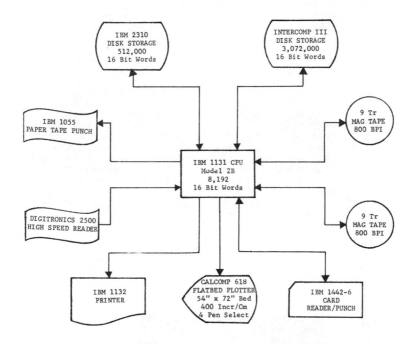

Figure 7.   Atlantic Marine Center Computer-Plotter System Block Diagram

Peripherals interfaced with the central processing unit
include:

- An IBM 1055 paper tape punch.

- A Digitronics 2500 High Speed Paper Tape Reader
  capable of 300 characters per second.

- An IBM 1132 Line Printer with a maximum speed
  of 120 lines per minute. This unit is being
  replaced by a 600 line per minute printer.

- Two Infotec TS-1130/6 Magnetic Tape Drives capable of reading 9-track, 800 BPI tape at 22,000 characters per second.

- An Intercomp III Disk Storage System with a storage capacity of 3,072,000 16-bit words and an average access time of 50 milliseconds.

- An IBM 2310 Disk Storage System with a capacity of 512,000 16-bit words.

- A Calcomp 618 Flatbed Plotter with 24-vector input command format. Increment size is 0.05/ 0.025 mm. Any one of four pens can be selected under program control.

The Calcomp 618 plotter will be placed under the control of a separate computer. The plotter, at a speed of 200 IPS, takes twelve hours of computer time to plot a 30,000 sounding data file. In order to increase processing speed and eliminate the endless hours of plotting on the IBM 1130, the plotter will be interfaced to a Digital Equipment Corporation PDP-8 computer. Plotter commands will be generated on the IBM 1130 and written on magnetic tape. The magnetic tape will then be processed by the PDP-8, and all plotting will be performed by that system, thus freeing the IBM 1130 system for other processing. This modification, along with the increase in core storage and high speed printer replacement, will correct what are now judged to be the three major drawbacks to the AMC computer-plotter system.

Figure 8.   Atlantic Marine Center Computer-Plotter System, from left to right: Digitronics Paper Tape Reader, IBM 1131 computer, INFOTEC Magnetic Tape Transports, IBM 1132 Printer

Software and processing

In August 1970, the Electronic Data Processing Branch of
the Atlantic Marine Center was established and development of the IBM 1130 software for hydrographic processing began. FORTRAN IV was to serve as the primary programing language, and assembler language was to be used
only in areas where FORTRAN was not feasible or where
significant increases in processing speed could be
achieved.

Approximately seventy-five operational programs have been
written to date for the shore-based processing of hydrographic data. All programs were written by AMC personnel.
The Electronic Data Processing Branch at AMC consists of
two full-time civilian professional programers, one full-
time civilian computer specialist, and one commissioned officer.

Of the five types of navigational control--hyperbolic,
range-range, visual, and the two hybrid systems, hyper-
visual and range-visual--the hyperbolic system was chosen
as the prime area of concern. Hydrographic surveys performed under hyperbolic control would be the first surveys
processed at AMC. Since the raw data for surveys made
under hyperbolic and range-range mode were recorded on
ship in the same format, minor changes need only be made
to the hyperbolic software system to enable the range-
range data to be processed. Visual surveys are recorded
in a different format; but since both hybrid systems use
the visual format, only two major programing systems would
be required to process any survey: one system to process
surveys performed totally in the electronic mode and another
system to process surveys utilizing visual navigation.

The processing of hydrographic data from the initial raw
data recorded on paper tape to the final smooth sheet
plot is accomplished in nine major phases.

Phase I

The raw data for a hydrographic survey and the associated sounding and position fix corrections are received in paper tape form. The paper tapes are read
on the high-speed paper tape reader, the data is
checked for possible errors (time errors, invalid
characters, invalid formats, etc.), all discovered
errors are listed on the printer, and the entire
survey is written in two magnetic disk files--one
for the raw data and one for the corrector data.
From this point on in the processing, the data is
invisible.

Phase II

The list of errors produced in Phase I is reviewed by
hydrographic survey verifiers, and the appropriate
corrections are submitted to the EDP Branch to be

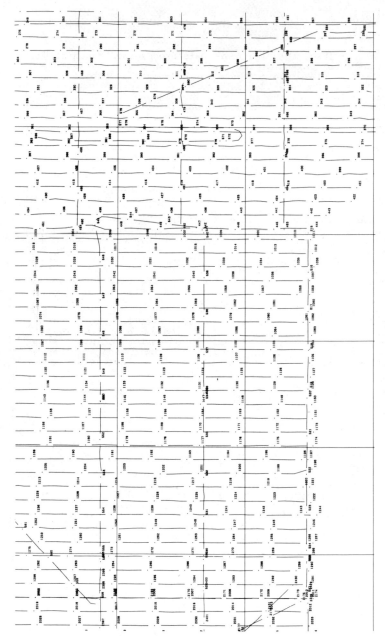

Figure 9. Machine Plotted Geographic Position Overlay

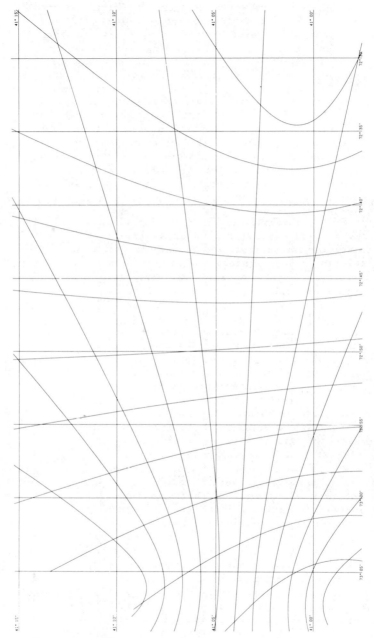

Figure 10. Machine Plotted Hyperbolic Lattice

167

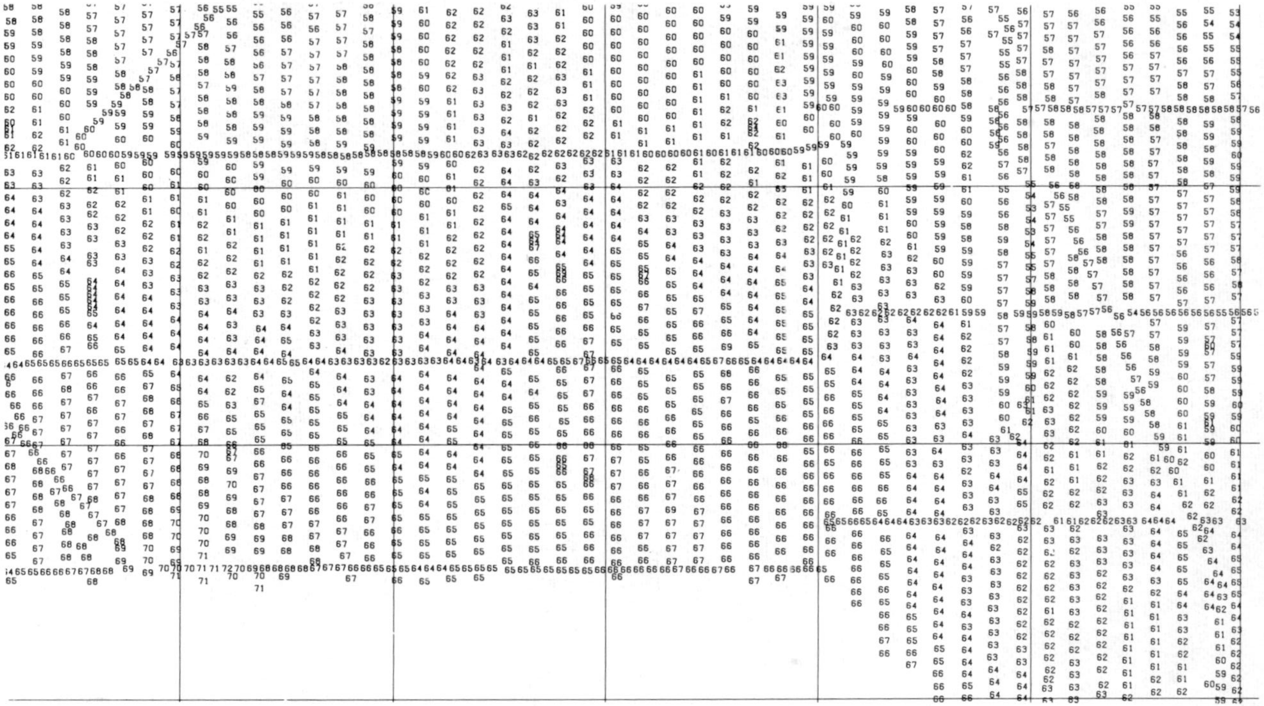

Figure 11. Machine Plotted Sounding Overlay

168

applied to the disk files. The corrections are key-punched and then processed on the IBM 1130 to update the raw data or corrector disk files.

Phase III

The raw data and corrector magnetic disk files are merged, creating one master disk file; geographic positions (latitude, longitude) are computed; a geographic position overlay is plotted, as shown in Figure 9; and a listing showing all geographic positions is produced. In addition to plotting a geographic position overlay, software has been designed to plot the polyconic grid with meridians and parallels labeled, plot a hyperbolic or range-range lattice, as shown in Figure 10, and plot geographic locations of triangulation and topographic stations.

Phase IV

The preliminary geographic position plot and associated position listing are reviewed, and a list of position corrections are submitted to the EDP Branch to update the disk files in the same manner as in Phase II. Data can not only be corrected, but also added or deleted from the disk file.

Phase V

Echo Sounder Transducer corrections, sound velocity corrections, and smooth tide corrections are applied to the soundings on the disk file, and a reduced sounding is computed.

Phase VI

A special excess removal program is executed, which analyzes the entire survey disk file and determines which soundings will overlap or overprint when plotted or are excess to plotting requirements or needs. The shoal soundings are selected to be plotted, and the remaining soundings are labeled on the disk file as excess information.

Phase VII

The preliminary smooth sheet and an overlay of all excess soundings are plotted. Figure 11 shows a section of a sounding overlay.

Phase VIII

The preliminary smooth sheet is reviewed, and corrections are submitted to the EDP Branch and applied to the data in the same manner as in Phase II.

Phase IX

The final smooth sheet and geographic position overlay
are plotted and the smooth data are copied from magnetic
disk to magnetic tape for submittal to Headquarters.

The above descriptions were not intended to totally define
the entire operation on the IBM 1130 Computing System.
The only intent here was to give the reader a broad picture of the overall system. However, a few of the
special features need to be pointed out.

1. The plotter subroutine package, called by all
   plotter programs to perform the actual plotting,
   was completely redesigned. Programers do not
   have to be concerned with the size or shape
   of any sheet to be plotted. Simply by telling
   the plotter software the sheet dimensions and
   whether it is a long N-S plot or a long E-W
   plot, the plotter routines will guarantee that
   no plotting will occur beyond the sheet limits.
   In addition, the software will notify the operator, on request, of any position which does
   not fall within the limits. Also, the plotter
   I/O command table will be automatically altered
   to perform an effective rotation of 90° for
   those sheets which require a long Y-axis.

2. The magnetic disk files are normally dumped to
   magnetic tape for storage purposes. No survey
   ever remains on disk from start to finish. The
   entire contents of a disk file can be copied
   to magnetic tape in eight minutes and also restored to the disk in the same length of time.

3. The contents of a disk file always remain in
   the same order as the raw data paper tapes were
   processed. In cases where the data needs to
   be sorted on time and day, such as for application of tide corrections, a modified tag sort
   is used. An entire disk file can be sorted in
   fifteen minutes, and the tags generated then
   become a permanent part of the disk file.

4. A disk file protection feature has been incorporated into the software system so that no
   disk file can be accidentally destroyed before
   copying it to magnetic tape.

5. Each sounding record is stored on the disk with
   all of the information needed for that record.
   In the case of hyperbolic control, each disk
   record contains:

   ● Vessel Identification

   ● Year

   ● Time

- Feet, Fathom or Meter Indicator

- Raw Depth

- Velocity Correction

- Tide Correction

- Transducer Correction

- Position Number

- Electronic Control Pattern I and its Correction

- Electronic Control Pattern II and its Correction

- Latitude-Longitude

- Reduced Sounding

- Excess Sounding Indicator

6. The same survey disk file can be listed on the IBM 1132 Printer in a number of ways as follows:

- Position data for each record

- Sounding data for each record

- All fields for each record

- Each record's sounding data and actual plotted depths. Plotted depths may not be in the same unit as raw depths. Figure 12 shows an all-field printout.

The IBM 1130 Computer-Plotter System at AMC has obvious advantages over its predecessor in Seattle. The card-oriented system has been all but eliminated. During program execution, less operator intervention is required. The IBM 1130 is a much faster computer, thereby significantly reducing processing time. The use of FORTRAN IV as the primary computer language makes programing tasks much simpler. And most important, the IBM 1130 is a disk-operating system in that the entire software system is resident on the disk; therefore, any program can be called into operation with only one or two statements, and batch processing is permitted.

Certainly, the new system has its disadvantages, but they are relatively minor. Even though individual programs are much simpler to write, the coordination of all programs into one major processing system becomes a much

VES ID	YR	DAY	TIME	IND	DEPTH	VTAB	VEL	TIDE	TRA	POS NUM	TYP	P1CR	P1C	P2CR	P2C	COORDINATES LAT	COORDINATES LONG	RECORD NUMBER	RED. DEPTH	EXCESS
2930	70	064	232806	0	38.0	2	6	6	114	3028	11	76.11	-0.45	279.28	-0.13	33 43 49.05	78 23 18.52	2305.	50.6	0
2930	70	064	232836	0	38.8	2	6	6	114	0	11	75.25	-0.45	279.32	-0.13	33 43 54.62	78 23 18.64	2306.	51.4	0
2930	70	064	232906	0	39.1	2	6	6	114	0	11	74.43	-0.45	279.35	-0.13	33 43 59.94	78 23 18.80	2307.	51.7	0
2930	70	064	232936	0	38.7	2	6	6	114	0	11	73.57	-0.45	279.47	-0.13	33 44 5.56	78 23 18.66	2308.	51.3	0
2930	70	064	233006	0	38.5	2	6	6	114	0	11	72.72	-0.45	279.63	-0.13	33 44 11.14	78 23 18.38	2309.	51.1	0
2930	70	064	233036	0	39.8	2	6	6	114	0	11	71.90	-0.45	279.91	-0.13	33 44 16.56	78 23 17.67	2310.	52.4	0
2930	70	064	233106	0	39.0	2	6	6	114	3029	11	71.06	-0.45	279.98	-0.13	33 44 22.12	78 23 17.73	2311.	51.6	0
2930	70	064	233136	0	38.0	2	6	6	114	0	11	70.24	-0.45	279.92	-0.13	33 44 27.56	78 23 18.24	2312.	50.6	0
2930	70	064	233206	0	37.5	2	6	6	114	0	11	69.40	-0.45	279.91	-0.13	33 44 33.16	78 23 18.60	2313.	50.1	0
2930	70	064	233236	0	37.5	2	6	6	114	0	11	68.56	-0.45	279.92	-0.13	33 44 38.79	78 23 18.89	2314.	50.1	0
2930	70	064	233306	0	37.0	2	6	6	114	0	11	67.75	-0.45	280.16	-0.13	33 44 44.28	78 23 18.37	2315.	49.6	1
2930	70	064	233336	0	37.2	2	6	6	114	0	11	66.93	-0.45	280.35	-0.13	33 44 49.86	78 23 18.04	2316.	49.8	0
2930	70	064	233406	0	38.0	2	6	6	114	3030	11	66.14	-0.45	280.37	-0.13	33 44 55.23	78 23 18.30	2317.	50.6	0
2930	70	064	233436	0	38.2	2	6	6	114	0	11	65.35	-0.45	280.36	-0.13	33 45 0.62	78 23 18.68	2318.	50.8	0
2930	70	064	233506	0	38.5	2	6	6	114	0	11	64.51	-0.45	280.44	-0.13	33 45 6.40	78 23 18.77	2319.	51.1	0
2930	70	064	233536	0	38.5	2	6	6	114	0	11	63.72	-0.45	280.65	-0.13	33 45 11.90	78 23 18.40	2320.	51.1	0

Figure 12. All-Field Data Printout

more complex task. Since the use of disk and magnetic tape has made the data "invisible," users, not completely familiar with computers, tend to distrust the reliability of software. In addition, the invisibility of the data requires special programs for the sole purpose of testing software reliability.

The Atlantic Marine Center system is only the second phase of shore-based processing for the production of smooth sheets. Undoubtedly, it is a major step forward in the total automation of processing marine data for coastal mapping.

CONCLUSIONS

The National Ocean Survey has developed computer-assisted data acquisition and processing systems which increase the speed and efficiency of producing a hydrographic survey. Computer-assisted acquisition enables the hydrographer to choose the survey pattern, unrestrained by the geometry of the electronic positioning system. Time, depth and position are recorded automatically at a much higher rate than could be recorded manually and with virtually no possibility of recording error. Automatically entered data correctors have enabled the development of new instruments and techniques, such as the real-time telemetered tide gage. The shipboard computer has opened new possibilities for the future; among these are the development of digital electronic sextants which may result in more efficient surveys in areas where visual control must be used, and a heave corrector to compensate for vertical motion of the sounding vessel.

The computer has established its usefulness beyond basic hydrography by assisting in calibration of electronic positioning equipment and in the detection of lane jumps in addition to the utility and off-line routines. Machine plotting under computer control has eliminated much of the inefficient drudgery of hand plotting the thousands of soundings of a typical survey.

The shore-based processing system provides a means of applying correctors to data quickly and efficiently, of selecting critical data and of eliminating superfluous data. The shore-based plotter provides a highly precise, neat plot at high speed.

Both shipboard and shore-based systems have been developed over a period of years, and both now offer modern equipment and refined, proven techniques. Development and implementation costs have been modest at a time when data processing costs have been high.

BIBLIOGRAPHY

Ferrara, Angelo A., _Shipboard Computers and Data Acqui-sion Systems_, 1970, paper prepared for the Public Seminar for Marine Engineering, Tokyo, Japan, March 1970.

Upham, Clinton D., Charles H. McClure, _The NOS HYDROPLOT/ HYDROLOG System_, 1972, paper prepared for the Eleventh Annual Canadian Hydrographer's Conference, Ottawa, Canada, February 1972.

Wallace, Jack L., _HYDROPLOT/HYDROLOG Systems Manual_, NOAA Handbook No. 24, NOS Technical Manual No. 2, September 1971.

THE LIMITATIONS OF PRESENT
COASTAL MAPPING PROGRAMME IN GUYANA
AND THE NEED FOR ITS EXPANSION

Mr. Paul L. Kranenburg
Superintendent of Coastal,
River and Engineering Surveys
Government of Guyana, South America

BIOGRAPHICAL SKETCH

Paul L. Kranenburg is Superintendent of Coastal, River and
Engineering Surveys, Ministry of Works Hydraulics and
Supply, Government of Guyana. Educated at St. Stanislaus
College, Guyana, he served an apprenticeship in Survey
Department of Public Works Department of Guyana, and was
licensed as a Surveyor in 1950. He has been involved with
coastal surveys and mapping in Guyana for 24 years. In
1960-61 he was attached to Delft Hydraulics Laboratory of
Holland while they were executing the United Nations
sponsored Demerara Coastal Investigation. In 1969-1970 he
was attached to NEDECO of Holland executing a Sea Defence
Feasibility Study for the World Bank. At present, he is on
training Programme with the U. S. Naval Oceanographic Office.

ABSTRACT

Coastal mapping of Guyana was done by the British prior to
independence in 1966. It is now performed by the Ministry
of Works Hydraulics and Supply. The present mapping
programme is limited to one-half of the coastline and a
width of only 10 miles. Of the 100 mile wide continential
shelf, a 30 mile wide zone adjacent to the shoreline is
comprised of mud which forms itself into waves with a
length of 30 miles. These travel along the coast at 1 mile
per annum. This phenomenon has a bearing on the hydraulic
problems of the country's low lying coastal zone; because
of this, improved mapping is desirable.

INTRODUCTION

Guyana lies roughly between 57-61°W longitude, and 1-8°N
latitude, and forms a part of that zone of South America
between the Amazon and Orinoco Rivers known as the Guiana
coast. Five countries, (Brazil, French Guiana, Surinam,
Guyana - formerly, British Guiana - and Venezuela) border
the Atlantic Ocean between these large streams. Figure 1
shows the location of Guyana in South America.

The country, which received independence from Britain in
May of 1966, has a population of 700,000 and a land area
of approximately 83,000 square miles. It's coastline
measures 275 miles, as the crow flies; along one half of
which the majority of the population lives. Due to the low
lying nature of the coast lands and the peculiar behavior
pattern of the seabed adjacent to it, coastal mapping is
an important factor to Guyana. Unfortunately, the instrumentation available for the work severely limits what can
be done.

FIGURE 1—SOUTH AMERICA, SHOWING LOCATION OF GUYANA

HISTORICAL BACKGROUND

First coastal mapping of the area was done in the mid 19th century by the British. This work was restricted to the major estuaries and the areas immediately adjacent. The first comprehensive chart of the area produced by the British Admiralty in 1852 was based on data from the Spanish of the Northwest zone, and Dutch and French of the Northeast. No further survey or mapping of the area was done until 1957 when a resurvey of the area was started by the HMS Vidal. This was never completed. Between the Corentyne and Essequibo Rivers, the surveys were completed prior to 1966, but no chart to my knowledge has been produced. The likelihood that the survey will ever be completed is very remote, as the status of the country has changed from that of colony to a sovereign state.

In 1935, because of engineering problems, the Ministry of Works Hydraulics and Supply, then known as the Public Works Department, commenced surveys of a 30 mile stretch of coastline immediately east and west of Georgetown, the capital city of the country. A 10 mile expansion to the west was made in 1940 and here it rested until 1968 when one-half of the coastline was surveyed. Data from the surveys 1935-1940 were not disseminated but used by the department.

PRESENT MAPPING PROGRAMME AND LIMITING FACTORS

Coastal mapping in Guyana is the responsibility of the Hydraulics Division of the Ministry of Works, Hydraulics and Supply. This has resulted because the hydraulic problems of the coastal zone of the country make engineers the greatest users of this type of data. There is little international and coastal maritime trade. The mapping is handled as three distinct phases of activity; Offshore, which is of primary interest, Foreshore, and finally, Topographic immediately adjacent to the coastline.

The present offshore programme extends from the Corentyne estuary to the Pomeroon estuary, a distance of approximately 125 miles. Seaward, the extent varies between 8 and 12 miles. The programme calls for the annual survey and mapping of this area with quarterly data off the areas of high economic value which are immediately east and west of Georgetown. Soundings are made on lines at predetermined locations which are at approximately 1 mile intervals. Figure 2 shows the offshore area surveyed under the present programme and target area proposed.

Offshore surveys are at present, executed by two small survey launches, the "H. N. Critchlow" and the "Sir Frederick." The Critchlow has a length of 62 feet, a draft of 6 feet, and a beam of 15 feet. It was built locally and put into service in May 1961. The other vessel, the Sir Frederick, was built in Scotland in 1948 and put into service in 1949. It has a length of 58 feet, a beam of 10 feet, and a draft of 5 1/2 feet. These vessels are fitted with Kelvin Hughes M. S. 26 Echo Sounders; none of them have aboard any Position Fixing Equipment. Positioning is done by the traditional method of sextant angles, with

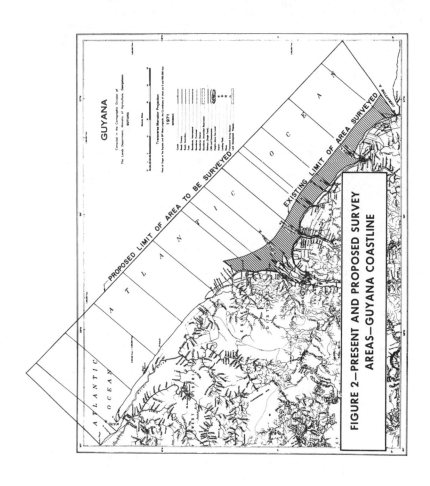

FIGURE 2—PRESENT AND PROPOSED SURVEY
AREAS—GUYANA COASTLINE

plots using Three Arm Protractors or Station Pointers.
Where high frequency surveys are required, sextant angle
charts have been produced to facilitate plotting. Because
of the importance of data close to the shoreline, 18 foot
wooden dinghies are used to link up from the inner limit
handled by the launches to the shore.

The coastal zone of Guyana which is on an average 25 miles
wide is a tidal area which is a mere 1 to 1 1/2 feet above
mean sea level. The spring range of the tides off the
coast vary between 11 feet at the Corentyne estuary, in the
East, to 6 feet at the Waini estuary in the Northwest.
Figure 3 shows mean tide curves in the vicinity of
Georgetown and the relationship of the average land level
to these. Only a small portion of the coastline has any
conspicious buildings or structures, the remainder is
forested by wild mangrove and courida.

The nature of coastline makes it imperative to build marks
along the shore to be used for position fixes. At present,
the method used is to construct towers 110 feet in height
and on these fly flags 10 feet by 6 feet. The Ministry
has 6 of these towers; these are erected at three mile
intervals and shifted along the coast as the survey proceeds.
The size of the marks and poor visibility, inherent to
tropical weather conditions, limit the offshore capability
of surveys to a mere 10 miles of the continental shelf,
which is on an average 100 miles wide. A photograph of the
launches and a tower is shown on the following page.

To further limit the work, the Ministry has no Electronic
Distance Measuring Equipment, and from the Pomeroon River
to the Waini River on the northwest coast, there are no
roads; it is, therefore, impossible to establish control or
build bases for the towers. For this reason, mapping of
this area has not yet been undertaken.

Foreshore surveys are made to study changes of the tidal
area immediately adjacent to the High Water Mark. The
section of coast covered is the same as under the offshore
programme and are executed with the same frequency. I have
not referred to the zone as beaches because the material is
silt, consolidated in some areas, and unconsolidated in
others. These surveys are made with engineer's level and
level rods. Again, sections are made of the foreshore at
predetermined distances varying between 1,000 feet apart
and 1 mile apart. The 1,000 foot interval is restricted to
zones of high economic value. The distance offshore that
the measurements are made varies between 600 feet and
2,000 feet. The surveys are most unsatisfactory as they
cannot be extended far enough seaward in areas of unconsolidated silt; a further disadvantage is that level readings
have to be taken over long distances with resulting in-
accuracy.

Aerial surveys would in my opinion, be the best approach to
foreshore mapping but the entire country has no capability
for this type of exercise. All photogrammetry must be made
by contract to foreign firms with the resulting high cost,
mobilization being a major item. Photogrammetry that has
been done to date is restricted to isolated areas mainly

SURVEY VESSEL—SIR FREDERICK

SURVEY VESSEL—
H. N. CRITCHLOW

SURVEY TOWER

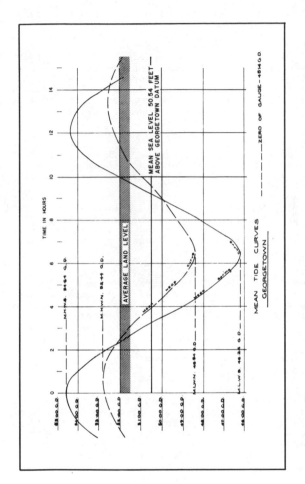

FIGURE 3—RELATIONSHIP OF AVERAGE LAND LEVEL TO MEAN TIDE CURVES—GEORGETOWN

inland. It is all at varying scales and is uncontrolled, which means that no comprehensive study of the foreshore can be made from this data.

Topographic mapping immediately adjacent to the shoreline is done for the planning and construction of Sea Defence Works, necessary because of the low shoreline, and the design, construction and maintenance of Drainage and Irrigation Works. Surveys for mapping are executed using conventional or rather traditional methods and equipment. It is a slow process especially with the small staff available for this work. True enough, the area is so flat that it is hardly likely that relief can be obtained by photogrammetric methods. It can be of use for the production of planemetric maps on which elevations can be superimposed. The swampy areas of the coastline along the N. W. Coast are so forbiding that no mapping has been undertaken here. The solution seems to be the development or utilization of some specialized transport equipment to make these areas accessible.

As can be appreciated from the above, the mapping programme in Guyana is severely hampered by the lack of proper instrumentation. Two other factors influence our mapping programme; these are outdated drafting techniques and lack of trained staff.

The old drafting techniques are still in vogue, this results in the slow processing of survey data from the stage of the smooth sheet to the finished maps and charts. The obstacle to improvement in this avenue is finance to purchase the modern reproduction equipment.

Surveyors, for work at sea, are recruited from personnel trained in Land Surveying who then receive on-the-job training. Unfortunately, not many are attracted to this branch of surveying. To further complicate matters, comes the issue of "Brain Drain." Many of the surveyors trained in Guyana migrate to the Bahamas where they are paid much more renumerative salaries, others go to Canada primarily to further their education, but never return to the same field of endeavor, if they do return at all.

SEA BED BEHAVIOR - GUIANA COAST

Studies by Deiphuis (Delft Hydro Lab, 1962) and Allersma (Delft Hydro Lab, 1969) using data collected in Guyana and Surinam, have established that to a distance of thirty miles offshore, the material which makes up the sea bed is silt, forming banks which are in a state of constant movement. Figure 4 shows an average section of the banks and its relationship with suspended matter.

Charts of the area such as the one at Figure 5 of the Surinam coast shows the wave-like pattern of the mud banks. Huge shoals extend obliquely seaward from the shore at more or less regular intervals. The average "wave length" is about thirty miles. Figure 6 shows the scheme of features of the mud shoals.

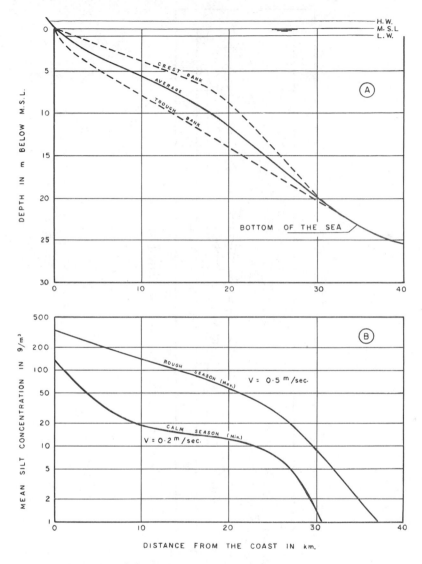

FIGURE 4—(A) AVERAGE SECTION ACROSS THE COAST
(B) DISTRIBUTION OF SUSPENDED SEDIMENT

183

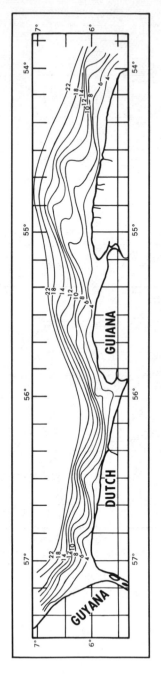

FIGURE 5—DEPTH CONTOURS OFF DUTCH GUIANA

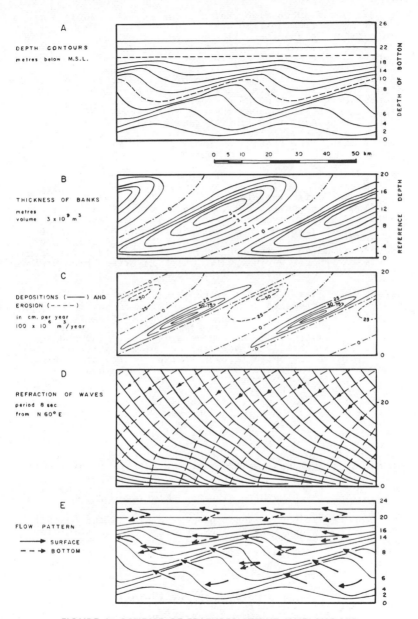

A

DEPTH CONTOURS
metres below M.S.L.

0 5 10   20   30   40   50 km

B

THICKNESS OF BANKS
metres
volume 3 x 10^9 m^3

C

DEPOSITIONS (———) AND
EROSION (- - - -)
in cm. per year
100 x 10^6 m^3/year

D

REFRACTION OF WAVES
period 8 sec
from N 60° E

E

FLOW PATTERN
———▶ SURFACE
- - -▶ BOTTOM

FIGURE 6—SCHEME OF FEATURES ABOUT MUD SHOALS

Comparison of successive charts shows that the whole pattern slowly moves from east to west. The average speed of propagation is about one mile per year which gives a periodic recurrence of thirty years. Figure 7 shows the changes of the sea bed in front of a portion of the Guyana coastline. The pattern of shoals is accompanied by a pattern of accretion and erosion of the adjacent shoreline. An advancing shore with a drying mud bank in front of it occurs where the crest of a shoal meets the coast. An eroding shore is found at the end of a trough. Figure 8 shows the changes resulting at the shoreline with time. From this figure, it is possible to evaluate the period of recurrence of the shoals and their rate of travel along the coast.

Major hydraulic problems on the coastal plain arise from the lowness of the land and the surcharge of water which accrues not only from plentiful rainfall but also from the overflow of the numerous rivers which traverse it. As mentioned previously, the coast is below sea level at high tides. Rainfall along the coast averages about 60 inches per year. Water runoff is slow and natural drainage poor. 90 percent of Guyana's population live along the coast in a constant struggle against water which involves three aspects: Sea Defence, Drainage, and Irrigation.

Sea Defence dams and walls are essential for the protection of developed areas and are a prerequisite to any developmental works. Wherever shoals occur in front of the Sea Defence, the area is protected from heavy wave attack, however, with troughs, the converse is true. The mud shoals also adversely affect drainage of the agricultural areas which is effected through sluices to the sea. Figures 9 and 10 show the effect of the shoals on the drainage.

Figure 9 shows Water Level Readings of a sluice which is operating in a zone of erosion and which is providing optimum drainage. Figure 10, however, shows the readings for a sluice in a zone of accretion and the resulting inefficient drainage. To further illustrate the effect, Figure 11 shows a comparison of tide curves offshore and just inside the mouth of one of the smaller rivers. Here again, it is evident how adversely the drainage and resulting run-off of these small rivers are affected.

THE NEED FOR IMPROVED MAPPING

The impact that the offshore phenomena has on the country's economy can be appreciated from the slight insight given. More knowledge about the processes occuring in the area are of importance in relation to navigation, fishing, possible offshore construction works, coastal protection, and agriculture.

Factors determining the behaviour of the sediments which form the shoals are waves, and swell, the currents, and properties of the sediment. There is need for instrumentation capable of measuring these parameters. Further, because the phenomena prevail along 1,000 miles of coastline, it is desirable that there should be coordination of efforts of the countries affected and foreign investigators.

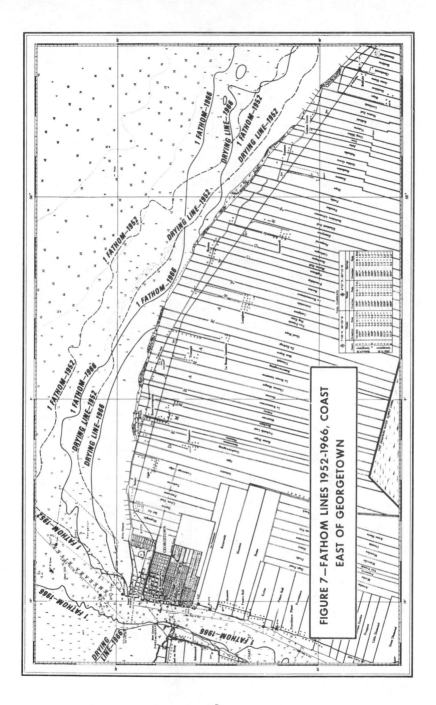

FIGURE 7—FATHOM LINES 1952-1966, COAST EAST OF GEORGETOWN

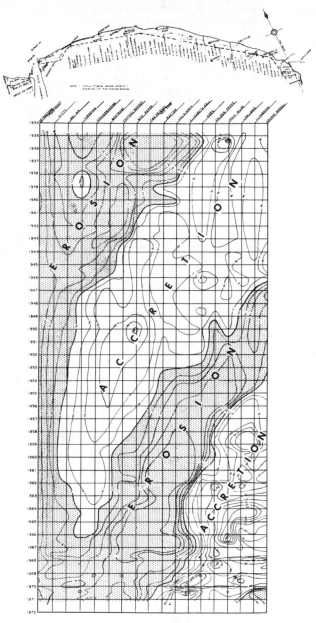

**FIGURE 8—MOVEMENT OF LOW WATER 1934-1971,
COAST EAST OF GEORGETOWN**

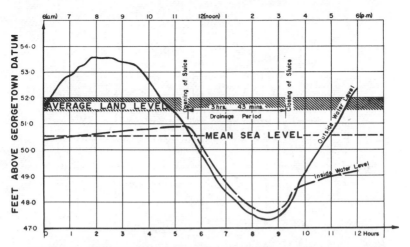

FIGURE 9—WATER LEVEL READINGS AT SLUICE IN EROSION ZONE

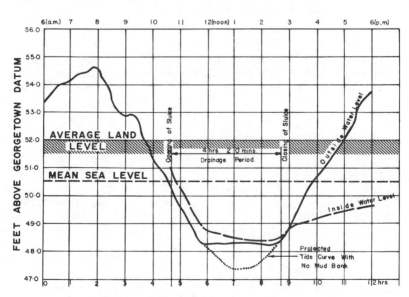

FIGURE 10—WATER LEVEL READINGS AT SLUICE IN ACCRETION ZONE

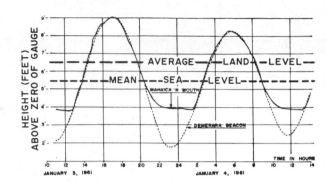

**FIGURE 11—TIDAL CURVES RECORDED AT DEMERARA BEACON
AND MAHAICA, 3-4 JANUARY 1961**

with the acquisition of more knowledge from coastal
mapping and investigation, proper prediction will be
possible. This, in turn, would greatly assist in the
programming and design of Sea Defence and Drainage Works
which are two major items of expenditure on the countries
annual budget.

REFERENCES

Delft Hydraulics Laboratory - Demerara Coastal
                              Investigation - 1962

Ministry of Works   - Sea Defence Programme 1968-72
Hydraulics and Supply   Guyana - 1967

NEDECO   - Surinam Transportation Study
                             Report on hydraulic
                             investigation
                             The Hague - 1968

E. Allersma   - Mud on the oceanic shelf of
                            Guyana - 1969

Ministry of Economic   - Recommendation for Pumped
Development   Drainage - Guyana 1970

190

SOCIO-ECONOMIC IMPACT MAPPING
FOR
COASTAL ZONE MANAGEMENT

E.W.Seabrook Hull, Editor, & John R. Botzum, Executive Editor
Coastal Zone Management
1056 National Press Building
Washington, D.C.20004

BIOGRAPHICAL SKETCHES

E.W.Seabrook Hull is Editor of the Nautilus Publications Ocean Science News,
Coastal Zone Management and World Ecology-2000. His undergraduate education was in physics at Union College, Schenectady, N.Y., interrupted by World
War II where he served as a Naval Aviator with the U.S. Marine Corps. In
1970 he received an M.A. degree in Marine Affairs from the University of Rhode
Island and shortly thereafter accepted a Fellowship at the Woodrow Wilson International Center for Scholars in Washington to develop the bases for an international
legal regime for global pollution management. Most of his professional career
has been as journalist, editor and writer in Washington and London. He is a consultant in coastal and ocean management problems, most recently having conducted an extensive survey and analysis for East Carolina University and the College
of the Albemarle of commercial fisheries problems, potentials and curricula
needs in the sound region of eastern North Carolina.

John R. Botzum is Executive Editor of the Nautilus Publications Ocean Science
News, Coastal Zone Management and World Ecology-2000. He received his A.B.
degree in liberal arts from the University of St. Andrews in Scotland and did
graduate work in English at the University of Connecticutt, where he also served
as an English instructor. During World War II he served with the U.S. merchant
marine. He has over 20 years editorial experience in Washington working for
newspapers, magazines and newsletters, including for some years Bureau Chief
for Penton Publications and as White House correspondent under both the Kennedy
and Johnson Administrations. He has served as a consultant to both industry
and independent research organizations on Washington affairs. He has been with
Nautilus for three years, having served before that as a regular contributing
editor.

ABSTRACT

A summary of the coastal zone, what it is and something of the nature of the
activities and conflicts encountered there. A proposal is offered for a system
of socio-economic impact charts to serve as valuable planning and management
tools at all levels of government and private interests. The system would
consist of a series of transparent overlay sets, each set to treat with a different
aspect of the coastal zone problem. The system would be computer-based and
its output would be available either in the form of overlays for manual/visual
manipulation or in the form of magnetic tapes for subsequent computer manipulation by the ultimate user. The overlays would be particularly useful to
local authorities at the county and smaller municiple levels where rural power
structures exercise great control over much of the nation's future coastal zone

development. Overlay sets are proposed to treat with such management sensitive areas as: Basic natural resources, use options, present uses, use impacts, use conflicts, use demand, resource alterations, future projections, and sources and nature of jurisdictions exercised in the coastal zone. NOAA is proposed as the administrative agency for this national coastal information system, which would function somewhat after the manner of the National Technical Information Service, though with the added capability of responding to specific sets of assumptions as proposed by the various users.

INTRODUCTION

Lew Alexander, Head of the University of Rhode Island's Department of Geography and Master of Marine Affairs Program and Director of the Law of the Sea Institute, has described the coastal zone as a "state of mind". If this is so, it is schizophrenic in the extreme, for there are about as many definitions of the coastal zone as there are people, agencies and institutions trying to define it. And, these are legion. A question, of course, is: How do you manage something you can't define?

There is one thing on which there is common agreement. In terms of population growth, rising economic activities and environmental stress, it is the nation's number one pressure point. Some 53 per cent of the U.S. population -- over 106 million people -- live within those counties and cities within 50 miles of our coasts. Some estimates see 80 per cent of the population living within that zone by the year 2,000 -- as many as 225 million people. We are talking about some 86,600 miles of detailed shoreline on the Atlantic, Pacific, Gulf and Arctic coasts, plus 11,000 miles on the Great Lakes.

Most of the housing construction, therefore, in the next 28 years must be within the coastal zone. New U.S. housing needs are placed at 1-to-2 million units per year -- most in the coastal zone -- with all that means by way of sewage and other waste disposal, transportation, public services, utilities, land consumption, etc.

Most of our so-called "energy gap" is going to be met near, at or close offshore of our coastline. Included are such activities as the construction of nuclear power plants on or close to prime coastal land (always the "best" site for many reasons), placement of floating or bottom-sited power plants just offshore, production of offshore oil and gas, enlargement of present port and harbor facilities to receive oil and gas imports, offshore petroleum terminals, points where pipelines transect the coast, associated refinaries, tank farms, etc....

Or, from another viewpoint, let's look at recreational boating in California, for example. According to one estimate the projected demand for boating slips between now and the year 2,000 would preempt all other uses of the shoreline in the southern third of California. Clearly, an unacceptable prospect.

DEFINING "COASTAL ZONE"

But, just what is the "coastal zone"? What are we talking about? Answers vary.

The seaward limits of the coastal zone are generally conceded by the coastal states as extending to the limits of the U.S. territorial sea (3 n. mi. off U.S. ocean and Gulf of Mexico coasts; to the international boundary in the Great Lakes) -- though even this is fuzzy. Regardless of official U.S. territorial sea claims, some states are disputing the limits of their seaward boundaries with the Federal government in the courts. Washington already concedes that state seabed mineral rights offshore of Louisiana and the west coast of Florida extend out to three marine leagues (over 10 n. mi.). In some areas the baselines from which such distances are measured are vague themselves. The mangrove shores of southern Florida have an exposed land difference of several miles between mean high and mean low water -- all of it hidden from view in an impenetrable tangle of mangrove roots. A similar situation exists in the Louisiana bayou country.

State fisheries legislation and regulations tend to control the activities of any vessels landing their catch within the state's jurisdiction, regardless of where the fish are caught -- within or beyond the territorial sea. Some states are attempting to push their pollution control authority to include all vessels which operate in such a manner as to pollute or threaten to pollute state shore and coastal waters regardless of whether they're in the territorial sea or not. The picture is not simple and clear cut.

Federal seaward coastal zone jurisdiction also varies with some authority exercised within the three-mile limit but other authority exercised to the limits of the legal -- as against the geological -- continental shelf. In consideration of the exploitability provision of the 1958 Geneva Continental Shelf Convention, this is a creeping definition: As oil, mining or other operations on the seafloor are undertaken successfully in progressively deeper water, so does coastal-nation jurisdiction over a large and important aspect of ocean space and operations creep outwards.

Both Canada and the Soviet Union have extended pollution jurisdiction over ships' operations in the Arctic regions well beyond their claimed territorial seas. And, upwards of a dozen or so nations have extended their territorial sea claims to 100-to-200 nautical miles from their shoreward baselines. You might say that the seaward limit of the coastal zone is a floating limit or, as Alexander says, a state of mind. Few have any illusions, incidentally, that the 1973 Stockholm law of the sea conference will do anything to clarify the situation.

If you stand on the beach with your back to the sea and look inland, the picture is even more confused. One report [1] out of Texas A&M University talks about the Texas coastal zone as including some 72 counties to heights above sealevel of some 2,000 feet and many miles inland. This is, in part, because they're using an impact of fisheries definition. The Office of the Governor's Coastal Zone Resources Program [2] defines the coastal zone as including 36 counties, extending seaward 10.35 miles, and rising to a land altitude of 500 feet (the limits of the coastal plain). Another Texas A&M reference pegs it at 47 counties. Take your choice.

Looking at the Gulf of Mexico as a whole, it can be argued that from an environmental impact point of view the Gulf coastal zone includes the drainage basins of all the rivers that feed into it, including the Mississippi and the Rio Grande. Thus, some could contend, the Gulf of Mexico coastal zone includes over half the states in the Union, the eastern watershed of Mexico and a few southerly fragments of Canada. Before you discard this as ludicrous, note that in 1968 some 696,000 tons of solid waste are estimated to have drained into the Gulf from this combined watershed and that the annual discharge of DDT into the Gulf is some 225,000 pounds -- most of both originating far away in America's heartland, hundreds of miles from the sea.

The state of Georgia defines the inland limits of its coastal zone [3] as extending "to a boundary which is the westernmost line of those counties which contain the Pleistocene 'Wicomico' (100-foot contour) shoreline." Interestingly, the "Wicomico Line" was arrived at by connecting straight baselines between those points in rivers, estuaries, etc., where tidal influences cease. Such baselines follow quite closely the contours of this ancient beach. Delaware has enacted legislation which "absolutely prohibits" the development within an area six miles deep along the Atlantic and Delaware Bay coasts and in offshore waters of any new industrial complex which has the potential to pollute "when equipment malfunctions or human error occurs." [4] New Jersey defines the landward portion of its coastal zone as: Land, water or subaqueous land lying between mean high tide and an elevation of

10 feet above sealevel.

The Florida Coastal Coordinating Council defines the coastal zone as the water and subsoil of the territorial sea and inland to a distance of 5-to-25 miles. In its Escarosa Project [5] this state is attempting to determine the feasibility of comprehensive and balanced-use zoning control over its coastal regions. It seeks to relate natural environmental support capacity and use-impact to permissible activities. A Wisconsin Shoreline Zoning Law concerns itself with land wit hin 1,000 feet of lakes and within 300 feet of river basins. Minnesota has a similar law. Hawaii has or had a proposal for prohibiting any activity which would mar the natural environment of a strip 100 feet wide along the ocean shore. This state also dreams of an Hawaiian archipelago claim which would include some 100,000 square miles and extend 1,500 nautical miles across the Pacific Ocean. The fact that Hawaii is the cross-roads for the Pacific drug traffic may or may not have any bearing on the origin of such dreams. Numerous states now have wetlands protection laws. A few have or are working towards master coastal zoning. One or two have and are beginning to enforce dune protection laws. Some have offshore mining laws; some do not. And, so forth....

If you begin to see what Alexander means by the coastal zone being a state of mind, a matter of viewpoint and terms of reference, fine, but this is only the beginning. There is hardly a coastal state that doesn't have in the works one or more pieces of major legislation affecting the coastal zone. Diversity of approach is the rule, not the exception. Just as there is little agreement on what constitutes the coastal zone, there is little agreement, too, on how best to approach its management.

Meanwhile, the National Coastal Zone Management Act of 1972 has passed the U.S. Senate and could conceivably become law this year. It, too attempts to define the coastal zone -- though we're not at all sure how much it narrows the field. In both the Senate and the House versions of the bill the coastal zone is defined thus:

> "Coastal zone means the coastal waters (including the lands therein and thereunder) strongly influenced by each other and in proximity to the shorelines of the several coastal states, and includes transitional and intertidal areas, salt marshes, wetlands, and beaches. The zone terminates in the Great Lakes waters at the international boundary between the U.S. and Canada and, in other areas, extends seaward to the outer limit of the U.S. Territorial Sea. The zone extends inland from the shorelines only to the extent necessary to control shorelands, the uses of which have a direct and significant impact on the coastal waters. Coastal waters means (1) in the Great Lakes area, the waters within the territorial jurisdiction of the U.S. consisting of the Great Lakes, their connecting waters, harbors, roadsteads, and estuary type areas such as bays, shallows, and marshes and (2) in other areas, those waters adjacent to the shorelines which contain a measurable tidal influence including, but not limited to, sounds, bays, lagoons, bayous, ponds, and estuaries."

At first glance this might appear to be pat, neat and to resolve all existing ambiguities. Not so! In the world at large 83 nations claim territorial seas in excess of three nautical miles. Some 55 claim 12 miles, and only 29 still claim three nautical miles. The U.S. is certain to go to a 12-mile limit (at least); the only question is when. When this happens, will state jurisdiction also extend to 12 miles? What happens to federally-issued mineral leases when that happens? Questions such as these can probably be resolved through legislation and/or court rulings, but even so the prospects for early order are not encouraging.

Even more dismaying are such imprecise terms (state-of-mind descriptors) as "coastal waters strongly influenced by each other..." and "...to the extent necessary to control shorelines..." Such language is hardly designed to pin down the limits of either the coastal zone or its management requirements. The Outer Banks of North Carolina and the extensive sound regions behind them, for example, have been described as "being within 500 miles of 100 million of the nation's population." Every one of these people has a potential for impacting on the North Carolina coastal zone -- depending on individual mobility and preference for sea and sound over hill and vale for vacations and holidays.

ACTIVITIES, CONFLICTS & IMPACTS

Coastal zone management and coastal zone impact considerations, therefore, must take into account factors which may be hundreds of miles from the coast and sited in quite different, entirely inland states. The flow of rivers to the coast and the pollutants they may or may not carry is quite analogous to the flow of people or of industry. Conversely, oil that is transported by sea and/or produced offshore and landed in coastal ports for inland consumption is also a case of distant but direct impact and involvement in coastal zone activities. The Federal Government, for example, would surely step in should the coastal states ban the landing of petroleum products in sufficient quantity to satisfy the demands of inland America. Unlikely? Not when you consider that this is precisely the kind of action Delaware has taken in banning deep-draught ports from its coast, or that New England and Maryland are trying to do in their efforts to prevent offshore oil exploration from occurring off their coasts. Alexander's "state-of-mind" approach takes on additional relevance.

Any individual's or organization's view of the coastal zone is tempered by background, both prior and contemporary exposure and, of course, vested interests. As we keep saying, a state of mind... A real estate developer's view of the value and utility of coastal wetlands, which he would dredge and fill, is quite at odds with the view of conservationists and commercial fishermen, both of whom would have them left in their natural state. The oil industry views 90-to-100-foot channel depths as a natural and necessary site for oil ports to handle mammoth tankers in the 200,000-to-500,000 deadweight ton range. Others view such facilities and tankers as totally unacceptable threats of massive oil spills. Machiasport, Maine, and the lower reaches of Delaware Bay are the only locations on the U.S. east coast where such deep water can be found. Citizens of each area have been successful, so far, in blocking such development -- though Washington is determined that there will be at least one such east coast facility.

Mariculturists view Puget Sound and the Florida west coast as ideal locations in which to fence in impoundments, build artificial ponds, set their cages and pens, etc., whereas watermen-all -- sport and commercial fishermen, sail and power boat enthusiasts, merchant shipping companies, conservationists and upland home owners -- fight bitterly and well against such activities, citing among their reasons: Hazards to navigation, deprivation of traditional rights of free access, ceding of common resources to private interests, confiscation of riparian rights, etc.

Local governments -- rural county commissions, town councils, etc. -- often find themselves in a dilemma. The pressure of the rising level, diversity and cost of services (schools, roads, welfare, law enforcement, pollution control, etc.) militates for policies and actions which will strengthen the tax base, such things as industry, other commercial development, housing developments, recreation-support facilities, and greater economic activity generally. Each of these consumes or otherwise acts adversely on the very natural resources which make the coastal zone both unique and desirable. Under present terms of reference many coastal resources are fixed and nonrenewable. The need is to strike a balance between development and conservation. In the interests of maximizing the use and productivity of those resources slated for development and coincidentally minimizing the rate of destruction of those resources, allowable development must be so sited and so ordered as to produce a minimum adverse impact, whether on public budgets, the natural environment or future options.

How is this to be done? That is a key question and one to which many scholars, government officials, industry leaders and others are addressing themselves. The simple answer is that all of those who make or participate in decisions affecting the coastal zone should understand thoroughly the nature, limits and interrelationships of the total coastal ecology -- and by "total ecology" here is meant the natural environment, all human activities and the interactions of the two. It is a simple solution to state but not simple to achieve. You can't reeducate a population or its officialdom overnight or even, perhaps, in a generation. But, you can try, and one way of trying is to provide tools that ease the problem recognition process, simplify the reduction of alternatives and enable decision-making to be made easier and more reliable. We feel that a major contribution to such an effort and concomitant coastal zone order may be found in expanded, innovative use of the mapmakers' arts and technics.

Among the major problems of coastal zone management and planning is the identification of the nature and extent of various types of impact, both primary and secondary, present and future. What kinds of activities concern us? At what times and locations and -- in terms of resources -- at what use rates? Once activities have been identified and quantified, it is necessary to define the impact characteristics of each such activity -- both the primary impact, such as crowding up a beach area and covering it with litter, and the secondary impacts, such as overstressing highways, parking lots, public services, etc.

It is possible to draw quite a precise picture of a region, whether coastal or otherwise, as it exists and is used at any given point in time: Soil or seabed type, topography or bathymetry, water table, agricultural/economic activity, population, transportation, climate, weather, living resources, non-living resources, use patterns, etc. It is possible to examine such a picture and to identify most development potentials -- housing sites, underutilized recreational potential, power plant sites, marina locations, commercial fisheries, light and heavy industry locations, port facilities, etc.

With the right kinds of base data properly presented, such potentials can be made to stand out in quite an obvious, exciting manner. But, there is more to it than the simple act of resource utilization. Suppose the decision is to develop a beach for increased recreational use. What's needed? You need expanded access -- roads, railroads, airfields. You need parking facilities. Food and sanitation facilities and service, lodging, law enforcement, waste disposal, and so forth. Where are these to be put? What impact do these support activities have on the resource being developed, the beach itself? Will the increased rate of sewage disposal pollute the beach waters, thus making it unusable as a recreation resource? Will beach development preclude use of the resource later for other purposes? Will it preclude the use of other resources? What is the plan with the greatest economy, the least social cost? What is the highest social benefit solution? How do you reach a common definition of "social cost" or "social benefit"?

A good example of an unforeseen secondary impact is found in the case of phosphate mining in eastern North Carolina. A few years back it was decided that the local region, a poverty area, would benefit from such operations, and approval was given. What was not foreseen, however, was that excavations would penetrate deep enough to cut through major aquifers supplying water to farms and cities alike. Unless they are continually pumped out, the excavations fill with water making further mining operations impossible. The result is that there has been a serious drop in the level of the surrounding water table, with considerable economic hardship to those whose accustomed water supplies have dried up.

We'd like to draw an analogy, if we may, between coastal zone management and

the process of making tuned bells, such as those found in carillons. This is not
an ancient art -- hardly 100 years old, in fact -- but it is an art and combines a
good ear for tone, a couple of sets of fine tuning forks and a large vertical bor-
ing mill. The bell is first cast in rough form of a special bronze alloy mixed
"by eye". It may weigh several tons. Once cooled, a matter of a day or day-
and-a-half, it is removed from the sand and placed upside down on a vertical bor-
ing mill. Now is when the good ears and tuning forks come in. A good team is
father and son: The older man is especially sensitive to lower frequency tones,
while the younger man has greater capabilities in the higher register.

The two first calibrate the bell -- that is, with activated tuning forks they determine the natural frequency of the bell as a whole and, in turn, of each zone of
the bell. From this they judge how much metal must be removed from each zone
of the inside bell wall. They're after a pure basic note and as many harmonics
as may be reasonably expected. If memory serves correctly, the Freedom Bell,
manufactured about 20 years ago in Croydon, England, has 18 harmonics.

Sound simple? Well, it's not and for the very reasons that managing the coastal
zone is not easy. It is easy to calculate where and how much metal to remove to
change one calibration point the desired amount. However, once that metal is
removed, not only does the target tone change, but all other tonal characteristics
of the bell are altered as well -- needless to remark, in varying amounts. So, it
is necessary frequently to recalibrate the bell. If at any time too much metal is
removed, there is no fixing it. It's back to the melting furnace and start over.

Managing the coastal zone is much like producing a tuned bell. Both are completely interrelated and complex systems. Any major action taken on or with respect to one part of the coastal zone affects many if not all other parts. If the
action is excessive one or more coastal values are degraded. If actions are excessive values are simply destroyed. And analogous to the different tonal zones
of the bell, you must count more than actions taken on specific value resources,
for an action taken with respect to one resource may have indirect impacts on many
other resources. It is necessary to evaluate cumulative effects of all impacts,
both direct and indirect, primary and secondary, present and future.

There have been countless studies of the coastal zone. Most contribute something. Several are excellent. None is 100 per cent complete. The definitive
book on coastal zone management has yet to be written -- even though there is
one available by that name [6]. No individual work fully identifies all the activities which do or may impact on the coastal zone. The same is true of the various types of impacts themselves. Both are quite numerous, and their interaction
is quite complex. From Sorensen[7] we have included in the appendix to this paper
his list of the multiple uses of the California coastal zone; also his list of the
"causal factors" resulting from those uses which impact on coastal resources.
He has worked these into a rather elaborate matrix which also shows under the
heading "Possible Adverse Impact" (1) Initial Condition, (2) Consequent Condition and (3) Effect.

One thing is clear: The demands on the coastal zone are high and rising rapidly.
Especially critical are recreational areas and facilities. Most of the U.S.
coastal shoreline is privately-owned or by nature of its topography totally unsuited to beach-based recreational activity. Recreational use in most cases
precludes other uses. There are other demands on coastal resources equally as
pressing and just as proscriptive -- ports, power plants, wildlife sanctuaries,
highways, urbanization, and other social/economic activities that benefit one way
or another from close-to-sea and estuary siting. Indeed, we cannot see how the
U.S. can avoid turning to artificial islands -- made-to-order coastal zone land
-- as some nations are doing already in the North Sea, English Channel and elsewhere. Such activity will relieve somewhat the pressure on the natural coastal
zone, but it will also raise special problems of its own.

NEW MANAGEMENT TOOL

When we first started working on this presentation we tried to think in terms of maps, charts and the technics involved in this particular activity. How can they be employed innovatively to ease the coastal zone management problem? And, we came up with several ideas -- at least one of which was new and might be made to be extremely useful. We soon learned, however, that we had reinvented the wheel and were just putting it on a different kind of vehicle. Our "innovation" was to prepare a system of socio-economic impact overlays -- "sensitivity overlays" we called them at first -- which would be shaded by nature and extent of impact. The idea is that simply by laying these over one another, one could get at least a first-cut idea of feasibility, nature and extent of costs, etc., attendant on proposed coastal zone use and development.

However, this sort of thing had already been done by Dr. Ian L. McHarg, Chairman, University of Pennsylvania's Department of Landscape Architecture & Regional Planning. In 1968 McHarg used this technic to show the least social cost route for Richmond Highway on Staten Island, N.Y.[8]. He prepared two sets of such overlays, with shading intensity varying with cost. One overlay set was concerned with such social cost factors as: Land, historic, scenic, recreation, residential, tidal inundation, wildlife and institutional values. Another set was devoted to construction costs, such as: Slope, soil drainage, surface drainage, susceptibility to erosion, bedrock foundation and soil foundation.

All of these were superimposed over a light table; the lighter-shaded, or least-cost route was obvious. Curiously, the route originally selected by conventional methods showed up as the darkest, or most expensive route.

This is an approach to land-use, regional or whatever planning. We think it would be especially valuable in coastal zone planning and management. Obviously, this isn't mapping in the sense accepted by cartographers and photogrammeters with benchmarks, transit lines, triangulation, etc. But, it does make use of many of the map-makers' arts; indeed before a complete system could be devised, a considerable amount of pretty much standard surveying would be required.

For coastal zone management purposes, we would like to see McHarg's "least social cost" approach considerably expanded. We would like to see a system of such overlays composed of specific data-type sets -- each set to be completely compatible and usable with every other set in any mix or sequence that decisional needs might dictate. Such data is readily susceptible to computer storage, manipulation and retrieval, thus greatly speeding and simplifying analysis for those with access to and faith in such facilities. However, we see the overlays as valuable in their own right -- as planning and decisional aids to those many, smaller rural communities which too often have neither the funds, time nor expertese to rely regularly on computers and associated graphic plotting equipment, but which often exercise telling jurisdiction over broad areas of largely unexploited coastal resources.

Perhaps what is needed is a "dynamic coastal data bank", a large, centrally sited and federally funded computerized system from which area and regional information sets can be extracted on a to-order basis. This would provide a valuable Federal planning aid, something we don't have now. States and larger municiple authorities could order out the data on computer-compatible magnetic tape or by direct telephone tie-in and use it for their own analyses. The system would also be programmed to print out overlays automatically for those who prefer them.

We cannot overstress the importance of the smaller, rural communities in coastal zone management. In Washington's mammoth, introverted Federal bureaucracy there is an almost universal tendency to be unaware of or otherwise ignore the nature and power of the rural power structure. To a lesser extent this is also true of state capitals, particularly those which are located far from their coasts. Yet these undeveloped areas are where the heaviest pressures are beginning to fall, where a wide range of options still remain and where sound management is still possible. If there is to be orderly coastal development anywhere, it is in such largely undeveloped areas that it must happen.

As to what form these data sets should take, we offer the following categories -- not as a final description but, rather, as a start for discussion: (1) Resource Charts, (2) Use-Option Charts, (3) Present-Use Charts, (4) Use-Impact Charts, (5) Use-Conflict Charts, (6) Use-Demand Charts, (7) Resource Alteration Charts, and (8) Projection Charts (future projections of the preceding).

Resource Charts

Resource charting means just what it says, though somewhat expanded in scope from traditional concepts. Every transparency in all overlay sets would show basic geographical outlines of land areas, rivers, bays, towns, cities, counties, etc. Resource overlay data would include but not necessarily be restricted to: Topography and bathymetry, hydrology, soil and subsoil types in terms of both engineering and biological considerations, groundwater (depth, quantity, type), living resources by basic type, tidal ranges (incl. MHW & MLW), maximum high water shoreline, flushing rates (for bays and estuaries), currents (ocean, coastwise and estuary), storm frequency, prevailing winds, erosion rates, non-living resources (if known), rainfall, etc. This set would present the basic physical/biological picture of the region in its natural state.

Use-Option Charts

Use-Option Charts would consist of a series of overlays showing the uses to which the existing natural resources could reasonably be put -- based solely on the fact of their occurrence without regard to market demand, custom, etc. An alternate title for this set might be "Use-Potential Charts". A 1,000-foot-high mountain peak, for example, doesn't have any potential for ocean beach recreation. A thin, low ocean barrier island of constantly moving sand has no potential as a heavy industry site. A beach has many use options: All of the recreation options, commercial fishing (haul seining), sport fishing, research pier siting, intensive resort development, sand mining, shell mining, heavy mineral mining, etc. Wet swampy land with the water table only inches below the surface has no reasonable potential for housing development or heavy construction, but it may have a good potential for forestry or wildlife preservation.

A recent study of the Albemarle Region of North Carolina[9] uses separate color-shaded maps to show soil suitability for : (1) agriculture-commercial crops, (2) agriculture-truck crops, (3)forestry land-hardwoods, (4) forestry land-softwoods, (5) rural residential development, (6) septic tanks, (7) urban development, (8) light industry, (9) recreation development and (10) trafficways. This is the sort of thing we would like to see expanded to include the entire spectrum of coastal resources and potential uses and presented in overlay form. Every activity has certain natural resource conditions on which it depends. These should be related to both present and foreseeable uses. In this set we are not concerned with whether there is a market demand for a particular use, whether there's a labor force, etc. -- only whether the potential itself exists based on geographical, geological, hydrological, oceanographic, biological, etc., conditions as they exist. It amounts simply to analyzing the Resource Chart data and determining what can or cannot be done without regard to whether anyone presently wants to do it.

This set would have a number of real values, including: (1) identifying heretofore unappreciated opportunities, (2) simplifying best use decisions, (3) identifying potential conflicts, and (4) assaying potential loads on highways, public services, etc. In preparing such a set careful consideration should be given to the potential for new and presently nonexistant uses: Artificial islands (which depend on water depth, bottom type, availability of fill, erosion regime, etc.), hovercraft and/or hydrofoil rapid transit routes (a fact in Europe), underwater power plant siting, and so forth.

Present-Use Charts

Present-Use Charts would be a set of overlays showing the existing pattern of use (including intensity) for both human and non-human activities. This set would be divided into two subsets. One would show human activities such as population density, rural-suburban-urban split, existing water use, transport network, recreational use, agriculture, forestry, commercial fisheries, sewage and other waste processing and disposal, heavy and light industrial distribution, public facilities, waterways, shipping, federal installations, academic facilities, research areas, wetland-use leases, water-use leases, public vs. private ownership, power plants and high tension lines, pipelines, etc. A second set would show natural or non-human uses including such things as migratory waterfowl settlement areas, fish spawning route areas, nursery areas, major drainage patterns, water-holding areas, natural channelways (flushing routes), etc.

Use-Impact Charts

Use-Impact Charts would show the location, nature and intensity of impacts that accompany different types of uses. Improperly treated sewage, for example, closes shellfish beds and reduces the recreational value of coastal waters. Highways interrupt drainage, break wildlife travel patterns. Housing and resort developments alter land characteristics, increase the demand for public services and trafficways; ship channels preclude the installation of gill and pound nets; power plants and certain industrial activities consume water and release it in altered form; mariculture operations may close an area to sport and commercial fishing operations; and so forth.

Use-Impact Charts should probably take two forms: (1) A subset showing the impact of present activities; and (2) a subset showing the impact of proposed activities. It is in this latter context that a computer-based data bank with suitable built-in programs and a low-cost, efficient graphic readout would be most valuable. It may be possible in theory but would hardly be practical to try to provide future-use impact charts to cover all options and combinations thereof. It should be possible for local authorities to pick their options and make their assumptions, including a number of alternatives, and then to order computer-printed overlays for quick, inexpensive delivery -- much as one is now able to obtain for 35¢ micro-fische reproductions of reports from the National Technical Information Service at Springfield, Va. Such overlays, however, would have to be full-size. A multiple overlay projection system for blowing up microfische-size overlays would probably be too expensive and complex -- though it may be worth investigation. Impact Charts are important for showing the cumulative effects of several concurrent types of activity on the receiving and support capacity of the environment, as well as on other types of uses. These charts would be basically but not exclusively environmentally oriented.

Use-Conflict Charts

Whereas Use-Impact Charts are mainly environmentally oriented, Use-Conflict Charts would be mainly human activity oriented. Use-Conflict Charts -- in their simplest context -- would show cases where one use of an environmental factor, such as a beach or a waterway, precludes or degrades one or more other uses. You can't dredge and fill a saltwater marsh and still maintain its biological productivity. These are preclusive uses. Not all conflicting uses are preclusive. Sport and commercial fishermen often go after the same fish in the same place at the same time. This doesn't mean they both don't fish, but they interfere with one another (or think they do) and there is conflict -- often vocal, sometimes physical. Power plant use of water may degrade the biosphere but doesn't necessarily destory the entire fishery potential. High intensity resort development and large crowds of people are inconsistent with wildlife areas and pristine natural beauty -- either or both of which may have been the reason for the development in the first case. An ancillary subset might be overlays showing compatible uses -- the opposite of the conflict set. Such manipulation would be easy and inexpensive with a central computer.

Use-Demand Charts

Use-Demand Charts might also be called Use-Source Charts. In other words, where does the demand for a particular resource use come from ? Where might it come from in the proximate future, in the distant future? Take Ocean City, Md., or Rehoboth, Del., for example. These are both intensive-use beach resort areas, and the holiday-makers who use them come mainly from over 100 miles away -- Washington, D.C., Baltimore, Wilmington, and Philadelphia. The existing traffic, if not obvious, is readily determined. But what about the future ? How many more people are or will there be in these areas, elsewhere, who do not now but may use these facilities in the future ? What are such use trends ? In preparing Use-Demand Charts the role of anticipated technological development (in transportation, for example) should be taken into account.

Such an overlay set would be especially useful in ordering the future development of those coastal areas not yet subject to intensive use -- areas such as the North Carolina Outer Banks and particularly the sound area behind them, or the Sea Islands of the coast of South Carolina and Georgia.

Many factors would have to go into the preparation of such charts, including the prospects for offshore mineral exploitation, future commercial fishery developments, power plant siting, basic regional energy need forecasts, etc.

Resource Alteration Charts

Use means environmental change, and Resource Alteration Charts would utilize all or much of the above-developed data to show change in environmental capacity to support coastal zone activities. Sometimes such activities in moderation may actually enhance the environment. Raised nutrient levels, within limits, may increase the desirable biomass without materially degrading an estuary for other uses, for example. Too often, however, the alteration produces undesirable results. Resource Alteration Charts should be limit-oriented, and they should be interaction-oriented. In the case of pollution, for example, there has been a tendency to think in terms of the safe limits of individual pollutants, whereas increasingly it is being realized that synergistic effects herald the first onset of undesirable results. All systems have some impact tolerance -- meaning that they can be used within limits without significant alteration. Nature itself is capable of major impact and change. Man is not alone in this respect.

In New England clamming with a hand fork and within the size limitations set by law for "keepers" probably doesn't materially hurt either clam stocks or their habitat, whereas a mechanical dredge used without restriction might quickly destroy both. Moderate recreational boating activity produces no material adverse impact, wheras a boating explosion , such as is occurring in many of our estuaries, strains the natural environment, other environmentally-dependent uses, access and transportation facilities, local public services, and materially interferes with the viability of the resource complex generally. A basic mission of this set of overlays would be to alert planners and managers to the danger of permitting activities which the existing environment would not support without the degradation and/or destruction of the very support capacity to be utilized. Its purpose would be to help avoid self-defeating activities.

Projection Charts

Projection Charting refers simply to the need in some instances for charts and computational services to project predictable future events and activities -- population growth over time and area, coastal erosion, highway construction, industrial growth, changes in land use, etc., all based on historical trends and analysis of future technologies and socio-economic preferences. Special provision should be made in this case, too, for local authorities to obtain overlay sets to order based on their own unique conditions and assumptions.

Jurisdiction Charts

One of the hair-raising aspects of coastal zone management is trying to determine which agency at which administrative trophic level -- local, state, regional or Federal -- has what jurisdiction over what aspects of which types of activity. This raises the possible desirability of a second system of overlays -- again to be computer supported and updated. This system might be called Jurisdiction Charts. Initially, these overlays would show the various jurisdictions -- color-coded as well as shaded to include agency-by-agency differentiation -- over major resources and activities in the coastal zone only at the state and Federal levels. Ultimately, as data became available and were fed into the system it could be expanded to include local county and municiple jurisdictions. Sets would be ordered according to resource and/or activity, while subsets could treat with the nature of the authority exercised: Financial assistance, taxation, enforcement, environmental protection, resource management, zoning, etc.

CONCLUSION

Obviously we are not detailing a final program. We have had but little time to think about it ourselves. We do know, however, that there is a real need -- particularly by local, rural power structures -- for simple, reliable, graphic representations of the resources under their control, the options available and the affects of alternative selection. For those who understand, trust and are accustomed to and can afford such services, computer analysis print-outs are both valuable and useful. But, many instinctively distrust both fancy electronic "gadgets" and long rows of figures. For them (and, indeed, many others) there's nothing so revealing, reassuring and convincing as being able to select the alternatives oneself. Shuffling overlays over a light table could perform just such a function. It's a process that county commissioners, mayors, etc., could do themselves. They could see the dense, black "don't" areas, and they could see the effects of alternatives as they themselves tried different option patterns.

Clearly such a tool would require much care in its organization and development, and it would require a considerable initial investment. However, it could be accomplished in phases, and, once the data were stored and the proper programs inserted, continuing and operating costs should be moderate and to a degree self-supporting. Standard overlay sets, to-order overlays and consulting services could be sold -- much as NTIS now sells its reports and microfische copies.

A considerable quantity of such data already exists in the records and charts of of the National Ocean Survey, Geological Survey, Bureau of Land Management, National Marine Fisheries Service, Weather Service, Navy Oceanographic Office, Bureau of the Census, and various other agencies of the Departments of Commerce, Interior, Defense, Labor, Housing & Urban Development, etc. Much other useful input can be found in the great and growing volume of coastal zone studies conducted, variously, by Federal, state and academic institutions -- with particularly productive reference to the series of publications developed under the National Sea Grant Program. The problem, of course, is to identify, locate, extract and manipulate such data into a standard, compatible format and to centralize it in usable form at a single central location.

What we propose is a centrally-operated and managed interagency, interdisciplinary approach -- probably best administered by the National Oceanic & Atmospheric Agency. The burden of responsibility for developing the overlay system itself for maximum utility and flexibility should fall heavily on innovative chartmakers and visual display specialists. The use of simple, graded screens is an obvious approach. This was McHarg's technic. The lower the cost, use or impact level, the lighter would be the screen and vice-versa. However, perhaps it is possible by using different screen patterns to obtain desirable secondary effects or to show exponential rather than simple arithmatical compounding of impacts and/or synergism. The possibility has also occurred to us that there may be available completely transparent, normally uncolored fluorescing inks which might enable current status and future projections to be printed on a single overlay. Simple rheostat controls could be used on the light table to switch from normal to ultraviolet light. There are undoubtedly many technics which are available or could be developed -- more familiar to you than to us. Clearly, anything that can be done to reduce the quantity of overlays without unduly complicating their use or format is desirable.

Our main purpose here has been to stimulate some thought both in the development of new much-needed tools for coastal zone planning and management and in the development of innovative technics for optimizing the utility of such tools. If we have been successful in doing this, then we have wasted neither your time nor ours. Thank you.

REFERENCES

(1)   ------------ Marine Resource Activities in Texas, Texas A&M University, August 1969.

(2)   Boykin, Rosemary E., Leatha F. Miloy & Kathi J. Jensen, Texas and the Gulf of Mexico, Texas A&M University, June 1971

(3)   ----------- Georgia, Florida Organize for Coastal Zone Management Coastal Zone Management, 2/11, November 1971

(4)   ----------- Delaware Law Bans Heavy Industry on Coast, Offshore Terminals, Coastal Zone Management, 2/6, June 1971

(5)   ----------- Escarosa: A Preliminary Study of Coastal Zone Management Problems and Opportunities in Escambia and Santa Rosa Counties, Fla., Florida Coastal Coordinating Council, April 1971

(6)   Brahtz, J.F. Peel, Coastal Zone Management: Multiple Use With Conservation, John Wiley & Sons, New York, 1972

(7)   Sorensen, Jens C., A Framework for Identification & Control of Resource Degradation & Conflict in Multiple Use of the Coastal Zone, University of California at Berkeley Department of Landscape Architecture College of Environmental Design

(8)   McHarg, Ian L., Richmond Parkway Study (A Least Social Cost Corridor) on Staten Island, University of Pennsylvania Department of Landscape Architecture & Regional Planning, May 1968

(9)   Blake, James G., III, A Region in Transition: The General Development Plan for the Albemarle Area, State of North Carolina Department of Conservation & Development, April 1967

APPENDIX

The following two tables are extracted from Sorensen's California Coastal Zone use matrices[7]. Table I shows coastal zone uses. Table II shows causal factors resulting from such uses and which impact on other uses and base resources.

Table I

Residential Development	Shopping - Boardwalking
Commercial Services	Ocean-View Dining
Crop Farms	Sightseeing - Pleasure Driving
Ranching & Dairying	Camping
Forestry	Commercial Shrimp & Finfishing
Motorboating	Commercial Shellfishing
Boat Fishing	Abalone Fishing
Water Skiing	Kelp & Seaweed Harvesting
Sailing	Shore Oil & Gas Wells
Surf Fishing	Offshore Oil & Gas Wells
Pier Fishing	Offshore Mineral Mining
Swimming	Shore Mining & Quarrying
Surfing	Sand, Gravel & Shell Mining
Scuba - Snorkling	Desalinization
Wading	Seawater Chemicals Extraction
Sunbathing	Marine Transport
Group Beach Games	Highway Transport
Beachcombing - Strolling	Air Transport
Clamming - Bait Collecting	Communications
Picnicing - Cookouts	Navy Operations
Contemplation - Observation	Military Facilities
Painting - Photography	Marine Research
Wildlife Observation	Industrial Operations
Hunting	Power Plants
Horseback Riding	Sewage Treatment Plants
Beach & Dune Driving	Sewer Outfalls & Offshore Dumping

Table II

Septic Tanks
Sewage Systems
Solid Wastes
Groins & Beachworks
Bulkheads & Seawalls
Signs & Billboards
Vehicles
Utilities
Structures
Fences
Roadways & Parking Areas
Grazing Stock
Landscaping
Vegetation Clearing & Logging
Irrigation
Water Impoundments
Groundwater Withdrawal
Chemical Contro Agents
Fertilization
Drainage Improvements
Plowing & Cultivation
Cuts & Fills
Protection of Species
Picnic Facilities
Toilet Facilities
Paths to Shore
Vehicle Trails
Launching Ramps
Roads to Shore
Turnouts & Vista Points
Channels
Breakwaters
Navigation Aids
Docks & Piers
Fuel Docks
Slips & Berths
Boatyards

Boats
Stock Introduction
Prospecting
Temporary Housing
Processing Plants
Refineries & Tank Farms
Towers & Platforms
Offshore Drilling
Excavation
Dredges
Gangue Dumping
Offshore Beneficiation
Wastewater Dumping
Seawater Intakes
Pipelines
Submerged Fencing
Evaporation Beds
Boats & Barges
Practice Ranges
Defense Operations
Power Pylons & Wires
Transmission Towers & Antennae
Runways
Aircraft
Railroads
Building Site Cuts & Fills
Roadbed Cuts & Fills
Bridges
Roadbed Fill & Causeway
Water Impoundment
Waste Water & Sewage
Nuclear Reaction
Fossil Fuel Combustion
Bulk Refining & Processing
Tanks, Elevators & Warehouses
Bulk & Fuel Loading
Shipyards Nuclear Ships
Ships

(NOTE: Neither of these lists should be taken as complete or as representative of all coastal zones. There are no abalone, for example, on the east coast or in the Gulf of Mexico. Sorensen stresses recreation. Others may wish to stress a different set of activities. The two lists do serve, however, to underscore (1) the variety of activities that can and do take place in the coastal zone (Table I), and (2) the secondary activities, "causal factors", attendant on the primary activities (Table II).)

THE NATIONAL SEA GRANT PROGRAM - A PROGRESS REPORT

Robert B. Abel, Director
National Sea Grant Program
National Oceanic and Atmospheric Administration
Washington, D. C. 20235

BIOGRAPHICAL SKETCH

Robert B. Abel is the Director of the National Sea Grant Program which constitutes NOAA's broadest interface with the academic community, through its grants to colleges and universities for activities looking toward the development and conservation of marine resources. Mr. Abel received his B.S. degree in Chemistry from Brown University and later went on to John Hopkins University, George Washington University and the American University majoring in Oceanography, Engineering Administration and Public Administration, respectively. Mr. Abel began his career with the Woods Hole Oceanographic Institution as a chemical oceanographer. In 1951 he transferred to the Hydrographic Office as Chief Scientist of the USS SAN PABLO and USS REHOBETH and, in 1956, was made Assistant to the Director, in which capacity he served until 1961 when he was appointed Assistant Research Coordinator and Executive Secretary of the Interagency Committee on Oceanography, Office of Naval Research. He came to his present position from the National Science Foundation where he was employed from 1967-70. Mr. Abel is affliated with the American Chemical Society, The Research Society of America, Joint Board on Science Education, Marine Technology Society, American Society for Oceanography and the New York Academy of Science.

INTRODUCTION

Our present Sea Grant goals are to continue involving scientists and engineers in the practical problems of the marine environment, and to accelerate the flow and application of results from research started in previous years. We are also continuing to take particularly hard look at education programs, evaluating those under Sea Grant funding in terms of probable trends in the manpower market.

In all, 89 Sea Grants were under way as of the end of FY 71. These grants encompassed 361 separate research projects, 111 education and training projects, and 96 advisory service activities, with 2,656 persons participating.

Aquaculture research, a field specifically named as part of the Sea Grant mission in the National Sea Grant College and Program Act, produced a number of useful results. Among them was the first handbook on shrimp culture methodology from the University of Miami. Development of a technique for management of shrimp in natural impoundments was reported by Nicholls State College of Louisiana, and a similar technique was used in artificial impoundments by Texas A&M University working with a Texas industry, a project that resulted in the first commercial harvest of cultured shrimp in that state. Texas A&M also identified <u>Vibrio parahaemolyticus</u> as the organism causing death in cultured marine invertebrates

(including shrimp), while the University of Washington identified the same bacterium as the cause of mortality in oysters.
Oregon State University, working with local oystermen, established an oyster seed hatchery capable of providing the local
industry with spat, which previously has had to be imported.
Virginia Institute of Marine Sciences reduced to routine operations the spawning and rearing of larvae, not only for oysters,
but for hard and soft clams, and bay and calico scallops.
Among finfish aquaculture projects, the Oceanic Institute of
Hawaii reported the first successful controlled spawning of
mullet, developing techniques that later will be applied to
other, higher value species.

Food scientists and technologists produced several significant
successes. Rhode Island demonstrated improved quality control
for fishmeal production by development of a new method for
analysis of "available" lysine. Oregon State found that shellfish toxin bonds to the melanin in affected clams, and so may
have opended the way to utilization of shellfish even at times
when the Northwest is plagued by the toxin-porducing organism.
In another project, OSU showed that shrimp wastes can be fed
to cultured trout to produce a beautiful red fleshed fish with
good growth and taste. The University of Washington demonstrated
on a laboratory scale a method for full utilization of shellfish wastes and moved toward pilot-scale operations with high
promise of solving the crab, shrimp, and lobster shell disposal
problem now faced in many parts of the country, by producing
a commercially useful product from the wastes.

Seaweed aquaculture also made substantial progress, with the
University of Hawaii demonstrating a system for farming valuable red seaweed, and the California Institute of Technology
making rapid advances in new techniques for expanding existing
kelp beds and establishing new ones.

Among Sea Grant marine technology applications, the Lamont
Doherty multiple system for use of deep ocean water showed
the feasibility of using the nutrients in such water for food
chain growth and shellfish culture. The development of a
hydraulic power takeoff from the outboard motors of Northwest
Pacific fishing dories opened a new era in efficient fishing
for dorymen and daily catch records of test boats demonstrated
that the income of a fisherman equipped with the hydraulic
system and lightweight gurdies can be doubled for a relatively
small investment. The University of Washington made an
important step in improving fish stock management with satisfactory field testing of an improved acoustics system for
estimating fish populations, and also created a computer
program for fish stock management, including a manager-
instruction game called "Simple Salmon." Stevens Institute
of Technology completed a computer program for analysis of
offshore platforms, for use in improving designs to make
platforms, for use in improving designs to make platforms more
resistant to ocean forces. A Stanford University/University
of New Hampshire project completed design and feasibility
studies for a submerged, buoyant, anchored pipeline for
transporting natural gas in the open ocean.

Ecological research produced several reports of value in
managing natural resources. The University of Miami identified the effects of thermal effluents on some estuarine

organisms, and published a detailed analysis of the value of
mangrove swamps. The University of Hawaii completed a systems
analysis of Kaneohe Bay, demonstrating the kind of damage produced when on-shore development causes siltation in a natural
area. In several states, including Rhode Island, Oregon,
Washington, Delaware, Wisconsin, Michigan, Alaska, California,
Texas and Hawaii, either the direct output of ecosystems
research or the dissemination of existing research by Sea
Grant Advisory Services is proving highly useful to state and
regional resource managers.

FY 1971 brought Sea Grant research lawyers into active consultation with their communities. Legal studies in Sea Grant
institutions provided a base for development of legislation,
alerted state and local officials to problems posed by existing
legal regimes, provided advice to conservation groups, translated legal technicalities into a form useful to fishermen and
others, and contributed substantially to the development of
background on international law of the sea. Sea Grant exono-
mists conducted studies ranging from the value of extending
the Great Lakes shipping season to specific guidance on book-
keeping for fishermen and small seafood processors.

Much of the year's activity was centered in Advisory Services,
a broad category that includes all useful forms of communica-
tion to user audiences. In addition to publications, there
was a considerable increase in extension agent activity, of
the kind described by Athelstan Spilhaus as "county agents in
hip boots." For example, at Oregon State, a seafood science
and technology extension agent assisted smoked fish processors
to upgrade their operations to meet new FDA standards, including making temperature measurements of their smoking processes with special equipment. The same agent also assisted
industry in devising new ways of using seafoods in convenience
packaged family meals. Other extension people accelerated
direct contact with industry, state and local government,
fishermen, and marine mining interests. One unusual example
of "mining" a living resources was the delineation of precious
coral beds off Hawaii and transmittal of details to local
industry. The University of Hawaii also described for industry
major deposits of manganese slabs or "pavements" in the Pacific.

In spite of cutbacks in marine and marine-related industries
Sea Grant technician training programs continued to maintain
their high record of placement of graduates, with 100 percent
employment reported in several instances. The lowest placement record was 85 percent for marine industry but even in
this case, the remaining 15 percent found jobs in which their
newly acquired skills were useful. But, given the uncertainties of the future employment market, Sea Grant began a gradual
re-emphasis in its training programs, responding to the demand
for fisheries technician training and for a limited number of
activities in marine engine and diesel mechanics, while reducing the number of oceanographic aide projects.

Fiscal Year 1971 produced what may be described as "phase two"
of the Sea Grant institutional program. Initially, the
relatively small unviersities organized quickly for the
broadly based Sea Grant institutional programs and began
productive operations almost immediately. The larger universities, which faced serious organization problems in

structuring the kind of multi-inter-disciplinary program Sea
Grant requires, began more slowly, and reached the "take-off
point" for full application of their very great competence in
1971. The year saw the development of Sea Grant in the entire
University of California system, involving nine campuses under
the leadership fo the San Diego campus and Scripps Institute.
Massachusetts Institute of Technology, which had participated
in Sea Grant projects--and produced a valuable series of ocean
engineering course books--developed a full scale progra. Rapid
expansion of the Sea Grant programs took place at the Universities of Washington, Michigan, Wisconsin, and Hawaii. Two universities, Louisiana State and Delaware, which had begun Sea
Grant activities as multi-disciplinary Coherent Projects, reached
the stage of development that justified their proposing full
institutional status for Fiscal Year 1972.

By fiscal year's end, 27 states, the District of Columbia and
the Virgin Islands were participating in the Sea Grant Program
through institutional or project grants.

Perhaps the single most difficult problem facing the Sea Grant
Program is how to get research results into the hands of potential users. The Advisory Service programs do a good job of s
serving their state and local communities, but an increasing
number of reports and papers are of national interest. The
academic and high technology industrial communities generally
keep aware of published results, but many important marine
users, including small business, are not subscribers of the
trade journals, abstracting services, or other routine sources.
As the flow of results continues and expands, the problems will
become more difficult. The NOAA Sea Grant Office will keep
working toward solutions, but ideas on how results can best
be targeted will be very welcome.

Development of the National Sea Grant Base

An underlying assumption of the National Sea Grant College and
Program Act is that the problems and opportunities of the nation's
marine environment are so complex and pervasive that provision
must be made for the continuing application of the nation's
best academic scientific and engineering talen over the next
few decades. To ensure the availability of that talent on a
continuing basis, the Act calls for a program of "Sea Grant
Colleges." While the actual designation of Sea Grant Colleges
is in the future, the intent of the Act is carried out be two
classes of continuing Sea Grant Programs:

Institutional Support is granted to universities or combinations of universities with a broad base of marine competence.

Coherent Project Support is granted to universities with core
competence and the expressed intention of further developing
that core to meet the needs of the state and region served by
the university.

Although both programs are continuing in nature, if the performance of the grantee warrants continuing support, the categories are essentially administrative conveniences under which
a single grant can encompass a variety of relevant, applied
activities, each of which is carefully reviewed and approved,
and each of which carries its own budget.

Historically, the national foci of marine competence developed
in relatively few places. On initiation of the Sea Grant
Program in FY 1967, most traditionally strong universities
and institutions made proposals and received grants, either
for continuing support or for individual projects. Those
proposing individual projects preferred to develop their continuing Sea Grant programs more slowly, fitting Sea Grant
requirements into their already heavy commitments, and
creating the organizations necessary for administration of the
Sea Grant Program. Other universities, primarily coastal in
location but without strong marine traditions, were just
awakening to the need for developing marine competence
essential to their states or regions.

Consequently, development of the national Sea Grant Base has
been a continuing process. Universities strong in marine
affairs have phased into the program as their Sea Grant
Programs assumed higher priorities, organization was created,
and faculty time became available. Universities determined
to develop the kinds of programs necessary in their areas
entered the Sea Grant Program under Coherent Projects and
began the process of growth.

The development of the continuing base is shown in the following tabulation by Fiscal Years:

Institutional Support	Pre-Institutional Coherent Projects
FY 1968	
Oregon State University	University of California, Scripps Institution
University of Washington	
University of Rhode Island	University of Delaware
Texas A&M University	Louisiana State Univ.
University of Wisconsin	
University of Hawaii	
FY 1969	
University of Miami	Virginia Institute of Marine Sciences
University of Michigan	
FY 1970	
University of Southern California	University of Alaska
University of North Carolina	University of Georgia
	Massachusetts Institute of Technology
FY 1971	
University of California	University of Maine
	Universities of Miss.

211

FY 1970 marked a change in the make-up of some grantee institutions. The University of North Carolina institutional program involves four main campuses, with the Sea Grant program administered by the consolidated university of the state. Similarly, the pre-institutional coherent project in Georgia is coordinated for the state within the Office of the Chancellor of the state system.

In FY 1971, the change was even more strongly marked when the entire University of California system of nine major campuses applied for institutional support, with the San Diego campus as leader, and the Sea Grant program administered for the Scripps Institution. Three Mississippi Universities and the Gulf Coast Research Laboratory combined in the Mississippi Coherent Project, with the state's Universities Marine Center as focus. FY 1971 also marked the maturation of two Coherent Projects started in FY 1968, when both Louisiana State University and the University of Delaware applied for Institutional Support. Both programs were reviewed and recommended for approval, with initial Institutional Support to be granted in FY 1972.

In summary, the Sea Grant base now represents 21 states, with the level of effort varying widely. In addition, Sea Grant Projects have been funded in an additional nine states.

The importance of maintaining and enlarging the base of National Sea Grant activity again was confirmed in FY 1971 through consultation with state and regional officials, industries, and professional societies. There was universal agreement that many problems and opportunities of the marine environment are so specific to a state or locality that general knowledge, principles, and procedures usually must be applied to the specific case by persons familiar with the local environment and with the competence to make the necessary adjustments.

ROLE OF THE U. S. ENVIRONMENTAL PROTECTION AGENCY
IN THE COASTAL ZONE

William S. Beller, Chief, Ocean Islands Programs
Environmental Protection Agency
Washington, D. C. 20460

BIOGRAPHICAL SKETCH

William S. Beller has degrees in mechanical and aeronautical engineering
from Georgia Institute of Technology and New York University, respectively. In 1969, he organized and led one hundred Hawaiian citizens
in preparing "Hawaii and the Sea," a program for the State's use of its
coastal assets. He performed a similar task for the Virgin Islands, and
currently is directing "Puerto Rico and the Sea." He was a member of
the staff of the President's Marine Commission. Beller organized and
chairs the Committee on Coastal Zone Management of the Marine Technology
Society. The Department of Interior gave him the Meritorious Service
Award in 1970.

ABSTRACT

The U. S. Environmental Protection Agency, which has the job of helping
the nation achieve and hold a healthful natural environment, is much
involved in coastal zone activities. With responsibilities that embrace
water and air pollution, disposal of solid wastes, noise pollution, and
the ultimate fates of pesticides and radiological substances, the Agency
is necessarily concerned with future developments of the coastal zone
including the facilities needed for increasing populations and numbers
of coastal industries. To properly conserve the nation's environment,
the Agency is preparing to work more closely with the States and industry on such matters as effluent standards, ocean dumping criteria, and
wastes from watercraft.

INTRODUCTION

I am very pleased to be here. Actually, I have had the pleasure of
speaking to the American Society of Photogrammetry before, in 1969 to
be exact. This was in connection with a balloon symposium I helped
organize for the Society. At the time, we were trying to re-introduce
the balloon as a stable platform--well, as a platform anyway--from which
to measure a number of ground activities. These were to include the
effects of pollution on the environment, land use, locating schools
of fish by the turbulence they cause in the water or possibly by the
oil slicks they leave after feeding, and other phenomena that we felt
could be detected economically and with limited commotion through the
neglected art of ballooning.

Alas, I cannot report to you that the ASP conference on ballooning galvanized the various Federal departments into action programs in aero-
statics. Yet as my colleagues and I see the resilience of some of the
political campaigners during this election year, we are loathe to recognize a lost cause. We are still persuaded that there is abundant merit
in balloon observations if only the potential users would recognize
this fact.

I must admit that EPA is reluctant to employ balloons to obtain the data
it needs to understand and help regulate the use of the environment.
The Agency, perhaps rightfully, considers it will gain more information
by using for this purpose satellites, aircraft, ships, bouys, and in
situ devices.

The state of one's environment is usually a subjective concept that
makes one think of social and cultural relationships as well as those
of more material import. As a result, the familiar factors that make
up an environment are often too vague to be useful for scientific or
regulatory purposes. For this reason, the description of the environment has to be quantified. This EPA is trying to do, and the activity
forms the basis for much of the Agency's work. For example, we can
determine the sedimentation in water, its biological and chemical oxygen demands, and the topography of stream thermals. We can measure
the particulate densities and amount of noxious gases in the atmosphere;
and similarly we can determine the alkalinity and acidity of earth, and
its pesticide content.

These values help tell us what the present state of our natural environment is, and provide baselines from which to measure how fast and in
what directions it is changing. Thus, we can do something about regulating the changes. What is very important to note, though, is that
while we stress the characteristics of the natural environment, we simultaneously involve much of the total environment of man. I believe we
can say that when we improve the natural environment of man we simultaneously improve his overall quality of life.

When I was first asked to speak on EPA's role in the coastal zone, I
thought that this would be a very easy talk to give. After all, EPA
is exceedingly active in the coastal zone, and has wide interests and
legislative authorities. These facts were almost my undoing. Just
about everything EPA does has ramifications in the coastal zone. Where
should we turn first: to the water programs? to the air programs?
to those in solid wastes, pesticides or radiation? I decided to concentrate on the water programs because these appear to be more directly
relevant to the coastal zone. With these programs, I shall speak of
those that are most pervasive and that may soon be experiencing some
major changes.

COASTAL ZONE RESEARCH

Please spare me a moment to note that when EPA was formed under Executive
Reorganization Plan No. 3, at the end of 1970, many of us looked upon
the Agency as chiefly regulatory. In its responsibility, it combined
five of the major environmental concerns of the nation: air and water
pollution, solid wastes disposal, pesticides, and radiation. Noise
pollution was added only weeks after EPA came into being.

At the time of its creation, then, EPA could have stood in many of our
minds for the "Environmental Policing Agency." But then as the full
scope of the problems became better defined, and as we looked into them
more deeply, we saw that we needed to answer the question of how can
we arrange for man to live better with his environment. How should he
use his land and manage his coastal areas? How many houses should be
situated on the land and at what density? Is there an optimum population that the natural resources of an area can support without undue
degradation of these resources and consequent degradation of the quality
of life they support? Only upon a base of considerations such as these,

which in part have found formulation in some of the land-use bills now in Congress, can we establish a lasting program aimed at protecting the nation's environment and citizens.

Let me go a little further on this. We must not only know what man wants, and incidentally, what he is willing to pay for it, but also how what he is doing is affecting the environment. With this information, we can better regulate our use of the environment. What do thermal effluents do to the food chain in coastal waters? We are indeed true believers in the natural religion that tells us that everything is attached to everything else, but this tenet does not help us very much unless we are told in what fashion the connections are made. To help establish what these connections are, EPA is working in the following research areas:

Water Quality

We have to have a sound scientific base of data and understanding of coastal processes in order to help the States set up environmental standards for their waters and for interstate waters. We are therefore getting data on estuarine and coastal water quality, and on some of the demographic and geographic factors that affect water quality. We are also trying to get information that will help us set standards that will encourage important marine fish and their food chain organisms to reproduce themselves. We are also trying to determine safe levels of pesticide derivatives in estuarine and coastal waters; and the effects of organic chemicals, heavy metals, petroleum, and petroleum by-products on marine life.

Disposal Sites

In a similar vein, we are trying to find out the effects of pollutants on marine life and also the fate of pollutants in marine waters. Specifically, once we know the life cycle of pollutants, we shall better be able to establish scientific criteria for selecting disposal sites for wastes and for disposal methods; and also ways to develop monitoring methods for waste-disposal operations.

Technology

EPA is also engaged in the engineering research needed for the building of waste-treatment plants for both municipalities and industries; in the problems of disposing and detecting wastes from watercraft; and in the science and technology related in the abatement of pollution from oil and hazardous materials.

This listing is far from complete even for the research we are doing in the coastal zone. It does, though, give you an idea of how far backward an environmental agency must step if it is to base its regulations on an understanding of processes instead of on fiat.

Let me now speak about some of EPA's operational programs for the coastal zone, and the agency's expectations. From these, you will get an idea, I hope, of the way the nation will be going--at least the Federal and hopefully State governments--in protecting and enhancing the natural environment of the coastal zone.

The regulations and laws that governments make usually start from simple notions, change, and at last mature. This process is as true of environmental rules and regulations as it is of hypotheses and inventions in science and technology.

Water Quality Standards

The Water Quality Act of 1965 offered the simple notion that the waters of the nation should be sufficiently clean to serve the needs of the people. Congress determined that the best way to do this was to have State governments decide what uses they wished to make of their interstate waters; then, in cooperation with the Federal Government, set up water-quality criteria and implementation plans to ensure these uses. This was done. The water quality standards of all States are now approved, either fully or with some criteria exceptions. Typical standards prescribe limits on such factors as temperature rise and variation, coliform, BOD, COD, turbidity, acidity, and noxious substances.

Water quality standards, once approved by EPA, become both State and Federal standards. They are enforceable first by the State; or if a State defaults, by the Federal Government. Unfortunately, these joint standards are presently limited to interstate waters. As a result, many of the nation's waters are unprotected unless the States themselves have taken the initiative. To their credit, some of the States have indeed established water quality standards for waters over which the Federal Government has no pollution abatement authority.

Legislation in front of Congress would extend EPA's authority to most of the waters in the nation. One version of the legislation calls for the application of water quality standards to the nation's navigable waters, which would include the intrastate waters. The legislation would also seek to abate pollution of ground waters; waters in the Contiguous Zone that would adversely affect water quality in the Territorial Sea; and waters of the high seas if the discharged pollutants would be carried into U. S. Territorial waters.

Effluent Limitations

The nation has used its coastal zone in a haphazard way because during most of the life of the nation there seemed to be enough coastal area for almost every use. Then as uses began infringing on one another, the Federal Government in sequence tried to preserve those it considered most precious: the protection of commerce, of course; the conservation of fish and wildlife; the striving for cleaner water; and more recently, the nation's decision to try to conserve all aspects of its natural environment. Except for the last two efforts, the others were simply piecemeal attempts to extract individual benefit out of the coastal zone. Unfortunately, the total well-being of the area was only of incidental interest.

The right of the Federal Government to regulate navigation is based on the commerce clause of the Constitution. The Refuse Act of 1899 is an exercise of this right. It puts the Army Corps of Engineers in charge of protecting the nation's navigable waters. Now this Act is a good example of a nation's looking at a single purpose of its waters and making provisions to safeguard it. By this law, we are prohibited from discharging into navigable waters any substances that will impede navigation. And this was surely a most important consideration at the turn of the century. The United States then could no more do without its water commerce than today it could do without its trucking commerce and industry. And I feel sure that we would have today a "Refuse Act" for highways if people developed the habit of throwing their wastes onto them.

The Refuse Act is not impervious because it does allow the Corps to issue permits to discharge wastes provided they do not impede anchorage or navigation in navigable waters. However, it was only recently that the nation decided to fully invoke this permit program. And it came through the initiation of President Nixon, who was also seeking some way to control the effluents put into the nation's waters by the nation's industries.

Under the current permit system, all industries discharging effluents directly into navigable waters have to file an application with the Federal Government describing the total amount and exact ingredients of all discharged effluents. Based on this information, each industry will receive a permit restricting its effluent in very specific terms. To underscore this strategy, EPA expects to publish guidelines later this year to help 19 major polluting industries achieve the best practicable control over their effluents.

While the permit-granting authority resides in the Army Corps of Engineers, there is very strong coordination between EPA and the Army. However, some current legislation calls for transferring most of the authority to EPA.

This example indicates how the environmental laws of the nation are tending to mature and be more pointed. Regulating the quantity and quality of effluents a point-source may discharge gives the nation a much firmer grip on the quality of water in its waterways than it has ever had before. Let us take a case in point because the new legislation, which embodies the permit concept, shows the seriousness of the President and Congress in their efforts to protect the nation's waters in the most direct way possible.

In 1970, a German Corporation, the Badische Analin and Soda Fabrik (BASF), was planning to build a major petrochemical complex near Beaufort, South Carolina. This chemical plant was destined for what the Secretary of the Interior described as a "splendid estuary, virtually free of pollution." (When he made this statement, the Federal water pollution responsibilities were in Interior.)

The Secretary strenuously opposed any action that would result in the degradation of the water quality of this South Carolina estuary and would continue to do so, he said, unless the company provided sufficient environmental safeguards. The threat of the Secretary was eventually sufficient to deter BASF from continuing with its plans. The problem could have been resolved much sooner had effluent standards been established so that BASF would have known from the start what boundary conditions they had to use; and Interior could have processed the case in a much more expeditious fashion.

It would be wrong to assume that effluent limitations or pollution control always puts its figures on the debit side of a ledger. We sometimes find that the need for a company to re-evaluate its waste treatments can result in savings. For example, at the Midland, Michigan plant of Dow Chemical, the company is building 28 cooling towers, which will cost $7.2 million, in order to cut back on the thermal load on the Tittabawassee River. By reducing corrosion and cutting daily water intake by 100 million gallons, the towers are expected to more than pay for themselves.

We have reports that the anti-pollution efforts at Midland have over the past three years saved the company an amount of chemicals worth more than $6 million. And at the Dow plant in Texas, $900 thousand put into controls saves $265 thousand worth of chemicals every year. In commenting on this example, William Ruckelshaus, EPA Administrator, observed that Dow's profit margin of 24.5 percent is well above the industry average of 18.7 percent. These results were obtained in the very highly competitive chemical industry.

There are two cautions that I hasten to mention in connection with the EPA permit program. First, the legislation for it is still in bill form as of this writing (April 14, 1972); and second, the proposed legislation provides that in specific instances the Administrator of EPA may modify permit requirements where the economic, social and environmental costs of keeping them outweigh the benefits that can be derived.

Ocean Dumping

As environmentalists seek stricter enforcement of water quality laws, as legislation is passed requiring industry to seek permits before they may send their effluents into waterways, and as urban areas generate increased amounts of wastes, then the seas become increasingly inviting as disposal sites. In his April 15, 1970, message to Congress, President Nixon anticipated this problem and asked his Council on Environmental Quality to conduct a study of ocean dumping. I won't labor the findings of the Council except to note that it did indeed affirm that "there is a critical need for national policy on ocean dumping." The Council's report pointed out that industrial liquid wastes are the largest sources of pollution in coastal and estuarine regions; and the next largest are municipal liquid wastes. Although the amount of wastes that are transported and dumped into the ocean are small in terms of the total volume of pollutants reaching the ocean, the Council anticipated that in the future the impact of ocean dumping would increase significantly relative to the other sources.

Ocean-dumped material includes dredge spoil; sewage sludge, which is the residue of the waste-treatment of human wastes; solid wastes, which is more familiarly known as garbage or trash; and industrial wastes. To this listing we can add construction refuse, and the very energetic wastes respired by activities involving radioactive processes.

Among the Council recommendations was that of requiring a permit from EPA for anybody who wishes to transport or dump materials into the nation's oceans, estuaries or Great Lakes. This recommendation was drafted into Amendments to the Federal Water Pollution Control Act. If these Amendments are signed into law, and there is a good possibility they will, then EPA will play a major role in controlling the discharge of wastes into the nation's waters. These waters include the Territorial Sea, the Contiguous Zone, and in some instances, waters beyond the Contiguous Zone.

EPA would be able to carry out its responsibilities effectively only if it can tell what the effects of dumping wastes in various parts of the sea will be. Recognizing this fact, the Amendments call upon EPA to establish guidelines, which would include the following factors:

- The effect of disposal of pollutants on human health and welfare.

- The effect of disposal of pollutants on marine life including the various ecological chains upon which this life is based.

- The effect of disposal of pollutants on aesthetic, recreation and economic values.

- The persistance and permanence of the effects of disposal of pollutants.

- The effect of the disposal and varying rates of particular volumes and concentrations of pollutants.

- Other possible locations and methods of disposal or recycling of pollutants including land-based alternatives.

- The effect on alternate uses of the ocean, such as mineral exploitation and scientific study.

These considerations, then, will provide the grist for EPA in its milling of the guidelines. Very important is the safety valve put in by Congress, which tells EPA that "where insufficient information exists on any proposed discharge to make a reasonable judgment . . . no permit shall be issued" under the discharge provisions of the Act.

These Amendments are another strong indication of the maturing of the environmental protection regulations and laws of the nation, particularly as they affect the coastal zone. In some aspects they do challenge a privilege that society, early in its life in the United States, with unlimited resources at hand, considered one of its rights--the dumping of wastes into the ocean. Yet as we realize that our resources are limited, we must also realize that some of our rights to use them become abridged. If we do not make these abridgments voluntarily, nature will surely force them upon us.

Construction Grants

Most of the money spent by EPA is in grants to States and municipalities for the construction of waste-treatment plants. The President has asked Congress to provide $12 billion for this purpose over the next three years. Simply to provide grants for such construction purposes would be wasteful unless the plants were part of an overall water-quality management plan for an area.

EPA does necessarily provide planning grants through the States and municipalities so that we will know that waste-treatment facilities will be adequate to serve the expected needs of an area, and will be located and sized so that these needs will be served economically.

Before concluding this sketch of EPA's role in the coastal zone, I should like to speak of the Agency's role in controlling spills of oil and other hazardous materials; and in the control of wastes from vessels.

Oil and Hazardous Materials

We can probably point to the Torrey Canyon disaster, and later to the Santa Barbara oil spills, as the two environmental episodes that showed the industrial nations of the world the essential need to actively protect their coastal environments. I don't doubt that many of the environmental protection agencies in the world today were formed in reaction to these two disasters.

We would rightfully expect that EPA would be involved in just about every major oil spill in the United States. The interests and responsibilities of the Agency do indeed include working with industry to prevent spills; and working with industry as well as other government agencies to help clean up a spill once it has occurred. These responsibilities are well known. What is of interest at this time is that most of the responsibilities that EPA has with respect to oil may soon be extended through current legislation to include all hazardous substances. For our purposes, we can define a hazardous substance as any chemical that when discharged into a navigable waterway will cause an immediate and grave danger to life and property.

Vessel Discharges

The commercial ports of the United States generally involve only single uses of the coastal zone. The reasons are apparent and stem in part from the dangers of waterborne traffic to other uses of the coastal area such as recreation and fishing; and in part from discharges coming from the craft, which can jeopardize fishing areas and make recreation unpalatable or dangerous. Yet multiple use of port areas can be envisioned if pollution of the areas were arrested.

Some of the pollution stems from sewage released by the vessels. Under current legislation, EPA is developing standards of performance for marine sanitation devices.

You can imagine the difficulty of trying to devise a rational system of standards when the types and missions of waterborne vessels are so many and so varied. Nevertheless, EPA after a number of public hearings and publishing a set of proposed standards, expects to have its final ones out by the end of this summer. Based upon these standards, the U. S. Coast Guard will promulgate regulations governing the design, construction, installation, operation and testing of marine sanitation devices. Then the standards and regulations will apply to all vessels equipped with marine toilets and that operate on the navigable waters of the United States.

CONCLUSION

EPA will play leading roles in the environmental management of the coastal zone. These will stem from (1) the Agency's responsibilities for performing the research needed to help the nation achieve a healthful natural environment; (2) the need for the same research and understanding of natural processes, and man-made as well, in order to write and help enforce environmental practices that are in the nation's overall interest; and finally, (3) the need to work with local governments so that their goals as well as national ones can be achieved.

COASTAL BOUNDARY MAPPING

Captain Jack E. Guth
Chief, Coastal Mapping Division
NOAA, National Ocean Survey
Rockville, Maryland 20852

BIOGRAPHICAL SKETCH

Captain Jack E. Guth received his B.S. degree in Civil
Engineering from the Missouri School of Mines and Metallurgy
in 1950 and became a commissioned officer in the U.S. Coast
and Geodetic Survey that same year. His accumulated ten
years of sea duty, including several commands, was primarily
in coastal charting activities. His five years in charge
of photogrammetric and geodetic field parties was mostly
in support of coastal mapping. His recent administrative
positions include Chief of Ship Construction and Facilities,
and Chief of Photogrammetry, from which he became the first
Chief of the Coastal Mapping Division in 1970. He is a
member of the American Society of Photogrammetry, American
Congress on Surveying and Mapping, American Society of
Military Engineers, and Marine Technology Society.

ABSTRACT

There is not an acceptable established system for mapping
coastal property boundaries, and consequently uncontrolled
exploitation of our coastline has resulted. Interest is
high on protecting our wetlands, but federal standards must
be stated to insure legal acceptance. Old procedures are
no longer acceptable, but a system for establishing permanent recoverable control and graphically displaying coastal
property lines based on observed mean tide lines is practical.
For the system to become a reality, the federal and state
authorities and private property owners must accept their
responsibilities. These responsibilities are identified and
solutions to the problems suggested.

INTRODUCTION

As old as our country is, and as sophisticated as our land
and ocean mapping programs are, we have never established
an acceptable system for mapping our coastal property
boundaries. This is hard to believe in light of the dollar
value of coastal property. In this paper, I will present
my opinions of how we arrived at this state, and what we
can do about it.

Historically, we have complacently assumed that land ownership extended to the water's edge and when nature saw fit
to change the coastline, property was lost or gained. Now,
we realize that in addition to nature, man has been altering
the coastline for a long time. We have tolerated the exploitation of the coastline for so long it has become a way of
life, and we have never made the effort to establish acceptable legal coastal property lines. Although most states now
have definitions of coastal property ownership, they have
not surveyed or mapped them.

For the past few years, a number of interested and conscientious groups have been attempting to straighten out this chaos. But it is very confusing because there are a number of diverse interests with logical but conflicting views.

Developers want to alter the coastline to boost the economy with bigger and better industry. Ecologists want to protect the environment. Both claim their interest are for the best local and national good. These conflicts will go on forever, and it is up to responsible coastal zone managers to use good judgment in intelligently controlling their coastal regions.

Lawyers are torn between powerful political pressures, old statutes and new principles, and conflicting surveying procedures and standards. They will have to deliberate on difficult problems for years before they can develop reasonable laws. However, their job, and the job of coastal zone managers, can be made considerably easier with help from federal mapping agencies.

The first immediate and pressing need, to ease the tensions, is to define property lines so that engineers and surveyors can recognize and adhere to acceptable surveying and mapping procedures and standards. This task, although under considerable controversy now, is really not too complicated or difficult, as I see it.

As far as defining a property line, I believe legal precedent has clearly established it. The principle that has been consistently endorsed is that a water-land property line is, or is measured from, the point where a local mean tide line intersects the land. The only problem remaining is to establish consistent terminology. The National Ocean Survey has been reviewing this with the idea of clarifying terminology so that surveyors and mappers can get on with the job.

Because there are not many areas of our coast which have adequate coastal boundary property lines mapped, our courts are at a tremendous disadvantage. They are required to base their decisions on historical documents which were never intended to be used for coastal property line determinations.

I believe that establishing procedures and standards which surveyors and mappers can work within, and which they can rely on for legal acceptability, is the most important task facing us.

Different procedures and standards are required for federal vs. state and state vs. private. Where the Federal Government versus a state, the National Ocean Survey has historically been responsible for determinations (based on the mean low-water (MLW) line). But, where a state versus a private property owner, the responsibility for determination (usually based on the mean high-water (MHW) line) is not so well defined.

Where federal vs. state, the National Ocean Survey has been utilizing a system of tide-controlled aerial photography for many years to accomplish MLW line mapping for marine charting.

The line is determined by observing the tide. The MLW plane intersects the land, providing the line for graphically displaying on a map. To provide these mean datum planes, tide observations are required at select points along the coast. Precision recording tide gages are installed and monitored for this purpose.

Black and white infrared aerial photography is taken at the exact time of MLW at these points, which provides a sharply defined line where the tidal water meets the land. An observer at the tide stations actually monitors the tide and radios the aircraft when to photograph the area.

When wave runup occurs along the beach, field survey profiles are required as often as necessary to properly delineate these lines.

Although this traditional system of tide-controlled aerial photography mapping of the MLW line is adequate for its purpose of marine charting, it does not meet today's stringent requirements for property lines, because the tide between the observed points may be different in time and range. In very gentle sloping areas, a difference in a tenth of a foot in the vertical rise of the tide may result in several hundred feet of horizontal displacement of the intersection line.

In the past, the National Ocean Survey has connected the tide observation points with adjusted geodetic levels to satisfy MLW line mapping between them. This is not acceptable for some of today's requirements of discrete measurements, because the water level along the coast is not always level, and straight line adjustments of the level net, when transferred to the local seashore, can result in major incorrect horizontal line displacements.

Fortunately, exact accuracies were not generally required for marine charting purposes, unless a dispute between the Federal Government and a state occurred, at which time precision surveys were made based on actual observed tides at the specific location.

The system is still the most practical and reliable for MLW line mapping, because the line is nearly always visible from an aerial photograph.

However, the major area of concern today is the establishment of procedures and standards for mapping the MHW line, because it is the line generally accepted as the base for measurements from which state vs. private property ownership is determined. As important as this line is to map, it presents difficult surveying problems not usually encountered with mapping the MLW line. The MHW line is not visible from the air in major portions of our coastal regions. These increasingly important areas are our wetlands.

As I see it, there are two pressing requirements for wetlands mapping. The first is for the evaluation and management, plus generalized property line mapping. There is a need for fast, economical, large area coverage. For this need, I believe remote sensing techniques (biological line or others) are the most practical. These techniques, although subject to personal interpretation, offer a good average mean tide line determination, and produce an excellent historical document. I must emphasize average mean tide line, because continual changes in the coastline, either manmade or by nature, accounts for the reason that a vegetation line, which takes time to grow, cannot always be accurately interpreted as a true existing tide line at any one time. The degree of reliable accuracy of interpretation is proportional to the amount of comparisons made with recoverable ground truth established from observed tides.

When a state accomplishes this type mapping, it will become the most acceptable data base for legally governing the wetlands until a precise survey is made.

This points out the second pressing requirement, which is for procedures and standards of control surveys for precise coastal property line determination. For this need, I believe the only survey control system acceptable is permanent recoverable ground truth.

During the past several months, I have made some extensive field trips to evaluate the practicability of establishing recoverable ground truth in the wetlands. I used the following technique in New Jersey and Florida.

At selected points, tidal datums were established by observing tides with accurate recording gages. The density of tide stations was dependent on the physiography, flora, range of tide, and accuracy desired. At the tide-gage locations and at many additional supplemental stations between, recoverable points were photoidentified and referenced vertically to MHW. The additional supplemental stations were established by interpolating elevations at the time of the survey from the tide gages located on either side. The stations are permanently recoverable by horizontal measurements and azimuths referenced to recoverable photoidentified points. The stations have accompanying index numbers, written descriptions, etc. The distance, azimuth, and elevation above MHW of the reference points were recorded for archiving along with the photograph.

This system proved practical in the areas I worked recently, and from personal field experience in most of the coastal regions of the United States, I am convinced it can apply equally well in nearly every area.

These control points can be utilized for any detailed coastal boundary line mapping and historical documents for legal proceedings.

I am pleased to report that the National Ocean Survey is cognizant of this pressing need and recently the Director of the NOS, NOAA, appointed a high powered Ad Hoc committee to make recommendations to him regarding its involvement in seaward boundary determinations and surveying procedures and alternatives that could be followed by states, and others, to assure the required accuracy and legal acceptance of such property delineations.

I suggest that where this control system is used, coastal property lines be considered the same as land property lines. It should be the responsibility of the property owner to have his line surveyed and recorded by a registered land surveyor.

Coastlines are continually changed by nature, but so are land lines to a lesser degree. The point is that we have historical precedent for registered land property line surveys and it is about time we institute a similar system for coastal property line surveys. Most of the wetlands coastline is reasonably stable and permanent recoverable control can be established for producing accurate surveys and maps. In areas where the coastline changes rapidly, special legal applications will have to be instituted to equitably satisfy property rights.

In some few wetlands such as the Florida Everglades, there is not presently a practical system for establishing permanent recoverable control or mapping the MHW line. In such areas, it will probably be necessary for states to institute new property laws based on procedures relying on other than tidal datums. Additional field investigation will have to be accomplished before good judgments in these specific areas can be made.

In conclusion, let me say that I believe reasonable alternative methods exist for mapping coastal boundaries. The Federal Government has a responsibility to set reasonable standards, recommend survey procedures, analyze and state tidal datums, delineate the MLW line where it is in the federal interest, assist states and the general public to the extent feasible in the delineation of coastal property boundaries and the resolution of coastal property boundary problems, and maintain a national data bank.

The states have a responsibility to provide generalized property line maps for evaluating and managing their wetlands. States also must establish basic permanent recoverable control, within federal standards, for use in accurately surveying and mapping coastal boundaries.

Private property owners should be obligated to provide registered surveys made from state established control, and within state standards, if they are to claim property rights.

If federal and state governments and private land owners cooperate and accept their responsibility, I believe our serious coastal boundary mapping problem can be accomplished equitably.

THE ROLE OF THE NATIONAL FLOOD INSURANCE PROGRAM
IN COASTAL AREAS

Mr. Richard W. Krimm
Assistant Administrator for Flood Insurance

Mr. Walter Sutton, Director
Engineering and Hydrology Division

Mr. Nicholas Lally, Director
Flood Plain Management Division
Federal Insurance Administration
Washington, D. C.

BIOGRAPHICAL SKETCH

Richard W. Krimm is the Assistant Administrator for Flood
Insurance, Federal Insurance Administration, Department of
Housing and Urban Development. He received his BA from
Dartmouth College in 1954 and he has attended New York
University's Graduate School of Business Administration.
From 1965-1970 he served as the Deputy Insurance Commis-
sioner for the Pennsylvania Insurance Department.

Walter G. Sutton, a civil engineer, has been involved in
planning the development of water and related land resources
since 1938, except for four years of military service, 1942-
1946. He worked for the Corps of Engineers from 1938-1941,
1946-1958 and 1961-1968--the last period, as Chief of the
Flood Plains Section in the Office of the Chief of Engineers.
From mid 1958 to 1961 he was on the staff of the Special
Assistant to the President for Public Works Planning. Early
in 1969, he joined the Federal Insurance Administration in
the Department of Housing and Urban Development as Chief
Engineer.

A Civil Engineer graduate of Northeastern University, Boston,
Massachusetts, Mr. Lally has worked for the Federal Government in the field of water resources for more than 25 years.
Much of that time was spent in the New England area with the
Corps of Engineers. As Assistant Chief, Hydrology and Hydraulic Section, he was involved in the design and operation
of many flood control projects. From 1962 until he left New
England in 1969, he was Chief, Flood Plain Management Services
for the Corps of Engineers. In July 1969, he transferred to
Washington, D. C., to work in the field of Flood Insurance
with the Federal Insurance Administration in the Department
of Housing and Urban Development. He is presently the Acting
Director, Flood Plain Management Division, with that agency.

In recent years, Americans have increasingly focused
their attention on the problems confronting persons subject
to severe loss, whether from natural disasters such as flood,
hurricane, and earthquake, or man-made perils such as crime
and riot. Despite continued efforts to both eliminate and
ameliorate the impact of these disasters on their victims, it
is unlikely that either natural or man-made disasters will
disappear as a factor in American national life. Therefore
it has become necessary to discover a way to minimize their
devastating effects and to aid their victims.

In the past, this concern has been expressed by the United
States Congress in one of two forms: disaster relief and rehabilitation measures for disaster victims, or the utilization
of various mechanisms seeking to employ the insurance principle.
In recent years, however, it has become generally recognized
that after-the-fact compensatory measures are frequently inadequate, often inequitable, and almost always degrading to the
recipients. As a result, Congress has been giving more emphasis
to the use of the insurance mechanism as is evidenced by both
the National Flood Insurance Act and the Urban Property Protection
and Reinsurance Act. These measures were enacted by the U. S.
Congress in 1968. The need for governmental involvement in programs such as these was intensified by the growing reluctance of
private insurance companies to make essential property insurance
coverages widely available to the public.

Prior to the enactment in 1968 of the National Flood
Insurance Act, flood insurance had never been generally
available in the United States. The private insurance
industry has found it uneconomical to write such coverage.
Only property owners living in flood areas were interested

in the coverage, with the result that adverse selection was
guaranteed, thus making any spread of risk impossible. In
these circumstances, the catastrophic potential of flood losses
could bankrupt an insurance company. Furthermore, property
insurance rates are based on loss and expense experience
recorded over a period of years; credible experience data was
lacking for flood insurance, but even on the basis of available
data those property owners located in a severe flood hazard
zone frequently would be unwilling or unable to pay the high
premium necessary to obtain coverage. Thus the insurance
industry concluded that it was unable to provide flood coverage
without Federal Government assistance.

The inability of property owners to obtain flood insurance
frequently resulted in a failure to rebuild and replace entire
areas stricken by major floods. People often failed to take
advantage of available government assistance. It was also
apparent that any program of land management and other control
measures to reduce the destructive effects of floods in
inhabited areas would require assistance and direction from the
Federal Government. Since the Federal Government was already
providing disaster relief as well as low interest loans to
assist in the reconstruction of damaged property, government
aid in providing low-cost insurance appeared to be a logical
extension.

As a result of Congressional concern, a Federally sponsored
flood insurance program was initially enacted in 1956. A major
problem at that time was the difficulty in developing a schedule
of rates which would be adequate to pay all the claims incurred
within a reasonable period of time. As presented to Congress
in 1956, the proposed flood program set forth a rate structure

which did not reflect the risk variation in different locations
on the flood plain. This tended to support the insurance
experts' belief that sound actuarial rates could not be established. The Appropriations Committee of the House of Representatives considered this rate structure inadequate as the basis of
a viable flood insurance program and concluded that a more
extensive study was a prerequisite for establishing a program of
this nature. As a result, the original flood insurance proposal
failed to receive the necessary appropriations from Congress
and thus never became operative. However, both the need for
such a program and an active interest in establishing one
remained.

In view of the demonstrated critical shortage of flood
insurance, following Hurricane Betsy in 1965, Congress, in the
Southeast Hurricane Disaster Relief Act of 1965, directed the
Secretary of the Department of Housing and Urban Development
to undertake a study of the feasibility of providing flood
insurance at the Federal level. The U.S. Department of
Housing and Urban Development conducted the required study
with the assistance of the Army Corps of Engineers, Geological
Survey, Tennessee Valley Authority, Soil Conservation Service,
and the agency that is now the National Oceanic and Atmospheric
Agency and other organizations with technical competence and
experience in the field of flooding and flood plain management.

Early in this study it became evident that while the
accumulation of credible experience data on which to base flood
insurance rates could be accomplished, the previous fear that
the rates thus developed would be too high to enable most
potential flood victims to purchase policies was confirmed.
Some type of public subsidy by the United States Government was

imperative during the initial development of the program in order
to obtain a broad-based sale of flood insurance and to give
private insurance companies an opportunity to build up their
reserves.

In August of 1966 the resulting report, "Insurance and
Other Programs for Financial Assistance to Flood Victims," was
transmitted to the President by the Secretary of H.U.D. Recognizing the fact that floods are the most serious natural disasters
facing the citizens of the United States, the report cited two
objectives for any relief measure: (1) it should help provide
financial assistance for victims of flood disasters in order to
aid them in the rehabilitation of their property; and (2) it
should, at the same time, help prevent unwise use of land in
those areas where flood damages would mount steadily and rapidly.
Insurance was the mechanism which was capable of maintaining an
acceptable balance between these two goals.

The report therefore concluded that a program of flood insurance was not only feasible but would also promote the public
interest. Flood insurance, if properly conceived and operated,
would have a complementary rather than a competitive relationship
with other Federal Government flood programs such as flood fore-
casting, warning, protection works, relief, and land use management programs. The report concluded that a program of flood
insurance was an excellent means of helping individuals bear more
easily the risks of flood damage to which their locations expose
them as well as an excellent means of discouraging unwise
occupancy of flood-prone areas.

In order to establish a workable flood insurance program,
certain factors had to be given primary consideration:

(1) As few as two percent of all dwellings can expect to

have more than fifty percent of the total average annual flood damage, and less than ten percent of all dwellings have any significant flood hazard at all;

(2) The timing and magnitude of specific floods are unpredictable but the <u>probability</u> of occurrence of a flood of given size is determinable;

(3) The location of flood hazards is identifiable, and the average annual damage by risk/is reasonably predictable;

(4) The short distance between very high-risk areas and low-risk areas will often make the economic use of some zones possible while at the same time avoiding the use of excessively hazardous zones; and

(5) The variation in damage rates among cities necessitates the establishment of separate actuarial premium rates for each flood-prone area.

In response to the obvious need for Federal Government assistance in establishing viable flood insurance coverage, Congress enacted the National Flood Insurance Act of 1968. A 1969 Amendment to the Act expanded the definition of flood to include mudslides. The program, administered by the Federal Insurance Administration within the Department of Housing and Urban Development, is a cooperative effort between the private insurance industry and the United States Government. An advisory committee composed of representatives of the insurance industry, State and local governments, lending institutions, the home building industry, and the general public assists the Federal Insurance Administrator in carrying out the program. Designed to make at least partial flood insurance coverage available against property losses caused by floods, the long-range goal of the program is to reduce or prevent future flood losses through improved flood plain management.

232

In order to obtain flood insurance coverage, the initiative must be taken by each individual municipality or by the unit which has authority over zoning and building code measures. A community must submit a complete application which meets all the requirements of the regulations governing the flood insurance program.

First of all, appropriate local officials must demonstrate that there is a local need for flood and/or mudslide insurance coverage and supply evidence of their desire to participate in the program. In doing so, the community's application must first cite the jurisdiction's legal authority to regulate land use; provide copies of maps showing the areas in the municipality prone to flooding and/or mud-slides and a brief history of flooding and/or mudslide experience in the community; and, if available, furnish copies of any official reports on the community's flooding or mudslide programs. Secondly, the community must have in force, for areas having special flood hazards, adequate land use and control measures (i.e., codes, ordinances, regulations) designed to reduce exposure to these hazards. The minimum area of control and regulations should be predicated on the risks associated with the 100-year flood probability.

The measures ultimately adopted must be consistent with criteria established by the U. S. Government and should: (1) constrict the development of land exposed to flood damage where appropriate; (2) guide development of proposed construction away from locations threatened by flood hazards; (3) assist in reducing damage caused by floods; and (4) generally improve the long-range land management and use of flood-prone areas. The community must also cooperate with the Administrator in

233

his efforts to bring the benefits of the program to the area.

Once a community has completed its application satisfactorily, it will be declared eligible for the sale of subsidized flood insurance policies.

An essential purpose of the National Flood Insurance Program is to encourage State and local governments to adopt and enforce land use and control measures. The law does not place responsibility for flood plain management throughout the country on the Secretary of the Department of Housing and Urban Development, but the statute requires that the objectives of a flood insurance program be integrally related to a unified national program for flood plain management.

Land use and control measures should encourage only development of identified flood-prone areas which represents acceptable social and economic uses of the land in relation to the hazards involved, and should discourage all other development in the identified areas of special flood hazards. Consideration should be given to first-floor elevations and the need for bulkheads, seawalls, pilings, or other devices and procedures designed to reduce damage from flooding and to improve the long-run land management of flood-prone areas.

Without the requirement to adopt land use and control measures there would be no incentive in the flood program to reduce losses, and the program would then encourage rather than discourage the injudicious use of the Nation's flood plains. It is hoped that States will develop criteria for their communities to employ in establishing local land use and control measures. The States can also play an important role in this program by reviewing these measures, as well as by assisting the Federal Insurance Administration in establishing program priorities.

Regional differences in storms of record and topographical characteristics as related to flood hazards must be considered.

Existing structures generally do not have to meet the new building requirements. There is ordinarily no requirement to either improve or modify existing structures for flood damage protection, since zoning and subdivision regulations are not usually retroactive. However, the flood-proofing of existing structures should be an objective of sound flood plain management in developing the highest and best uses of land and in protecting owners against unnecessary losses.

Zoning ordinances, subdivision regulations, building codes, health regulations, and other controls for the health, safety, and welfare of the people should be designed to develop the wisest or most economic use compatible with the flood risks. The areas most frequently flooded might be reserved for open space types of use such as playgrounds, parks, parking areas, agriculture, and storage areas. Areas less frequently flooded might be used for industrial, commerical, and multi-story residential use with controls on first floor elevations, use, and occupancy to minimize damages from flooding. The fringe areas which are least frequently flooded might permit all uses, including single-family homes, provided the structures are anchored properly and first floors are above a safe elevation.

Flood insurance coverage is marketed through a voluntary pool of private insurance companies organized under the auspices of the National Flood Insurers Association. Any qualified company licensed to write property insurance under the laws of any State may become a member. Currently there are some one hundred participating insurance companies which have subscribed a total of over $40 million in risk capital. Companies which do not wish to pledge risk capital may act as fiscal agents for the association; thus, small companies with limited capital resources are not excluded from participating in the program.

NFIA administers and services the selling of insurance. It appoints an insurance-related firm, generally on a State-wide basis, to act as the serviciing office for all flood insurance policies sold in that State. This servicing office disseminates information both to the public and to insurance agents, processes all insurance policies, and handles the adjustment of claims for loss payments.

Any insurance agent may sell NFIA's flood insurance policy, regardless of whether or not he is licensed through a company which is a member of the insurance pool. The agent must submit the property owner's application for insurance to the appropriate servicing company, which then handles the actual processing of the application and the subsequent issuance of a policy. The agent's commission is paid by the pool at an established rate.

With respect to existing construction, premium rates are maintained at an affordable level by Federal subsidy. The subsidy pays for a share of the operating expenses of the companies and for a share of the losses, thereby permitting the actual premium collected from the property owner to be artificially lowered. Subsidized insurance is prohibited under the Act with respect to new construction located in areas identified by the government as having special flood hazards. In these areas the purchaser must pay an actuarial rate based upon engineering and hydrological evaluation of the actual risk involved. To the extent that the new construction includes flood proofing and higher first-floor elevations, the actuarial rates can be substantially reduced.

Property owners are encouraged to buy enough insurance to give them adequate protection where Federal flood insurance is available and all but low-income persons will be denied disaster relief to the extent they could have purchased flood insurance coverage after December 31, 1973. Many private lending institutions are now requiring that Federal flood insurance be purchased to protect their mortgage loans. Although there is no recommended amount, there are minimum premium provisions of $25 per policy and $4 for any increase in coverage during the life of the policy.

At present, the statutory limits applicable to the subsidized program are $17,500 in coverage for single-family dwellings, $30,000 for two-to-four-family dwellings, and $30,000 for non-residential properties. Additional coverage equal to these amounts can be made available at actuarial rates. Contents can also be covered up to $5,000 at subsidized rates. Congress has placed a limitation of $2.5 billion on the amount of flood insurance coverage outstanding and in force at any time and a limitation of $250 million on funds borrowed from the U. S. Treasury to pay for losses and expenses.

A flood insurance policy covers losses resulting from the inundation of normally dry land areas from (1) the overflow of inland or tidal water, (2) the unusual and rapid accumulation or runoff of surface waters from any source, and (3) mudslides which are caused by accumulations of water on or under the ground. It does not, however, cover water damage which results principally from causes on the insured's property

or within his control, or from a condition that does not cause
general flooding in the area. Claims are filed with the
policyholder's agent or broker. The industry pool pays its
share of any losses out of what remains of collected premium
after outlay for allowable expenses. When these funds are
exhausted it draws on the fund established by the risk-sharing
members of the pool up to a point called the stop-loss point.
Beyond this point, all of the industry share of the losses is
paid by Federal reinsurance. These reinsurance payments are
made out of the National Flood Insurance Fund which is composed
of funds borrowed from the Treasury plus reinsurance premiums
collected from the pool.

The principles inherent in the flood insurance program
are sound, but there have been several problems in making it
operational. One initial difficulty was the apathy on the
part of local governments and individuals--even those with a
high probability of being affected by severe flooding. Improved
publicity and an awareness of the benefits of the program combined to help increase vastly the number of applicants as well
as the number of participant communities.

Another key problem was the difficulty in developing
actuarial rates for communities. The rate studies required
at the beginning of the program took up to ten months for a
single community, and at the time of Hurricane Camille in 1969,
only two communities in the United States had been able to
qualify under this program. The enactment of an amendment to
the program in December 1969 authorized the Federal Insurance
Administration to provide flood insurance for a two-year emergency period ending December 31, 1971, without the necessity of
first determining the individual community's actuarial premium

rates. The authorization was further extended to December 31,
1973. These amendments have enabled the Federal Insurance
Administration to qualify more than 1100 communities for insurance as of May 5, 1972.

No change was made in the Act's requirements for the adoption
of local land use and control measures as a condition of obtaining
flood insurance, and no change was made in the requirement
that new construction in special flood hazard areas must pay
full actuarial premium rates.

The emergency program is intended primarily as an interim
program to provide earlier coverage for potential flood victims
pending the completion of actuarial studies. The Federal
Insurance Administration has no authority under the emergency
program to offer additional limits of coverage to existing
construction, and new construction within a special flood
hazard area cannot be covered by any Federal flood insurance
under the emergency program but must await the establishment
of actuarial premium rates.

A simplified actuarial rating procedure has now been
instituted, and it is expected that its use will hasten the
end of the emergency program and permit flood insurance to be
provided broadly under the regular program contemplated by the
1968 Act.

There has been some misunderstanding regarding the requirement to enact and to maintain in force appropriate land use and
control measures based on the hundred-year flood probability.
Many communities think this prerequisite for coverage will
restrict development unnecessarily. Either they do not appre-
ciate the hazards of building in a zone with such a high
probability of suffering severe damage from flooding or are

unwilling to take the necessary action to reduce such losses.
The Federal Insurance Administration is still involved in the
task of assisting in the education of local planners and
builders in the necessity of wise flood plain management.

It is hoped that, at some future date when land management
control and land-use programs have been well established and
have reduced the flood loss potential, when the use of flood
insurance becomes widespread, and when the actuarial rates
have been tested, adjusted and proven establishable, private
industry may be able to assume the entire program without
subsidy. Until that time, the Federal Government will continue
to be the major participant in this program, so that no consumer in a flood hazard area will be denied this much needed
protection.

MARINE TECHNOLOGY IN THE COASTAL ZONE

John G. Housley, PE
Office of the Chief of Engineers
U.S. Army Corps of Engineers
Washington, D.C.   20314

BIOGRAPHICAL SKETCH

Mr. Housley is a civil engineer specializing in staff planning for coastal and estuarine research in the Planning Division, Civil Works Directorate, Office of the Chief of Engineers. Previous assignments involved coastal engineering research in the Great Lakes, and wave dynamics research, including the physical modeling of harbors and shore protection works, at the Waterways Experiment Station. He holds a BS from Lehigh University, an MS from Massachusetts Institute of Technology, professional engineer registration, and membership in several professional societies, including American Society of Civil Engineers, Marine Technology Society, and American Geophysical Union.

ABSTRACT

Estuaries are an anomaly in the coastal zone. They are the transition from an oceanic environment to a terrestrial one; they serve the needs of man in terms of transportation, recreation, water source and sink, and the whole gamut of living and non-living resources; and they are poorly understood. To increase the knowledge of estuaries and how to use them for man's benefits requires an increase in the ability to predict the effects of man on the estuarine environment. Marine technology is being developed to answer the questions and objections raised to such activities as dredging, jetty and groin construction, beach nourishment, hurricane barrier construction, aquatic weed control, and wetlands modification. One tool for understanding basic physical processes in an estuary, such as tide heights, currents, and salinity, is a scaled physical model. Major estuaries like Delaware Bay, Galveston Bay, and San Francisco Bay have been modeled to help solve some of the engineering problems associated with proposed channel realinements, dikes, and other modifications. Chemical and biological processes, which are indicative of environmental problems, are also derived with the help of physical models. Mathematical models of estuaries are now under intensive development. Although the state of the art is not yet what is required to solve the myriad of problems, great strides are being made in the development of two-dimensional mathematical models of physical processes. The Corps of Engineers has embarked on a program intended to establish the proper mix of physical and mathematical models to help solve specific problems. Concurrent with this study, an evaluation of data collection methods, both remote and contact, for the data required for either type of model is being pursued. Galveston Bay and Delaware Bay are the initial test sites for these investigations. The Corps' responsibility in coastal zone construction including that in estuaries, demands that the impacts of its works on the environment be predictable. The improvement in the art of modeling estuarine phenomena will help.

TIDELANDS MANAGEMENT MAPPING
FOR THE COASTAL PLAINS REGION

Philip Guss
Lockwood, Kessler & Bartlett, Inc.
One Aerial Way
Syosset, New York 11971

BIOGRAPHICAL SKETCH

Philip Guss is Project Manager for Ecological Services at LKB, Inc.
He received his B.S. in Biology and Geology at The City College of
New York, and has had subsequent training in Civil Engineering, Photogrammetry and Photo-Interpretation at six universities and The U.S.
Navy School of Photo-Interpretation. He has close to 30 years experience
in photogrammetry, photo-interpretation, and the application of aerial
photography, remote sensing, biology, geology and hydrography to environmental engineering, urban planning and development and associated legal
services. He has taught geometronics and photo-interpretation at graduate
and undergraduate levels.

Philip Guss is a registered professional engineer in the Commonwealth of
Massachusetts, and a member of ASP, ASCE, SAME, and the Marine
Technology Society. He is currently Program Manager for a NASA/USGS
funded project on Coastal Wetlands Ecology Research.

ACKNOWLEDGEMENTS

The author expresses appreciation to Mr. John L. Renkavinsky, Associate
Wildlife Biologist of the New York State Department of Environmental
Conservation, and Dr. Edward Yost and Robert Anderson of Long Island
University, for their contributions to the development of the photo-inter-
pretation systems and procedures.

ABSTRACT

The South Carolina Water Resources Commission instituted a pilot project
study early in 1971 to evaluate the feasibility of using aerial photography and
photo-interpretation to produce multi-purpose Tidelands Management Maps
as well as delineate other important physical and ecological features of the
wetlands of South Carolina.

Tide-controlled color, color-infra-red and multispectral aerial photography
was secured for comparative photo-interpretation of marsh vegetation, pollution, and other ecological features. Alternative photogrammetric and photo-
base map presentations at various scales were developed and tested for optimum
utility by various governmental agencies as wetlands management base maps.
Biological and field-survey ground truth corroborated the validity and accuracy
of the mapping and photo-interpretation procedures. The recommended map
format was a photo-base map at a scale of 1"=400' in undeveloped areas, and
1"=200' in urbanized areas, prepared to national map accuracy standards, upon
which would be delineated all conventional planimetric features, marsh vegetation

boundaries, and a coordinated mean high water line as derived from growth characteristics of marsh vegetation in relation to frequency of tidal flooding. The coordinate location of the mean high water line, with an accompanying metes-and-bounds description, would provide the State with a legal line of demarcation between upland ownership and lands under water.

The optimum photographic combination for achieving this map product was conventional color to prepare the photo-map base, and block-coverage with multi-spectral photography to provide the finest discrimination capability for marsh vegetation classification.

BACKGROUND

A pilot study program was instituted early in 1971 under contract with the South Carolina Water Resources Commission and funded through the Coastal Plains Regional Commission, with the objective of determining the feasibility of the use of various types of aerial photography and professional photo-interpretation to delineate and establish important physical and ecological features of the tidal wetlands in the Port Royal Sound area of Beaufort County. These data would supplement a comprehensive Environmental Base Line Study in the area and provide the State of South Carolina with standards and methodology to establish guidelines for the management, protection and development of all tidal wetlands in the State.

One of the first complex factors to be resolved prior to an acceptable management program for tidal wetlands, is in connection with the ownership. South Carolina, through the State Attorney General, holds that the State owns all of the tidally affected marshes and all submerged lands lying between the mean high water line and the mean low water line except those lands granted to private ownership by an unbroken chain of title from the Crown or by a legislative grant. Current population growth and demands for scenic, aesthetic, and recreational locations have brought new pressures in challenging the State-owned land concept. There are examples of land fills being made in marsh areas without consent on the part of the State. Currently, there is little or no effective method for State management of these lands. Most conflicts are being resolved only through court procedures a slow, costly, and inadequate method to cope with the rate at which private interests are moving to claim lands that may be in question of title. This problem exists in similar areas along the Atlantic Seaboard and other sections of the country with tidal wetlands.

The establishment of a mean high water line by conventional field survey methods in a tidal marsh property parcel is costly, time consuming, and of questionable accuracy. Such a procedure requires a minimum of 90 days of observation at a locally established tide gauge which has been tied into the sea level datum of 1929 by a level run to Coast and Geodetic Survey or Geological Survey bench marks. It is then necessary to reduce the tide gauge data to tidal datum planes to an accuracy of 1/10 foot by comparison with simultaneous readings at a primary tide station such as Charleston, S. C. and then carry the plane of mean high water by levels and traverse into a flat tidal marshland area with saturated organic soil and dense vegetation cover, which is subject to tidal inundation twice daily. Depending on the physical configuration, width and depth of tidal channels within the marsh, the actual elevation of mean high water could be several tenths of a foot different less than half-a-mile away. This could be a significant difference when attempting to establish an accurate high water line in such an environment.

A more realistic approach to mapping the physical location of the mean high water line in tidal wetlands is by aerial photographic interpretation to delineate the perimeters of those key marsh vegetation species which can only thrive in an environment subjected to average daily alternate flooding and exposure. The mean high water line can then be located to national map accuracy standards on a map base prepared from the aerial photography by conventional photogrammetric methods. A recent decision in the State of New York (Dolphin Lane Assoc., Ltd., v. Town of Southampton, Supreme Court, Suffolk County, Index No. 73873-68) has recognized the validity of utilizing vegetation species to define the location of the mean high water line in tidal marshes.

PURPOSE

The purpose of the pilot project, as stated in the agreement with the South Carolina Water Resources Commission, was to determine the feasibility of the use of various types of aerial photography and professional photo interpretation to delineate and establish important physical and ecological features which will augment the results of the Environmental Base Line Study in Beaufort County, South Carolina.

The program was centered around developing from aerial photography, a multi-purpose tidal wetlands management map prototype for the State of South Carolina, upon which would be delineated major associations of tidelands vegetation species, the mean high water line, and both the mean high water line and mean low water line along ocean shorelines. The aerial photography would also be evaluated for development of data on other physical and ecologically significant features.

Specific activities to achieve this purpose were:

a) Secure various types of aerial photography, at various scales and at specific stages of the tide for comparative photographic interpretation and photogrammetric mapping.

b) Develop a practical procedure for identifying and delineating vegetation species and the upland limits of tidal marshes.

c) Develop a practical procedure for determining the physical location of tidal datum planes by methods other than conventional field survey.

d) Development of alternate map and photo-map formats to national map accuracy standards at different scales, for selection of the optimum format and map scales to serve as a Tidelands Management Map.

e) Field verification and testing to determine the degree of accuracy

e) Continued

of tidal datum boundary lines and vegetation classification on the maps.

f) Evaluate the capability of utilizing the various types of photography for detection of pollution and its dispersion, location of oyster beds and assessing viability within these beds, detection of ground water upwelling in estuarine waters, and assessment of water depth penetration for channel bottom mapping.

g) Prepare a narrative report on procedures, problems, limitations, legal interpretations, and recommendations on the methodology for expanding the project on a state-wide basis.

PROJECT AREAS

The specific project areas within the Beaufort County Base Line Study Area were selected as follows:

1. Basic Interpretation and Mapping Area - an approximate 6 x 4-1/2 mile area centered around Spring Island, Callawassie Island, Victoria Bluff and adjacent waterways. It was also requested that the capability of aerial photographic interpretation to differentiate between viable and diseased oysters be investigated in a mud flat of the Colleton River within this area.

2. Mouth of the Beaufort River at the confluence with Port Royal Sound - an approximate 3-1/2 x 1-1/2 mile area. It was requested that the capability of aerial photographic interpretation to locate a sub-bottom source of ground water discharge into the Beaufort River, be investigated in the area east of Parris Island.

3. Ocean Shoreline Mapping Area - within an approximate 1 x 3 mile strip fronting the ocean at the north end of Hunting Island State Park, where a beach erosion control project by the U.S. Corps of Engineers was actively in progress.

Additional areas were subsequently selected at Broad River near the Laurel Bay Naval Housing Area and at Whale Branch near the Tenneco Chemical Plant for pollution detection. Fig. 1 locates the project areas.

MAPPING REQUIREMENTS

It was the intent of the Pilot Project Mapping Program to produce an accurate Tidelands Management Map prototype which would serve the widest range of users. The Water Resource Commission agreed that conventional planimetric maps and photo-base maps covering the Spring Island-Callawassie Island mapping area be developed at alternate scales of 1" = 800' (1:9600) and 1" = 400' (1:4800), with a sample compilation at 1" = 200' (1:2400). The selection of map scales was particularly appropriate because of their compatibility with the basic tax maps covering Beaufort, Charleston and Georgetown Counties. Fig. 1 outlines the 27.5 square mile area of a 30" x 40" map format at a scale of 1"=800', within which area could be developed 1" = 400' map sheets at a similar or smaller size.

The perimeters of the area were also selected to tie into the South Carolina State Plane Coordinate System in a manner compatible with the extension of a map sheet layout to cover the entire State at the selected scales.

Field survey reconnaissance during the month of April, 1971, determined that most of the U.S. Coast and Geodetic Survey and Geological Survey horizontal, vertical and tidal bench mark control within the designated project areas was recoverable, and accessible for preflight targeting. The density of existing horizontal control monuments in the mapping area was sufficient for aerial analogue or analytical triangulation to establish supplemental control for producing photogrammetric maps and photo-base maps to national map accuracy standards. Tide staffs at Bailey's Landing and Colleton (Victoria Bluff) could be readily established and tied into tidal bench marks at those locations for controlling and monitoring times of aerial photography to specific stages of the tide. A tide staff at Harbor River Bridge in Hunting Island could also be established and calibrated to the tidal bench mark for rigidly controlling times of aerial photography along the ocean beach to mean high water and mean low water.

Biological reconnaissance during the month of April, 1971, determined that tidal marsh vegetation, particularly upland species, were at an early stage of growth and it was questionable whether adequate mapping of species could be achieved by photographic interpretation any sooner than the end of the month of May.

AERIAL PHOTOGRAPHIC REQUIREMENTS

In recent years, research has demonstrated the capability of aerial photographic interpretation to classify species of tidal marshland vegetation from conventional color and color infra-red film with varying degrees of reliability. Most recently, the advent of multispectral photography coupled with additive color viewing has provided a powerful tool for discrimination of vegetation species. By control of hue, brightness, and saturation in each spectral band during the viewing process, the highest degree of precision can be achieved in simulating all other types of photography. By switching filters to create false color viewing renditions, fine differences in spectral reflectance of vegetative species can be accentuated for classification purposes.

Vegetation classification not only provides important planning data for wetlands conservation and recreation management, but also provides the means for establishment of the tidal datum plane of mean high water. The optimum time of photography for marsh vegetation interpretation was selected as mean low water to provide maximum exposure of the wetlands.

In ocean beach areas, where the mean high water line separates State-owned lands under water from upland ownership, and the mean low water line is the line from which the offshore State/Federal boundary is determined, both planes can be established by tide-controlled infrared aerial photography (black-and-white or color), utilizing the capability

247

of infra-red photography to image a sharply defined interface between land and water in non-vegetated areas. Tide-controlled aerial photography requires close liaison between an observor monitoring a tide staff and the photographic aircraft to insure that photography is secured at the times of mean high water and mean low water.

Photographic films selected for comparative evaluation of the capability of aerial photographic interpretation to classify tidal marshland vegetation were conventional color and color infrared for the Wild RC8 precision aerial mapping camera, and black-and-white infrared for the four-lens multispectral camera.

Photographic films selected for evaluating the precision of establishment of ocean beach tidal datum planes by tide-controlled aerial photography were black and white and color infra-red for interpretation purposes, and conventional color as a mapping base, to be utilized in the RC8 camera. Multispectral exposures were also to be secured for comparative purposes.

All film/camera combinations listed for vegetation interpretation were to be used to secure photographic coverage for evaluation of the capability of aerial photography to detect water pollution in tidal wetlands, for assessment of viability in oyster beds, and for detection of sources of ground water upwelling in tidal rivers. Water depth penetration capabilities of minus-blue color film would also be tested if time permitted inclusion of this film in the photographic missions. The minus-blue mode could also be simulated in multispectral additive color viewing of water areas for this analysis.

For the purpose of the pilot project, the rigid constraint of tide-controlled aerial photography severely limited the times of aerial photography to those days when predicted mean low water and mean high water coincided with daylight hours suitable for photography, preferably avoiding the 11 AM to 1 PM Standard Time interval to minimize specular water reflection. Such periods of time normally extended from three to four days once or twice a month during the flying months of June through November, when marsh vegetation could be speciated by aerial photographic interpretation.

Flight lines for interpretation photography in the mapping area were laid out to follow the progression of the tide through the major waterways. Flight lines for the mapping photography were similarly laid out, with the additional constraint of adjusting their orientation to take maximum advantage of the pattern of targeted horizontal control monuments for the aerial triangulation required to provide supplemental control for map production.

AERIAL PHOTOGRAPHIC OPERATIONS

Reconnaissance photography was planned during the optimum tidal/daylight periods of May 18-19 and May 23-25, but was cancelled because of poor aerial photographic weather at the job site. The intent of reconnaissance was to secure representative strips of aerial photography in multispectral and color infra-red for the purpose of selecting optimum filters for use in the multispectral cameras, and to perform preliminary photographic interpretation for vegetation speciation, water pollution detection, oyster bed

analysis, fresh-water upwelling, and water penetration capabilities.
The multispectral aircraft was dispatched to South Carolina on June 10
during a reported break in the weather, encountered clouds over the
Beaufort area, and secured very limited photographic coverage with
two sets of filters during breaks in the clouds. Preliminary interpretation of this photography, which was examined in simulated true
color, color infra-red, black-and-white, and false color renditions
on the additive color viewer, confirmed that vegetation had reached a
stage of growth suitable for classification by photographic interpretation.
The optimum set of filters for complete coverage aerial photography in
the pilot project area was selected as follows:

    505-558 nm (nanometers) - green
    585-680 nm - red
    712-745 nm - near infrared
    805-930 nm - far infrared

It was determined that two bands (585-680 and 805-930 nm) were most
sensitive in discriminating marsh vegetation species; that three bands
(505-558, 585-680, and either 712-745 or 805-930 nm) provided the
capability of simulating color infrared film, and that three bands
(505-558, 585-680, and 712-745 nm) were particularly valuable in
detection of water pollution.

Considering the extremely limited periods of time in the following
months when optimum daylight hours for aerial photography coincided
with desired tidal datum planes, the decision was made to go ahead with
operations during such periods if long-range weather forecasts were
good or marginal. Although the June 15-20 aerial photographic weather
forecast was marginal, a field survey party was committed on June 7
for pre-flight targeting of control, setting up and calibrating tide staffs
and establishing required traverse and level lines in preparation for
tide-controlled photography and ground-truth survey operations. An
advance photographic party arrived June 14 and set up test panels at
Walterboro Airport for calibration of the multispectral photography.
Two photographic aircraft were standing by in New York awaiting a
favorable photographic weather forecast at the job site to be confirmed
by the advance photographic party, and the project manager arrived on
the job site on June 15 to coordinate joint field-flight operations. Unsuit-
able weather conditions (thunderstorms, heavy cloud cover, fog and haze)
developed and remained in the Beaufort area during the entire planned
period for aerial photography, and the operation was cancelled for the
month of June.

Field and flight plans were adjusted for the next period suitable for aerial
photography, July 12 - July 16. The field survey party arrived on site one
week before July 12; the advance photographic party arrived on July 11
with test panels for multispectral calibration; the project manager arrived
July 12. Thunder-shower activity on July 12 prevented the arrival of the
two photographic aircraft until July 13, and solid cloud cover on July 13
precluded photographic missions. Aerial photographic coverage was
successfully obtained under marginal conditions during the July 14-16
period as follows:

Spring Island - Callawassie Island Mapping Area

a)   Color photography at mean low tide at a scale of 1" = 1000'; and at a
     scale of 1" = 2000' about 1-1/2 hours after mean low tide.

b)   Color infra-red photography at mean low tide at a scale of 1" = 1000'.

c)   Multispectral photography at a scale of 1" = 1600' about 1/2 hour
     after mean low tide.

The oyster bed areas in the mud flats were also covered by color
multispectral photography at mean high tide. The Victoria Bluff area
was similarly covered by color, multispectral and color infra-red
photography.

Hunting Island

Tide-controlled strips of photography:

a)   Color - @ 1" = 1000' at mean high water and @1" = 1000' and 1" = 2000'
     at mean low water.

b)   Color infra-red - @ 1" = 1000' and 1" = 2000' at mean low water, and
     @ 1" = 1000' at mean high water.

c)   Multispectral = @ 1" = 1000', at mean high water, and at mean low water.

Beaufort River

a)   Color and color infra-red @ 1" = 1000' at predicted slack tidal current.

b)   Multispectral - @ 1" = 1600' at predicted slack tidal current.

Broad River at Laurel Bay Village

a)   Color @ 1" = 1000' at mean low tide.

b)   Color infra-red @ 1" = 1000' at 1/2 hour after mean low tide.

c)   Multispectral - @ 1" = 1000' approximately 1 hour after mean low tide.

Whale Branch - Vicinity of Lobeco Village

a)   Color and color infra-red @ 1" = 1000' at approximate local mean
     low tide.

b)   Multispectral @ 1" = 1000' at approximately 1/2 hour after local
     mean low tide.

Color infra-red photography was given precedence over black-and-
white aerial photography, when weather forecasts indicated poor photographic weather for the remainder of the operational period. Tide-
controlled color infra-red photography would not only serve its primary

function of vegetation classification by photo-interpretation, but would also provide a sharply defined land-water interface at beach areas.

Tide staffs were established and monitored at Hunting Island, Victoria Bluff and Bailey's Landing, and tidal datum plane information was transmitted to the aircraft to control specific times of photography during flight operations. It was noted that Tide Table predictions of the times of mean high water and mean low water fell within twenty minutes of the actual times as observed at the tide staffs.

Ground-truth survey lines locating mean low water and mean high water at Hunting Island beach were established by conventional field survey on July 17.

On October 28, a photographic aircraft was dispatched to secure black and white pancromatic film coverage at a scale of 1" = 2000' covering the entire block-mapping area as well as selected strips of color infrared photography at a scale of 1" = 1000' covering ground-truth areas within the mapping area.

PHOTOGRAPHIC INTERPRETATION

a) Tidal Marsh Vegetation and the Mean High Water Line

Field reconnaissance by the biologist in late April 1971, correlated with background information on South Carolina marsh vegetation by other investigators, developed the following relationships between specific vegetation species and tidal datum planes:

Spring high tide - the line of demarcation between Sabala, Pinus and Quercus (palmetto, pine and water oak) and the most upland of the following high marsh species:

    Juncus roemerianus (needle rush)
    Iva frutescens (marsh elder)
    Distichlis sp. (salt grass or spike grass)
    Spartina patens (salt meadow grass or salt hay)

Mean high water - the line of demarcation between high marsh species (or the tree-line in the absence of high marsh species), and Spartina alterniflora (salt marsh cord grass) or annual Salicornia sp. (saltwort).

In tidal marsh "barren zones" with little or no vegetation, mean high water would be defined by the upland perimeter of a zone of high saturation. The upland boundary of the barren zone falls within the lower range of spring tide. The lowland boundary falls within the range of neap high tide and normally adjoins Spartina alterniflora, a species which requires average daily tidal inundation, or a bank of Salicornia sp. between the barren zone and the S. alterniflora.

Annual Salicornia sp. require two to three days of exposure above water level during the month for seeds to germinate and penetrate the substrate then regular tidal inundation for growth, thereby serving as excellent indicator species for the plane of neap high water.

Windblown dead S. alterniflora known as "wrack" may overlie the vegetation bracketing the plane of mean high water. Scattered S. alterniflora growth will normally be visible in this wrack zone, and the upland perimeter of this growth serves to locate the mean high water line.

"Wrack" may also overlie the barren zone. The zone of saturation would still be apparent (particularly in multispectral photography) for defining the mean high water line.

Figures 2 and 3 illustrate the relationship between marshland vegetation species and tidal datum planes in the mapping area, where the tidal range varies from 6 1/2 to 7 1/2 feet.

All modes of aerial photography secured within the mapping area were critically analyzed and compared by our biologist. It was apparent that the only physical features shown on about 50% of the photography were intertidal marsh and water, and the only vegetation species was Spartina alterniflora in various stages of stand vigor, with the most vigorous appearing on the banks of tidal creeks and in lower areas within the marsh which were subject to longer periods of inundation during the tidal cycle.

Low tide color infrared photography at a scale of 1" = 1000' imaged lush growth of S. alterniflora along stream banks as a deep magenta color. The magenta color weakened as grass heights diminished with increasing height of terrain within the tidal prism, and the blues normally associated with saturated soil became the predominant colors. Multispectral photography was examined in a simulated color infrared made with enhancement in the magenta color range to accentuate the color signature of S. Alterniflora and confirm its presence in the "blue-tone" areas imaged in the conventional color infra-red photography.

Differentiation of species in the area bracketing low marsh, high marsh and upland was accomplished primarily with multi-spectral photography. Imagery in false color modes was examined at a scale of 1" = 400' on the additive color viewer, and species boundary lines were annotated on 1" = 400' black and white enlargments by image matching. The mean high water line was then drawn in relation to the species boundaries. Conventional color photography and color infra-red photography were not sufficiently discriminating for rapid visual separation of species, and for detection of the critical perimeter of sparse S. alterniflora growth in "wrack" areas.

The color infrared photography covering ground-truth areas which was flown on Oct. 28 showed most species of the marsh vegetation in a lush, mature stage of growth, and confirmed the vegetation photographic interpretation from the coverage of July 14-16. The late October photography also confirmed that the optimum flying season for tidal marsh vegetation classification in South Carolina bracketed the period of June through October, and probably could extend through to the middle of December with slightly modified interpretation keys.

In early December, the biologist returned to the project area to check out several questionable interpretation areas, and to spot check the accuracy of his photo-interpretation of marsh vegetation species. The ground-truth confirmed the validity of species identification utilizing the described aerial photographic interpretation procedures.

b) Oyster Bed Areas

Low tide color infra-red photography and multispectral photography proved to be the best media for locating shell banks and oyster bed seeding areas in the mud flat and marsh environment. Relative viability of the oyster beds could not be differentiated. The shape and size of artificially seeded oyster beds could readily be interpreted for subsequent plotting on a map medium.

c) Fresh Water Upwelling in the Beaufort River

The attempt to locate a source of fresh-water upwelling in the Beaufort River by local differences in turbidity was not successful in any types of photography tested, although photography was flown as close to slack tide as feasible to maximize the surface effect of turbidity dilution by fresh water. Density and color differences observed in the water were closely correlated to the patterns of underwater topography and submerged tidal flats which were shown on the local Coast and Geodetic Survey nautical chart. The area for photography which was designated for this investigation extended from the mouth of the Beaufort River northerly to Cat Island, and it is doubtful that the ground water table was significantly breached within this reach of the river. Such an investigation could best be carried out as a separate research project with coordinated ground-truth, utilizing other sensors such as infra-red scanning to supplement aerial photography.

d) Water Pollution Detection

Source and dispersion of domestic pollution from the sewage treatment plant serving the Laurel Bay Village area, was visible in all photography - color, color infra-red and multispectral. The greatest detail on local dispersion within the tidal creeks of the intertidal marsh prior to discharge into Broad River, was achieved with several false color renditions of the multispectral photography.

Photography in the vicinity of the Tenneco Chemical Plant outfall at Whale Branch was critically examined in all photos - color, color infra-red, and multispectral - with no apparent evidence of a water pollution point source or dispersion pattern. This lack of evidence, however, is explained by the fact that the photography was secured in the area at approximate low tide, and it was subsequently learned that the effluent was discharged only at high tide to take advantage of maximum downstream flushing.

e) Water Depth Penetration

Because of priorities in securing aerial photography during the limited July 14-16 period, minus-blue color film could not be flown in the RC-8 mapping camera. Multispectral coverage over Broad River, Colleton

River and Beaufort River was examined in the additive color viewer in a simulated minus-blue mode, and it was noted that water penetration was limited by high turbidity in the water. Secci disc observations in the Beaufort River during the aerial photographic period showed extinction at a depth of 3-1/2 feet.

PHOTOGRAMMETRIC MAP AND PHOTO MAP COMPILATION

Aerial triangulation utilizing the 1" = 2000' photography covering the block mapping area provided the necessary network of supplementary control required to produce photogrammetric compilations and photo-maps at alternate scales of 1" = 800', 1" = 400', and 1" = 200', which would meet national map accuracy standards. (i.e. - 90% of all sharply defined map features shall be within 1/40" at map scale of their true geographic positions, and the remaining 10% displaced no more than 1/20" at map scale.) The following photogrammetric compilations tied to the South Carolina State Plane Coordinate System, showing all visible planimetric features within the marshland and adjacent upland areas, were independently prepared:

Coverage of the entire block mapping area at a scale of 1" = 800', within a 40" x 30" format.

Coverage of the entire block mapping area at a scale of 1" = 400' in four sections.

Coverage of an 8000' x 6000' area at Victoria Bluff at a scale of 1" = 200'.

Rigidly-controlled photo-mosaics covering the block mapping area at scales of 1" = 800' and 1" = 400' were prepared, and a special 1" = 200' mosaic was prepared covering a limited area bracketing Victoria Bluff.

A photogrammetric compilation at a scale of 1" = 400' was prepared covering the Hunting Island Beach area, upon which was added the mean high water and mean low water lines from the tide-controlled aerial photography.

After review of the compilations and preliminary photo-maps, the following alternate finished map products were prepared:

a) A photogrammetric planimetric map and a photo-base planimetric map at a scale of 1" = 800', covering the entire block mapping area in a 40" x 30" size within a 48" x 36" map format. Map content included visible planimetric and drainage features, the South Carolina plane coordinate grid system, names of geographical and cultural features, civil division boundaries, tidal marshland vegetation classification, boundary of the tidelands management area, and locations of recoverable horizontal and vertical control including tidal bench marks. The locations of the mean high water line as transcribed from photographic interpretation was added as a solid line on the planimetric map only. Marginal data on the plani-metric and photo-base maps included a title block, a tabulation of

horizontal control monuments and coordinates, bench mark
elevations and tidal bench mark datum plane elevations; location
diagram, symbol legend, and explanatory notes pertinent to the
map content.

A tidal datum plane overlay at map scale was prepared, upon which
was delineated a computer-generated series of points representing
points of intersection and points of tangency along the mean high
water line and impounded areas. Marginal data on the overlay
included tabulations of coordinate positions of each point in the
South Carolina State Plane Coordinate System to tie down the
physical location of the mean high water line in relation to Coast
and Geodetic Survey, Geological Survey, and South Carolina
horizontal control monuments. The information on the overlay
was photographically added to the photo-base map to incorporate
all information pertinent to both tidelands management and tidelands
ownership in one format. The overlay then became the second part
of the planimetric map format to illustrate an alternative presentation in which tidelands management map information was separated
from tidelands ownership information.

A separate computer print out tabulated bearings and distances from
point to point along the tidal datum plane along with bearings,
distances and acreages of impounded areas, to provide the basic
information required for legal descriptions. Bearing and distance
ties to governmental agency horizontal control monuments were
also established to facilitate occupation of the tidal datum plane by
conventional field survey methods.

b)   Four photo-base maps and two planimetric maps at a scale of
     1" = 400', with each map covering 30" x 25" of area at this scale
     within a 37-1/2" x 30-1/2" format, were prepared to the same
     specifications as the 1" = 800' scale maps.

c)   Although it was considered desirable to prepare a sample planimetric
     and photo-base map at a scale of 1" = 200' as an example of the need
     for this scale in urban, suburban and moderately developed rural
     areas, density of urbanization within the block mapping area was
     sparse and did not warrant any finished map products beyond the
     sample photogrammetric compilation.

d)   All photogrammetric maps and overlays were prepared on dimen-
     sionally stable polyester-base materials. One master set of photo
     base maps was prepared on opaque dimensionally stable material,
     and a set of screened positives suitable for providing paper ozalid
     reproductions were also submitted.

e)   The photogrammetric map covering the Hunting Island Beach area
     was ink-drafted, and the field survey locations of the mean high
     and mean low water lines were added to evaluate the precision of
     location of tidal datum-planes by tide-controlled aerial infra-red
     photography.

FIELD SURVEY TESTING OF TIDAL DATUM PLANES

a) Hunting Island State Park Beach Area

On July 17, 1971, on the day following color infra-red tide-controlled aerial photography of the Hunting Island beach area, a 3400'± field survey base line was established along the beach and tied into horizontal control monuments. From this baseline, the Harbor River Bridge tide gauge elevations of mean high and mean low water were located on the beach by offset distances along 8 profiles. These field locations were plotted on the 1" = 400' scale photogrammetric map of the area and compared to the photo-interpreted mean high and mean low water lines. The maximum horizontal offset along the mean low water line, where the gradient was steepest, did not exceed 1/40" at map scale, and most field established positions coincided with the photo-interpreted location. The correlation at the mean high water line ranged from coincidence or near coincidence to a maximum horizontal offset of 3/80" at map scale at a local area with a flat gradient. The close correlation between field survey location and photo-interpretation location of the mean high and mean low water lines, supports the validity of establishing tidal datums along beach areas from tide-controlled infra-red photography.

b) Mapping Area

During the period of Jan. 7-15, 1972, a field survey party carried the elevation of 3.6 feet above the sea level datum of 1929, into the tidal marsh by triangulation, traverse and leveling and physically located ten points at this elevation within the marsh. The elevation of 3.6 feet represents the height of mean high water at the river bank fronting Bailey's Landing, based on a tidal bench mark at that location. The physical locations of these points as compared to the photo-interpreted mean high water line ranged from coincidence to 1/40" offset in 8 of 10 points; offset 1/32" in the 9th point, and 1/8" offset in the 10th point.

The field party chief reported that his horizontal locations were indefinite, in that he could have moved his level rod at least 30 feet radially from each location and found a number of points at the same elevation. He also noted that the marsh vegetation between Point #10 (offset 1/8" at map scale) and the photo-interpreted mean high water line was Spartina alterniflora, the species which requires average daily tidal inundation to survive, and that a difference of 1/10 of a foot vertically at this location could have shifted the point several hundred feet horizontally.

The mean high water line established from photographic interpretation of vegetation species is considered to be of greater validity than the conventional field survey method of carrying a fixed elevation into the marsh from a tidal bench mark located outside of the marsh. To approach the same degree of accuracy by conventional field survey would require the establishment of a great density of tide gauges deep within the marsh, preferably spaced 1/4 mile apart, monitoring the gauges for at least 90 days, reducing the data to local planes of mean high water accurate to the nearest 1/10 foot, then running a traverse within the marsh at the level of local mean high water while adjusting this level to conform to differences in elevation between successive tidal bench marks. The accuracy of conventional field survey location of a mean high water line is further compromised by the inability to establish a discrete location of an elevation point in a tidal marsh since the same elevation can be encountered within a wide radius in the flat terrain.

CONCLUSIONS

The pilot study has demonstrated that it is feasible to produce from aerial photography and professional photographic interpretation, a multipurpose Tidelands Management Map upon which is delineated a valid mean high water line for determining the various ownerships in the wetlands of South Carolina. The methodology and techniques which were developed to produce the map products could equally serve to provide similar management map series for the adjacent States within the Coastal Plains Region.

RECOMMENDATIONS

Aerial Photography

The recommended types and scales of aerial photography to produce the South Carolina series of Tidelands Management Maps are:

a) Conventional color photography with a precision mapping camera at a scale of 1" = 2000' (1:24000) for map compilation of the 1" = 400' scale maps, and at a scale of 1" = 1000' (1:12000) for map compilation of the 1" = 200' scale maps covering urbanized areas. This photography should be flown at approximate mean low tide, with flight lines laid out sequentially and geographically to follow the progression of the tide upstream in major drainageways.

b) Color infra-red photography in a precision mapping camera at the above specified scales covering ocean beach areas. This photography would be flown at local mean high water and mean low water, with times of photography controlled by observors monitoring tide gauges.

c) Multispectral aerial photography at scale of 1" = 1600' covering rural areas and 1" = 800' covering urbanized areas, with flight lines laid out in a pattern similar to the conventional color photography to provide approximate mean low tide coverage.

Aerial photography should be acquired with the County as the basic subdivision, conforming to a schedule of priorities established by the State of South Carolina. Flight lines, however, would straddle County boundaries to logical terminations based on tributary drainage basins.

Photographic Interpretation

Multispectral photography was recommended as the optimum photographic medium for accurate, rapid photo-interpretation to differentiate

tidal marsh species, and thereby arrive at the physical location of the
mean high water line based on the viability of these species in relation
to average frequency of tidal flooding. As mapping progresses in the
tidal wetlands, photographic interpretation would be regularly supplemented by ground-truth investigations correlated to tide gauge observations to confirm the accuracy of vegetation interpretation and the location
of the mean high water line within the various types of tidal marshes in
the South Carolina coastal region.

Map Compilation

It was recommended that the photo-base prototype map with accompanying computer print-out bearings and distances be adopted as the standard
format for a Tidelands Management Map series covering the tidal wetlands of the State of South Carolina. Map scale would be 1" = 400' (1:4800)
in rural areas, and 1" = 200' (1:2400) in urbanized areas. Overall map
size would be 37-1/2" x 30-1/2" within which the mapping area of
30" x 25" is laid out to tie into the South Carolina State Plane Coordinate
System.

Map content is designed to provide the maximum amount of information
pertinent to multi-agency useage of the map series:

a)   Each map is tied into the horizontal control network of South
     Carolina and is prepared at a precision which meets national
     map accuracy standards.

b)   Maximum density of planimetric detail in the marsh and adjacent
     upland areas is provided by the low tide aerial photographic base
     map.

c)   Tidal marsh vegetation species are differentiated and identified.

d)   The mean high water line (and the mean low water line along
     oceanfront shoreline) are represented as a series of numbered
     connected points, which are physically located by coordinate
     positions in a marginal tabulation on the map sheet, and by
     bearings and distances tied to horizontal control monuments
     in a separate computer tabulation.

e)   All impounded areas are also described by coordinates, bearings
     and distances, along with computed acreages of impoundments.

f)   The plane of mean low water in the tidal marsh could similarly
     be coordinated and described if the upland owner holds valid
     title to low water, since the basic aerial photography is flown
     at approximate mean low water.

Inventory of Tidal Wetlands

It was also recommended that acreages of high marsh, low marsh and
open water areas be computed during the course of map preparation to
provide an accurate inventory of tidal wetlands by map sheet, town,
county and for the entire State.

OTHER CONSIDERATIONS

A partial tabulation of the broad spectrum of management uses for the recommended map series are:

1. The establishment of the boundaries of State, Federal and private ownership in the tidal wetlands, along with an accurate inventory of acreages of ownership. Adverse possession by encroachments or impoundments would be documented in a form providing legal descriptions and acreages.

2. A comprehensive base map of the tidal wetlands for establishment of a system of zoning classifications, and for the evaluation of the environmental impact of proposed dredging, filling or other alterations.

3. An accurate base map for comprehensive planning of the development, improvement and maintenance of navigation systems and facilities, including selection and designation of long-term disposal areas for dredging.

4. A comprehensive base map for fish and wildlife management in the tidal marshes and adjacent upland areas. Leased oyster bed boundaries could be accurately located to resolve conflicting lease claims, and to develop information on non-utilized leased acreage.

5. A highly detailed base map for recreational management, including planning of access and facilities improvements for boating, fishing and bathing.

6. A base map for sanitary control of estuarine waters, upon which sewage and industrial outfalls can be pinpointed, and pollution survey data can be plotted and analyzed in relation to shellfishing, fishing, bathing and other recreational uses.

7. An up-to-date base map showing the status of land and improvements, which can be utilized for the assessment of real property by local governments.

8. A map medium showing the extent, density, and access to forested tracts adjacent to tidal wetlands, which can be used for game management and for planning of selective cutting.

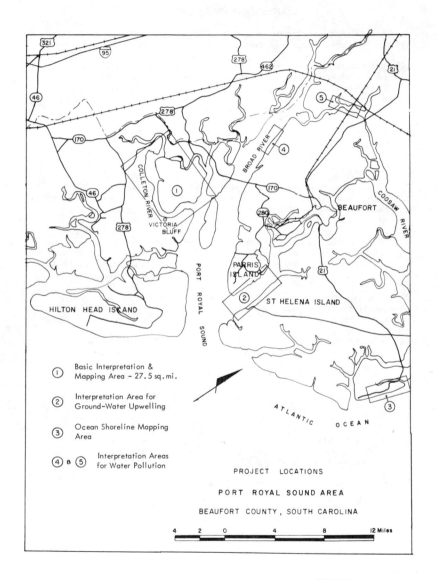

Legend:

① Basic Interpretation & Mapping Area – 27.5 sq. mi.

② Interpretation Area for Ground-Water Upwelling

③ Ocean Shoreline Mapping Area

④ & ⑤ Interpretation Areas for Water Pollution

PROJECT LOCATIONS

PORT ROYAL SOUND AREA

BEAUFORT COUNTY, SOUTH CAROLINA

4 2 0 4 8 12 Miles

FIGURE 1

COMPOSITE MARSH PROFILE COLLETON-CHECHESSEE AREA

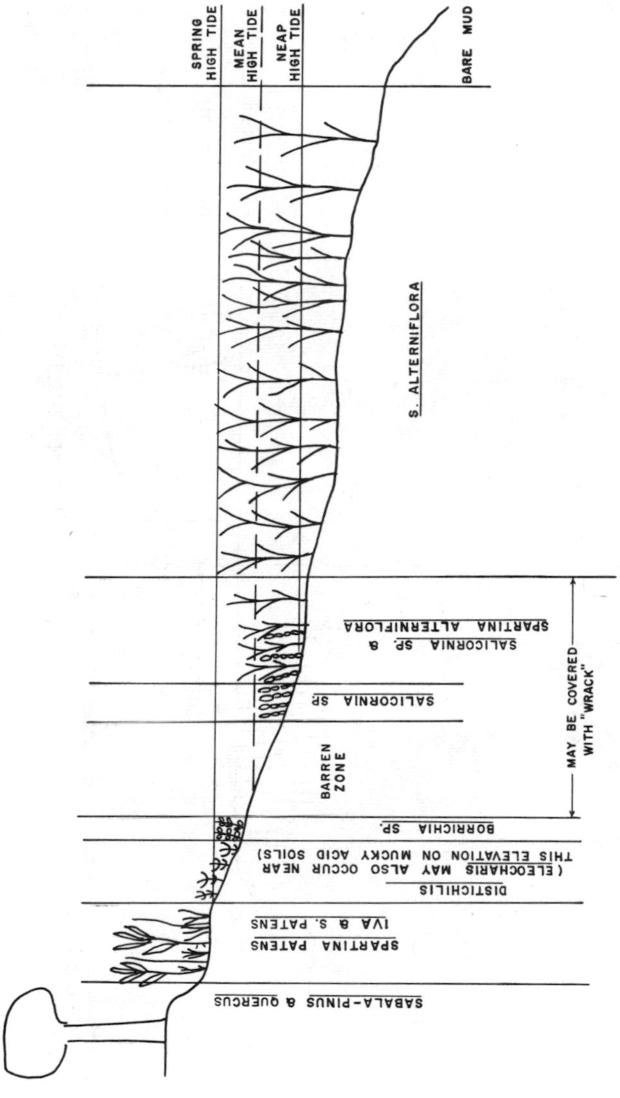

SPRING HIGH TIDE
MEAN HIGH TIDE
NEAP HIGH TIDE
BARE MUD

S. ALTERNIFLORA

SALICORNIA SP. & SPARTINA ALTERNIFLORA

SALICORNIA SP.

MAY BE COVERED WITH "WRACK"

BARREN ZONE

BORRICHIA SP.

(ELECHARIS MAY ALSO OCCUR NEAR THIS ELEVATION ON MUCKY ACID SOILS)

DISTICHILIS

SPARTINA PATENS IVA & S. PATENS

SABALA-PINUS & QUERCUS

FIGURE 2

261

MARSH PROFILE INCLUDING _JUNCUS_

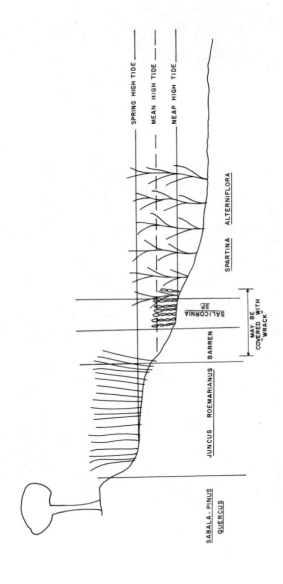

SABALA - PINUS
QUERCUS

JUNCUS ROEMARIANUS

BARREN

SALICORNIA SP.

SPARTINA ALTERNIFLORA

MAY BE COVERED WITH "WRACK"

SPRING HIGH TIDE
MEAN HIGH TIDE
NEAP HIGH TIDE

FIGURE 3

HYSURCH - A SYSTEM DEVELOPMENT
FOR COASTAL CHARTING

Halford Woodson
Engineering Department
U. S. Naval Oceanographic Office
Washington, D. C. 20390

BIOGRAPHICAL SKETCH

Halford Woodson is HYSURCH Project Officer at the Naval Oceanographic Office. Prior to this assignment he worked in the field of navigation first with the Navigation Science Division and later with the Precise Positioning Branch of the Research and Development Department. Woodson is a graduate of the U.S. Naval Academy and served on active duty for 21 years, a number of which were spent in aircraft navigation and bombing system development. He is a member of the U. S. Naval Institute.

ABSTRACT

HYSURCH is a system development for the improvement of acquisition rates of coastal survey data and subsequent on site data compilation and display. An advanced development model of the system is in the final stages of integration prior to a technical evaluation in the summer of 1972. The system will then undergo an operational evaluation in a coastal survey ship prior to final integration for coastal survey operations.

INTRODUCTION

In mid 1967 the Naval Oceanographic Office undertook the development of an advanced HYdrographic SURvey and CHarting system. This development has become known as HYSURCH, an acronym derived from the name. Its objective, simply stated, is to improve the Department of Defense capability to produce coastal charts faster with greater accuracy. All facets of survey data acquisition and chart production have been analyzed and the development pursued from a system standpoint. Work has progressed from a conceptual phase through an equipment hardware development and test phase. Upon completion of an initial technical evaluation, the system will undergo an operational evaluation aboard a coastal survey ship prior to its integration for normal survey deployments.

SYSTEM DEVELOPMENT

System Concept

The concept for HYSURCH (Figure 1) evolved from a study made by the System Measurements Laboratory, Massachusetts Institute of Technology under a Navy contract. The guidelines were to study coastal survey and charting with a goal of increasing acquisition rates of survey data by a factor of ten with the capability of producing charts on site within 24 hours after completion of the survey. Specific areas of investigation included: depth sensors for mounting on high speed craft, both surface and airborne; advanced methods and techniques for on site data reduction and compilation; and improved procedures for display of hydrographic data. An added requirement was a positioning technique that would not require the occupation of land areas by a shore team. The system must be capable of operating on a worldwide basis in support of naval requirements. Also, it should meet the requirements of the Office in support of general maritime operations.

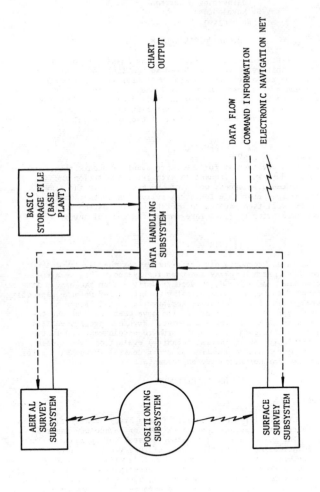

Figure 1. HYSURCH Functional Concept

CHART
OUTPUT

BASIC
STORAGE FILE
(BASE
PLANT)

DATA HANDLING
SUBSYSTEM

AERIAL
SURVEY
SUBSYSTEM

POSITIONING
SUBSYSTEM

SURFACE
SURVEY
SUBSYSTEM

DATA FLOW
COMMAND INFORMATION
ELECTRONIC NAVIGATION NET

During the study several major unknowns arose. The performance of
sonic depth sounders on high-speed surface craft was undetermined.
Previous sounding had been done at speeds of 12 knots or less. There
was considerable question as to wheather the precision depth sounders
could operate successfully from high-speed surface craft such as
planing craft, air cushion vehicles, or hydrofoils. As a first step,
the Naval Ship Research and Development Center at Carderock, Maryland,
designed and tested a universal high-speed housing in the tow tank to
observe the onset of cavitation. Speeds to 45 knots were attained with
no appreciable occurrence of cavitation. In addition, a precision
depth sounder was installed and tested in HIGH POINT, a Navy experimental
hydrofoil. Limited success was attained at speeds to 40 knots in water
depths 100 fathoms or less.

Another area of considerable doubt was the performance of a positioning
net in a buoy-mounted configuration. Of particular concern was the
possible degradation of the net stability due to buoy watch circle
excursion and signal loss due to antenna roll and pitch. A Sea-Fix
slave station was mounted in a taut wire moored buoy and tested as
part of a station pair with the master station installed ashore. The
buoy watch circle in currents up to 2 knots with wind conditions 20
knots or less was kept to less than 10% of mooring line scope. Signal
stability was excellent.

Investigations of side-look sonar that would operate from a high-speed
vehicle and detect objects or obstructions between sounding lines were
made. An experimental ahead-looking, obstacle-detection sonar
developed for use in hydrofoils was mounted to look abeam in a vertical
pattern. This was tested in HIGH POINT with some success. However,
additional engineering development is required to provide a useful
side-look sonar for high speed application.

Investigation into sounding of the shallow water of the near beach
areas in depths to 30 to 40 feet directed the study to airborne
sounding. The laser showed promise as a sensor for this application.
An experimental laser depth sounder, the Pulsed Light Airborne Depth
Sounder (PLADS), was build by Raytheon under contract to the Oceanographic Office. In its initial tests it acquired data to depths of
40 feet in coastal areas. A great deal of work remains to improve its
reliability and signal-processing techniques prior to fabrication and
and test of a prototype model.

As a result of the MIT study plus the supporting investigations, the
system concept evolved for a near shore hydrographic survey and
charting system or HYSURCH. The concept included a mother ship with
embarked high-speed boats and helicopters as the nucleus. The boats
and helicopters ,equipped with sonic depth sounders and laser depth
sounders respectively, acquire the depth data. Position information
and horizontal control are provided by a buoy-mounted or land-installed,
hyperbolic positioning net. Tidal data are obtained from data buoys
moored in the survey area. All data are recorded on magnetic tape and
returned to the mother ship at regular intervals during the survey.
Aboard ship the data are reduced and compiled. The hydrographic data
are merged with land map information from source files for the on site
production of limited quantities of charts. During actual survey
operations samples of data collected by the boats and the tide-data
buoy are telemetered upon command to the ship. They provide the survey
control central with a means of real-time monitoring of the survey
and a capability to change or adjust the survey during operations.

Advanced Development Model

Based upon the above concept a contract was negotiated with Kollsman
Instrument Corporation, Syosset, New York; to design, fabricate, and
test an Advanced Development Model (ADM) of the system. Decca Survey
Systems of Houston, Texas, and Hermes Electronics of Halifax, Nova
Scotia, are major subcontractors. The model includes only those
elements of the system necessary to demonstrate the concept. It is
configured with the shipboard collection/compilation computers and
peripherals in a portable shelter so that the initial tests can be
made from a shore site. The ADM can then be embarked in a survey ship
for operational type testing. The model is in the final stages of
hardware and software integration and is to receive initial testing
during the summer of 1972. Basically it consists of a data acquisition
group and a compilation group. The major elements of the ADM are two
soundboats, one tide-data buoy, a positioning net with two buoys, and
a collection/compilatio shelter.

The soundboats (Figure 2) are standard fiberglass, 36-foot Uniflite
Sport Sedans equipped for sling and davit hoisting. They are powered by
two 300-horsepower diesel engines and develop speeds of approximately
30 knots in calm water. The soundboat can be handled by a three-man
crew; a helmsman, a survey-equipment operator, and an engineer. Survey
equipment is configured in a console on the starboard side of cockpit.
It consists of a Decca Sea-Fix position receiver, at Atlas DESO-10
precision depth sounder with 100-kHz and 210-kHz sounding heads, a data
transceiver, a Kennedy 1600 tape recorder, a Control Data Corporation
5102 computer, and an interface unit. These equipments are connected
to a control panel, which gives the operator centralized access. A
navigation display panel at the helmsman's station provides steering
signals to control the boat along the sounding lines.

The data buoys (Figure 3) are 31-inch spherical buoys equipped with a
counterweight and self-deployable anchor system. The buoy supports a
20-foot whip antenna. A battery power supply, a cassette tape recorder,
and a data transceiver are located in the buoy compartment. Attached to
the anchor is a pressure transducer and temperature unit that sense the
water temperature and pressure changes during the tidal cycle. These
data are recorded on the magnetic tape and also stored in the data
transceiver for transmission upon command. Power supply is sufficient
for 30-days of operation.

A Decca Sea-Fix system used in the hyperbolic mode provides the
positioning net. The stations can be mounted in buoys (Figure 4) or
installed ashore. For the ADM, two buoys are included which are
configured to take a master or slave station. The buoys contain two
compartments one for the station electronics and the other for the
power supply consisting of 24-volt batteries with a diesel-powered
generator for battery recharging. The buoys are moored submerged on
a taut wire, with only the antenna superstructure piercing the surface.
A 35-foot whip antenna is mounted on the structure. A tide winch operated
by a pressure switch allows the buoy to follow the water depth with the
buoy being submerged about eight to nine feet below the surface. The
moor is designed for implanting the buoy in water depths from 20 to 200
feet.

The collection/compilation center (Figure 5) is housed in a 20x8 foot,
air-conditioned shelter. It contains a collection group with a Honeywell
H-316R computer interfaced to a cathode-ray tube (CRT) and a data
transceiver; a compilation group with a Honeywell H-516R computer inter-

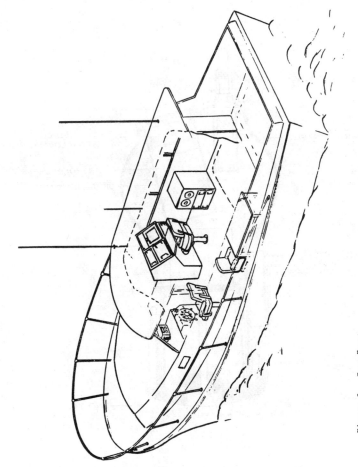

Figure 2. Soundboat

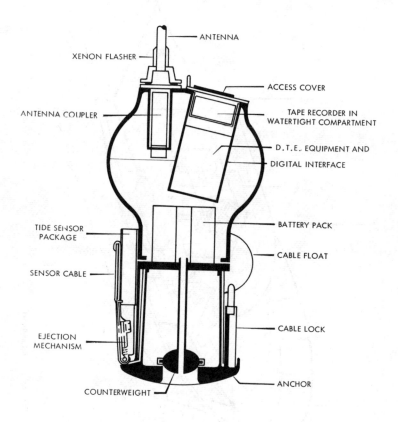

Figure 3. Data Buoy

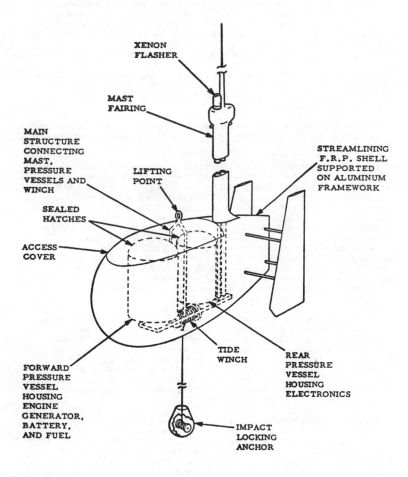

XENON
FLASHER

MAST
FAIRING

MAIN
STRUCTURE
CONNECTING
MAST,
PRESSURE
VESSELS AND
WINCH

LIFTING
POINT

STREAMLINING
F.R.P. SHELL
SUPPORTED
ON ALUMINUM
FRAMEWORK

SEALED
HATCHES

ACCESS
COVER

FORWARD
PRESSURE
VESSEL
HOUSING
ENGINE
GENERATOR,
BATTERY,
AND FUEL

TIDE
WINCH

REAR
PRESSURE
VESSEL
HOUSING
ELECTRONICS

IMPACT
LOCKING
ANCHOR

Figure 4. Positioning System Buoy

faced to a CalComp plotter and magnetic tape drives. Both groups share an ASR-35 teletype unit and a fixed-head disk storage. The collection group communicates with the boats and data buoy, displaying real-time survey data on the CRT. The compilation group compiles the data in a format suitable for graphic output on the CalComp plotter.

A 2.5 to 2.9 mHz data transceiver (Figure 6) has been developed for the interchange of data between the boats and buoy, and the collection group. This unit has been designed for a 50-mile overwater path at a data rate of 160 bauds. The reliability of transmission is such that the undetected word error rate will not exceed three in 10,000. Initial tests have indicated its performance to exceed the design specifications.

These equipments are being integrated into a system capable of acquiring water-depth data and then outputting these data in a chart format for on-site production of nautical charts. An essential effort in this integration is the computer software.

Three major software programs are being developed; that for the soundboat computer, that for the collection computer, and that for the compilation computer.

The soundboat computer program is functionally subdivided into three subprograms. The first is the navigation program which **converts** the hyperbolic data to XY position, compares present position with input track information, and outputs steering signals to the helmsman's navigation display in the form of left/right error signals and distance-to-go along track. The second is a data management program which combines depth with position data and writes these data on magnetic tape. This program has a limited editing capability in that redundant and spurious data are eliminated prior to recording. The third subprogram controls the data transmission to and from the soundboats including the formatting, coding, and decoding. The depth data are scanned to determine the data characteristics plus maximum and minimum depth within a specified interval. These are stored in a register for transmission upon command to the collection computer.

The collection computer programs control the real-time monitoring of the survey. One subprogram controls the data transmission equipment providing the interrogating commands to the soundboats and data buoy. It encodes and decodes the information transmitted and received via the data link. A second subprogram computes tidal data and corrects received depth data to a common datum. Another subprogram controls the display of data on the CRT. Three formats are displayed; a navigation display showing soundboat progress, a single sounding-line-analysis display, and a depth profile display.

The third major programming effort is for the compilation computer. The soundboat tapes with depth and position data, and the data buoy tape with tide data are input to the compilation computer. The tide data are processed and combined with the depth data to correct the depths to a common datum. Soundboat position data are processed through a smoothing routine. These corrected and smoothed soundboat data are then used as the input to generate an equally spaced data grid, (Figure 7) which is output on the plotter with a contour overprint. A subroutine regenerates the soundboat line from the grid points and compares this with the soundboat tape. Actual tape-data-points from the soundboats that exceed a preselected allowable error are retained in the grid tape as spot depths. In a similar manner, regenerated cross-check data are compared with actual cross-check data to evaluate the validity of the survey.

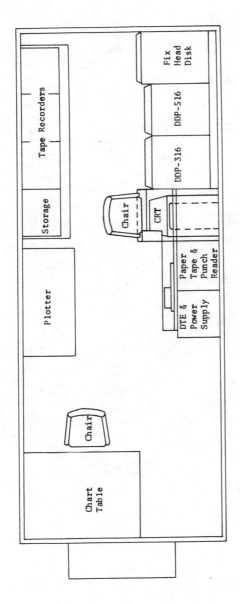

Figure 5.   Collection/Compilation Center

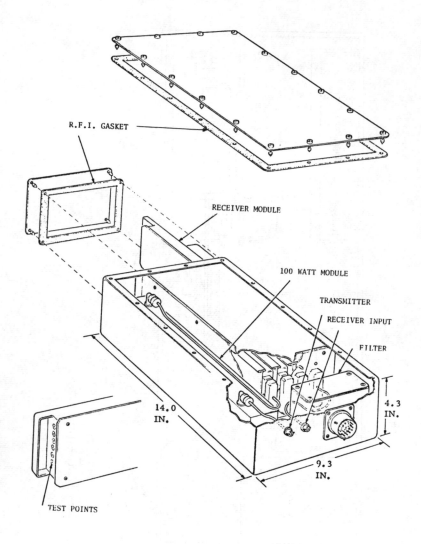

R.F.I. GASKET

RECEIVER MODULE

100 WATT MODULE

TRANSMITTER

RECEIVER INPUT

FILTER

4.3
IN.

14.0
IN.

9.3
IN.

TEST POINTS

Figure 6. Data Transceiver

272

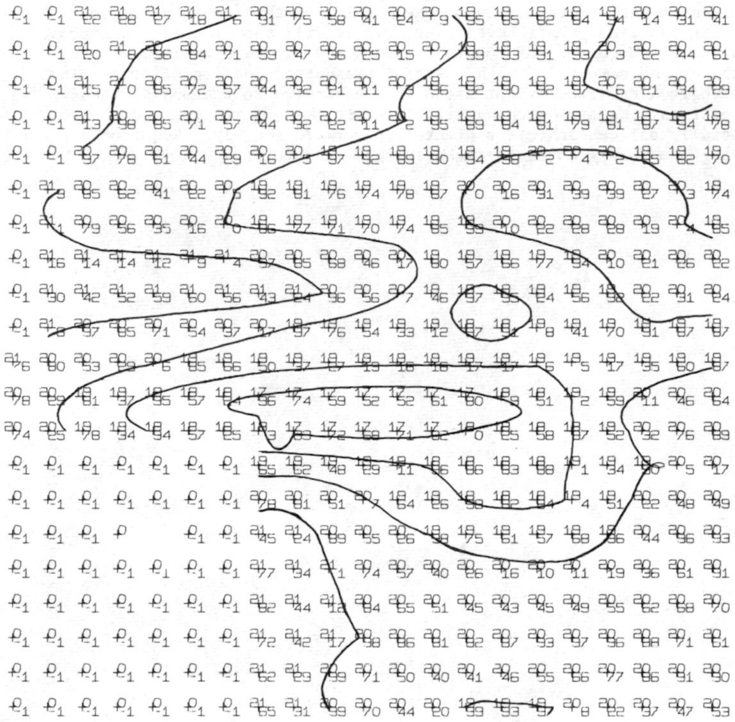

Figure 7. Data Grid Plot

273

The grid plus the spot depths then becomes the data base for the graphic output of the final hydrographic chart master. The hydrographic data are output in the form of selected contour lines and spot depths at the desired chart scale. This master is then combined with the land map master for on site production of charts.

CONCLUSION

HYSURCH is now near the test stage of the full system. With its completion we will have demonstrated the capability to increase substantially the data acquisition rates and to significantly decrease the time required to compile the data for output. On-site reduction of the data and data portrayal in graphic form will provide a realistic and comprehensive evaluation of the quality of the survey prior to leaving the area. This development effort will show the way to improve the speed and quality of coastal surveys and at the same time reduce manpower and associated high costs of present collection efforts. The Oceanographic Office is not alone in the concern to accomplish these objectives. We are watching with interest the efforts of others. Hopefully all can achieve a giant step forward shortly. Requirements facing the survey community make success mandatory.

PRELIMINARY RESULTS AND NEW PRODUCTS
DEVELOPED FROM A CIRCULATORY SURVEY
OF BOSTON HARBOR

R. Lawrence Swanson
Chief, Oceanographic Division
National Ocean Survey
Rockville, Maryland 20852

BIOGRAPHICAL SKETCH

Commander R. Lawrence Swanson, born October 11, 1938, in
Baltimore, Maryland, graduated from Lehigh University in
1960 with a B.S. degree in Civil Engineering. He also
attended Oregon State University graduating with a M.S.
degree in Oceanography in 1965 and a Ph. D. degree in
Oceanography in 1970. Swanson joined the Coast and
Geodetic Survey in 1960 serving as a junior officer on
several survey and oceanographic ships. In 1966 he was
appointed Commanding Officer of the USC&GS Ship MARMER
a circulatory survey vessel assigned to the east coast
of the United States. Presently, Swanson is serving as
the Chief of the Oceanographic Division of the National
Ocean Survey. He is a member of the American Society of
Civil Engineers, American Geophysical Union, and Phi Kappa
Phi.

ABSTRACT

A physical oceanographic survey of Boston Harbor is described with particular emphasis given to the remotely
sensed photogrammetric current and the thermal mapping
surveys. A few of the preliminary results are presented
along with much of the data displayed in a map format for
easy reference and utilization.

INTRODUCTION

The National Ocean Survey has been developing an estuarine
and coastal circulation program over the past several years
which has been an extension of our ongoing program of providing tide and tidal current data to the public for navigational, scientific, engineering, and recreational uses.
This program has and will contribute significantly to the
knowledge necessary for understanding estuarine and coastal
processes and provide information on which to base sound
coastal zone management decisions. Summarizing our efforts,
they are:

1. Extension of traditional tidal
   current surveys along with
   initiation of estuarine flushing and nontidal current
   predictions.
2. Integration of remote-sensing
   techniques with methodology
   traditionally employed for
   estuarine and coastal circulation studies.

3. Coordinated estuarine studies
   with other interested agencies.

In view of the above objectives the National Ocean Survey
conducted a circulatory survey of the Boston Harbor and
Massachusetts Bay area during the summer of 1971. The City
of Boston and the New England River Basins Commission
stressed the importance of the survey for use as baseline
data on which to form sound environmental policy and
planning. Field operations were augmented to include input
from the Environmental Protection Agency.

The NOAA Ship FERREL - a special purpose research vessel
designed to carry out physical oceanographic observations in
estuarine and near-shore areas - commenced operations in
Boston Harbor in early May of that year. Instrumented arrays
maintained by the FERREL were used to collect such physical
oceanographic data as temperature, salinity, and current
speed and direction. Time series data of this type varying
in length from a week to as long as five months constituted
the basic survey. Synoptic coverage of some of the physical
properties was considered to be of significant importance to
the further understanding of the hydrodynamic processes.
However due to the large area involved, synoptic coverage
was impossible from instrumented arrays. Thus a photogrammetric tidal current and thermal mapping surveys were
developed to supplement the classical shipboard operations.

The general objectives of the remote-sensing project were:

1. To further investigate the circulation patterns of Boston Harbor.
2. To develop new methods of remote-
   sensing techniques for water
   quality studies.
3. To develop new products and services particularly in the area of
   water quality.

OPERATIONAL PROGRAM

The Coastal Mapping Division of the National Ocean Survey
developed in the early 1960's a technique whereby surface
currents could be described by photogrammetric methods.
The x and y parallax caused by movement of a surface target
with the current can be measured on a pair of stereoscopic
photographs. Any number of targets can be released and the
speed and direction of each can be determined.

Targets consisted of flaked aluminum powder. Measurement
of current speed and direction were obtained from metric
photography using a Wild RC-9 camera. It was operated at
23,150 feet, MSL, true altitude giving a scale of 1:80,000.
The single flight line over the project area was flown at
30-minute intervals (Figure 1).

In addition to the photogrammetric measurements of the surface currents, infrared imagery was obtained for the purpose of tracing the temperature distribution throughout the
tidal cycle. These investigations led to increased detail

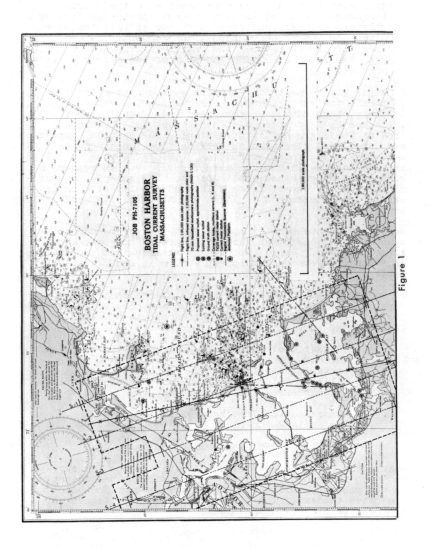

JOB PH-7105

BOSTON HARBOR
TIDAL CURRENT SURVEY
MASSACHUSETTS

Figure 1

277

of the water mass movements within the estuary as a result
of correlation with the in situ measurements of current,
temperature, and salinity.

Imagery was obtained for the entire tidal current cycle.
An HRB-Singer Reconofax IV single channel scanner, operating in the 8 - 14 micrometer region, filtered to 8 - 12
micrometers, recorded the imagery on 70 mm photographic
film and on magnetic tape in the analog mode. Scanner
flights were planned to be concurrent with the metric
photography. Infrared imagery was not limited to daytime
flights and weather conditions were not as restrictive as
required for metric photography. Consequently, when
weather appeared to hinder the entire effort, the thermal
mapping was undertaken independently of the metric coverage
(Figure 2).

A number of ground truth stations were occupied in order to
calibrate the remote-sensing observations. Temperature,
salinity, turbidity, current speed and direction, were
collected as a function of depth throughout the project
area at these ground truth stations. In addition, surface
wind speed and direction as well as tidal measurements
were obtained. This information, besides serving as calibration data, will also be used for research in remote-
sensing techniques and applications. For example, investigations of the use of false color and density slicing is
already being examined in light of our turbidity measurements.

Because a remote-sensing survey of this type requires
sophisticated equipment, aircraft, ground support, and a
large number of people, NOS sought and acquired cooperation
from other Government agencies, academia, and private
concerns.

In addition to NOS which had the total responsibility for
development, operation, coordination and completion of the
project, the following organizations provided valuable
input to the survey:

> The National Aeronautics & Space Administration
> The U.S. Coast Guard
> Lockwood, Kessler, and Bartlett, Inc. - Long
>   Island University (C.W. Post Research Center)
> Grumman Aerospace Corporation
> U.S. Navy
> Massachusetts Institute of Technology
> New England Aquarium.

PRELIMINARY RESULTS

Due to the wealth of the data collected during the survey
and also the number of diverse organizations participating
in the project, analysis has been preliminary and uncoordinated to date. The first steps towards integration
of the data are now being taken.

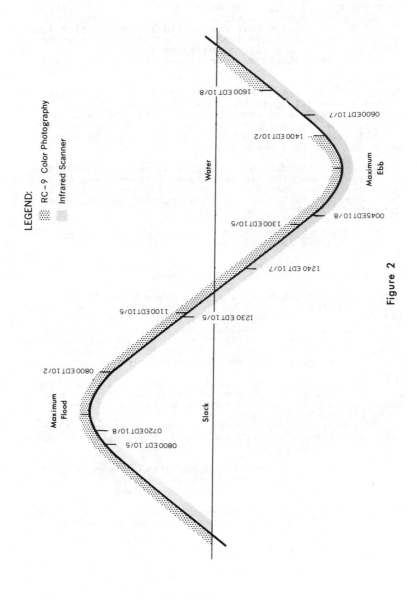

LEGEND:

⬚ RC – 9 Color Photography

▓ Infrared Scanner

Maximum
Flood

0800 EDT 10/2

0720 EDT 10/8

0800 EDT 10/5

Slack

1100 EDT 10/5

1230 EDT 10/5

1240 EDT 10/7

Water

1300 EDT 10/5

0045 EDT 10/8

Maximum
Ebb

1400 EDT 10/2

0600 EDT 10/7

1600 EDT 10/8

Figure 2

279

There are some generalities that can be established during these early stages of analysis. The tidal currents in what has been called the outer harbor are significant and will have a pronounced effect on the distribution of various properties. For example, one of several recommendations is that the Nut Island and the Deer Island sludge be combined and discharged approximately one mile north of The Graves. It can be anticipated that due to tidal currents plus a net drift to the South, undesirable distributions of adverse conditions such as coliform concentrations might be expected in the vicinity of Deer Island, the Brewsters and possibly Nantucket.

Drogue and dye studies in the area of Finn's Ledge were performed on several different occasions during the month of October. The drogues were tracked at five foot and 20 foot depths. The dye (Rhodamine WT) was diluted with methanol so that the mixture would seek a density level between three and five feet below the surface.

Comparison of the data on the flood current indicates good agreement between the two techniques (Figure 3 and 4). It must be realized when first scrutinizing the two sets of data, that the ratios of the flood current maximums for the area on October 8 and 19 were:

$$\frac{\text{maximum tidal flood current - Oct. 8}}{\text{maximum flood current} \quad \text{- Oct. 19}} = 1.24$$

When the data is reduced to the same base, agreement in both speed and direction is quite good.

Temperature and salinity data from casts taken in fall indicate that the structure of the water column is well mixed in this particular area. An exception is in the surface layer, due to diurnal heating. The shear indicated on a plot of the drogue data (Figure 3) in the vicinity of Finn's Ledge can be attributed to the frictional effects as the tidal current reverses near the bottom prior to the surface.

The decrease in the concentration of the dye in both time and space is a good indicator of the diffusive processes taking place. As expected the concentration (Figure 5) along the longitudinal axis over a half tidal cycle was found to decrease logarithmically from the source. The mean concentration for ebb and flood as a function of distance from the point source is $c = e^{6.35 - 2.052\,x}$

$$\text{where c is the concentration in ppb}$$
$$\text{x is the distance from the}$$
$$\text{source in nautical miles}$$

The drogues and dye indicate that the flood is channelized, apparently as a consequence of the dredged Boston North Channel.

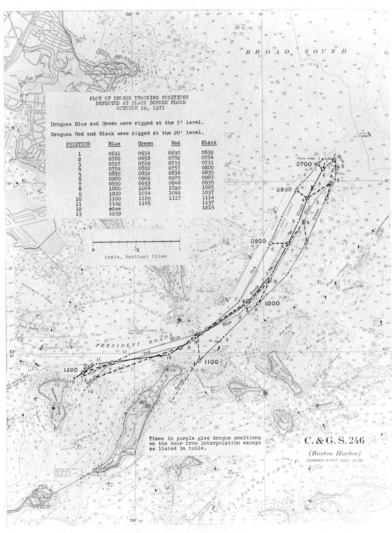

PLOT OF DROGUE TRACKING POSITIONS
DEPLOYED AT SLACK BEFORE FLOOD
OCTOBER 19, 1971

Drogues Blue and Green were rigged at the 5' level.

Drogues Red and Black were rigged at the 20' level.

POSITION	Blue	Green	Red	Black
1	0631	0634	0630	0632
2	0700	0658	0702	0704
3	0727	0729	0733	0731
4	0754	0802	0757	0800
5	0830	0832	0836	0835
6	0900	0902	0905	0903
7	0930	0933	0940	0935
8	1000	1004	1010	1005
9	1030	1034	1042	1037
10	1100	1105	1117	1114
11	1142	1145		1137
12	miss			1215
13	1239			

Scale, Nautical Miles

Times in purple give drogue positions
on the hour from interpolation except
as listed in table.

C. & G. S. 246

(Boston Harbor)

SOUNDINGS IN FEET—SCALE 125,000

Figure 3

281

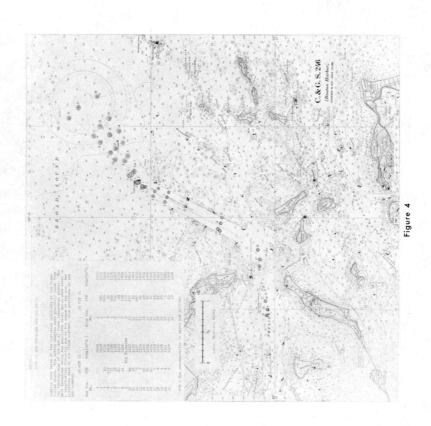

Figure 4

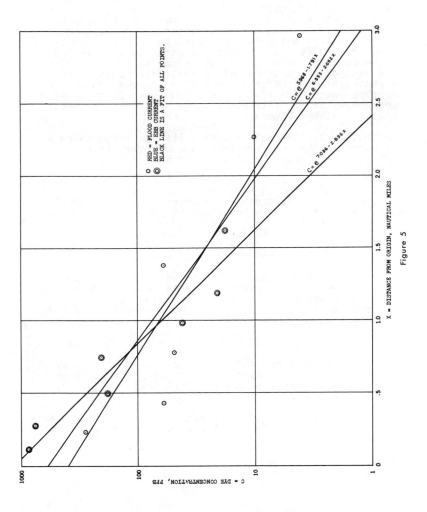

RED = FLOOD CURRENT
BLUE = EBB CURRENT
BLACK LINE IS A FIT OF ALL POINTS.

$C = e^{5.968 - 1.791X}$

$C = e^{6.833 - 2.022X}$

$C = e^{7.036 - 2.896X}$

X = DISTANCE FROM ORIGIN, NAUTICAL MILES

C = DYE CONCENTRATION, PPB

Figure 5

NEW PRODUCTS

It is our intent to incorporate the information obtained by
conventional observational techniques with that collected
via remote-sensing. The ultimate product is to be a publication describing the physical processes in Boston Harbor
and environs. However, the extraction of information from
such publications is often of more value to the scientist
then to the practitioner. As a result we have decided to
map a great deal of the diverse information in a format
that will be an effective tool for both the research and
management oriented.

A series of charts have been constructed which display the
data as observed, calibrated, and processed through various
error detection schemes. The data has been brought to a
unified scale using a bathymetric background as a base.
The temperature values which should be used to show trends
as opposed to absolute values are shown as a series of
isotherms. The currents are displayed as a series of vec-
tors with color differentiation indicating data collected
by photogrammetric techniques and by drogues and metered
observations. Tone changes have been used from the metric
photography to indicate distinctive water mass movements
such as effluent plumes.

Marginal data will include such pertinent information as
the anomalies between predicted and observed values of
tide, and tidal current at the reference stations in the
area.

It is the intention to have these charts available throughout the tidal current cycle. However, the first charts
which are ready for limited distribution are for:

> Max Flood plus one hour
> Slack water
> Max ebb.

These preliminary products will be made available to potential users who will hopefully benefit from the mass of information displayed. We are also looking to the users for
constructive criticism and suggested improvements for data
presentation.

SUMMARY

The large quantity of useful data collected on this project has given us a tremendous versitility in both types of
analysis, development of new products, and, of course,
basic research.

It is anticipated that this experience will further NOAA's
efforts to develop a sound but dynamic estuarine program.

AREAL SAMPLING FOR THE MAPPING OF
NEARSHORE ENVIRONMENTS

Dr. Richard B. McCammon
Department of Geological Sciences
University of Illinois at Chicago Circle
Chicago, Illinois 60680

BIOGRAPHICAL SKETCH

Richard B. McCammon is a Professor of Geology at the
University of Illinois at Chicago Circle where he
specializes in geostatistics. McCammon received his
B.Sc. in geology from M.I.T., his M.Sc. in geology
from the University of Michigan and his Ph.D. in
geology from the University of Indiana. He served as
a research geologist for seven years with Gulf Research
& Development Company. Since joining the University,
he has served as consultant to Gulf Oil Corporation
and TRW,Inc. For the past two years, he has been
engaged in research supported by the Geography Programs
Branch, Office of Naval Research, in the development
of statistical procedures for sampling nearshore
sedimentary environments. He is currently an
associate editor of the Journal of the International
Association of Mathematical Geology.

ABSTRACT

The areal sampling of coastal environments involves the
problem of pattern reconstruction under uncertainty.
Many of the mappable variables which are of interest
exhibit complex patterns with regard to their spatial
distribution. The distribution pattern for the
sedimentary environments of the Mississippi Delta region
of southeast Louisiana can be characterized however
by the average distances which separate the seven major
types of depositional environments. An optimal sampling
strategy for mapping nearshore environments is proposed
whereby the probability of intersecting environmental
boundaries between successive samples is maximized.

INTRODUCTION

Today, with the new awareness of the coastline, as it
relates to the Nation's population growth, urban
planning and environmental quality, a requirement for
new kinds of maps which convey specialized information
is clearly indicated in certain areas and for particular
uses. The country in effect has begun to measure the
impact of a growing population on our coastlines. It
is not surprising therefore that environmental mapping
has assumed a major role in the development of effective
environmental control programs.

For the nearshore environment, many of the variables of
direct interest cannot be mapped as continuous by remote
sensing methods but rather their spatial distribution
must be determined by areal sampling at selected geo-

graphic locations. While is is assumed that these variables
vary continuously over a given area, nonetheless, the
maps that are prepared are based on discrete data points
located on a traverse or on a grid. Examples of such
variables are bottom sediment types, concentrations of
trace elements, biotic composition, suspended matter and
pollutants to name a few. Since the main concern with
these variables is their spatial distribution and its
relationship to the environment, the problem arises as
to how many samples should be taken and where should they
be taken in order to reconstruct adequately the
underlying spatial pattern.

PATTERN RECONSTRUCTION

There is an elusive relationship that exists between
the size and arrangement of areal units of observation
and the underlying structure of a spatial pattern. For
the former to be chosen in some optimal manner, it is
necessary to have some knowledge of the latter. As an
example, the areal distribution of sediment types in the
Mississippi Delta region of southeast Louisiana exhibits
a complex pattern of depositional environments shown in
Figure 1.

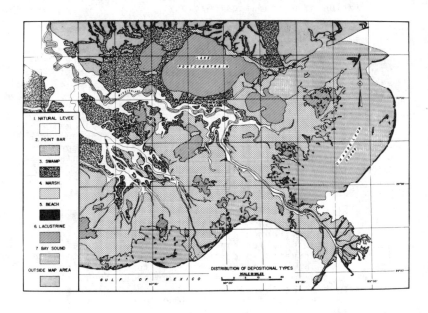

Figure 1. Depositional environments in Mississippi
Delta region after Kolb and others[1].

The pattern for each type environment however is
readily identifiable to the trained eye of the
coastal geomorphologist. Thus,though the Mississippi
Delta is for the most part subaerially exposed, it
is not unrealistic to suppose that a geomorphologist
could reconstruct the sedimentary environmental pattern
given a fraction of the original data. This it is
possible has been demonstrated by the geologist who
extrapolates his knowledge of deltaic patterns to
locate sites favorable for petroleum accumulation in
buried sediments whose areal extent is known from
well cuttings and rock cores taken from widely scattered
boreholes. Thus, pattern reconstruction based on
sample data is feasible.

The feasibility of reconstructing a pattern based on
sample data however must be tempered by the cost
involved in sampling. Such cost should reflect the
desired level of accuracy to be achieved in any re-
constructed pattern. For a fixed cost, moreover, it
is reasonable to assume an optimal sampling strategy
exists.

The difficulty comes when one considers how to give
quantitative expression to the complex spatial forms
of areally distributed variables which are actually
observed. Taking the spatial pattern of the Mississippi
Delta sedimentary environments, for example, it is
not yet possible to devise a geometric model to serve
as the basis for an optimal sampling strategy for
mapping deltaic patterns in general. Lacking a generalized
model, an alternative is to consider the Mississippi
Delta region which has been studied and mapped
extensively for several decades and to perform sampling
experiments on this pattern so that the results
obtained by experiment can be used to establish
guidelines for future surveys in areas where the
underlying pattern is unknown.

Figure 2 is a point pattern composed of 4034 points
which were taken from a grid superposed on the map in
Figure 1. The points were generated by choosing a point
at random within each cell of the grid and recording
the type environment situated at the point. Over 90
percent of the cells were found to contain no more than
two different types of environments which led to the
conclusion that the pattern represented by the 4034
points was an adequate representation of the underlying
continuous pattern. These 4034 points constitute a
parent population.

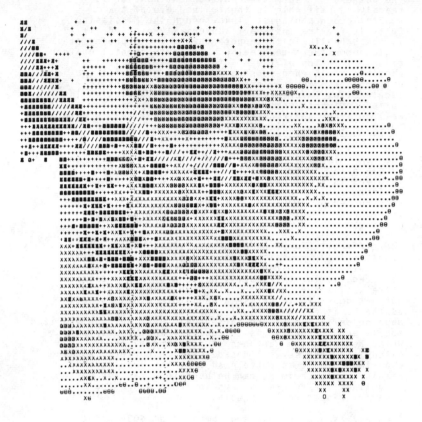

Figure 2. Pattern of depositional environments in
Mississippi Delta region based on 4034
points taken from a grid. Environments
represented by symbols are: ▇, natural
levee; /, point bar; +, swamp; X, marsh;
θ, beach; ▨, lacustrine; ., bay-sound.

Figure 3 is a composite made up of 4 proximal maps based on random samples of 100, 200, 500 and 1000 points drawn from the previous parent population. Continuity from one map to the next results from having retained the points drawn for each size sample for the next larger size sample. A proximal map is generated by assigning to each print location on a grid the type environment of the nearest sample point. Thus, proximal maps follow a nearest neighbor rule in their construction. For uncorrelated samples, a proximal map is an unbiased estimate of the underlying pattern.

     Figure 3. Proximal maps of Mississippi Delta region based on random sampling. Top left, 100 samples; Bottom left, 200 samples; Top right, 500 samples; Bottom right, 1000 samples. The symbols represent the same environments as in Figure 2. The maps were generated using the SYMAP computer program[2].

A visual examination of the above maps and comparing them to Figure 2 or Figure 1 leads to the conclusion that the map based on 500 random points is adequate to reconstruct the pattern of sedimentary environments in the Mississipppi Delta. In terms of an areal sample if we consider each point to represent an area equal to 1/4034th of the total area, it would amount approximately to a 10 percent sample.

Random sampling sets an upper bound on the number of
samples necessary to reconstruct adequately an underlying spatial pattern. It assumes no prior knowledge
of the population under study. For an areally distributed
variable in which some degree of spatial correlation
exists, it would seem more appropriate to consider
systematic sampling. Taking samples on a grid for
instance eliminates the variance introduced by uneven
spacing associated with random sampling. Aside from
the greater convenience of sampling on a grid, however,
it has been found for the Mississippi Delta data that
systematic sampling does not lead to any significant
reduction in the number of samples necessary to
reconstruct the depositional environment pattern[3].
A possible explanation is that the pattern is sufficiently
complex so that whatever differences exist between
random and systematic sampling is reduced to a
minimum.

An optimal sampling strategy precludes therefore some
degree of prior knowledge of the spatial structure of
the pattern to be mapped. Lacking quantitative models
at present, we turn to descriptive statistical measures.

NEAREST UNLIKE NEIGHBORS

Insight into the spatial structure of a pattern can be
gained by considering the nearest neighbor relationships
among sample data. For the Mississippi Delta map data,
we consider the distribution of nearest type environments
in the point pattern of Figure 2. Since the different
environments occupy a different percentage of the total
area, it is more appropriate to consider nearest unlike
type environments. Table 1 contains the number of
different nearest unlike type environments. The rightmost
column and the bottom row contain the row and column
sums respectively. Because the original data were
generated from a grid, equidistant unlike nearest
neighbors were weighted in proportion to their number
and for this reason, the numbers in Table 1 are rounded
to the nearest integer. The totals remain exact however.
Each row contains the number of nearest unlike type
environments for each environment. The relationships
are summarized graphically in Figure 4 in which a
comparison is made between the frequency each environment
serves as nearest unlike neighbor and the frequency of
each environment in the parent population. The line
which bisects the axes represents a perfectly symmetric
relationship. The extent which the points representing
the different environments depart from this line is a
measure of the diffuseness or compactness of the
separate pattern of each environment. Such a measure
could be used to classify pattern structure. Clearly
this needs more investigation.

Table 1

Number of nearest unlike type environments for
the point pattern of Figure 2

Nearest Unlike Type Environment

	natural levee	point bar	swamp	marsh	beach	lacus-trine	bay-sound	Σ
natural levee		93	241	138	0	1	0	473
point bar	96		25	14	0	1	2	138
swamp	285	24		172	0	138	9	628
marsh	494	17	167		45	308	272	1303
beach	0	0	1	29		0	72	102
lacus-trine	2	1	168	291	0		20	482
bay-sound	0	3	88	505	290	22		908
Σ	877	138	690	1149	335	470	375	4034

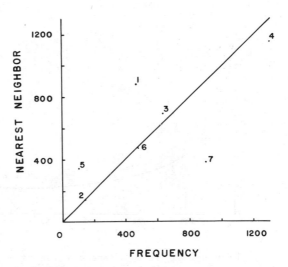

Figure 4. Scatter diagram comparing the frequency
each environment serves as nearest unlike
neighbor to the frequency each environment occurs in the population. The numbers represent: 1, natural levee; 2, point
bar; 3, swamp; 4, marsh; 5, beach; 6,
lacustrine; 7, bay-sound.

The data in Table 1 can be recast into proportions by
dividing each of the numbers in the table by the total
number of points. These proportions become the
probabilities that one type environment is nearest
to another. We can estimate how nearly these probabilities can by approximated by random sampling. As an
experiment, a series of 10 sequences of random samples
ranging in sample size from 10 to 1000 were drawn from
the parent population and for each random sample the
nearest unlike neighbors were tabulated and a measure
r defined as

$$r = \sum_{\substack{i,j=1 \\ i \neq j}}^{7} |\hat{c}_{ij} - c_{ij}|/42$$

was calculated where $\hat{c}_{ij}$ is the sample estimate for c_{ij}
defined as the proportion of occurrences in the parent
population where the jth type environment is the
nearest unlike neighbor to the ith type environment.
Figure 5 is a plot of the average value of r for the
10 sequences of random samplings. It is seen there is
little improvement beyond a sample size of 500 which
agrees with the earlier observation that a 10 percent
random sample was adequate to reconstruct the underlying
pattern.

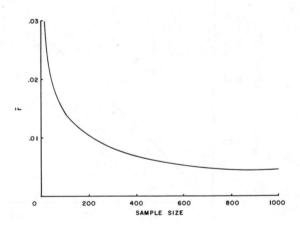

Figure 5. Plot of average value of r
calculated for a serier of 10
sequences of random samples
ranging in sample size from 10
to 1000.

Although the type and number of nearest unlike neighbors give evidence of the underlying structure for a given pattern, additional information is needed before an optimal sampling strategy can be devised. What is needed are the average spacing distances that separate nearest unlike neighbors. For any given point, it is required to have an estimate of the average travel distance to the nearest boundary of some other specified type environment. This is illustrated in Figure 6 for a random point X in region A which is part of a larger area subdivided into 5 different regions.

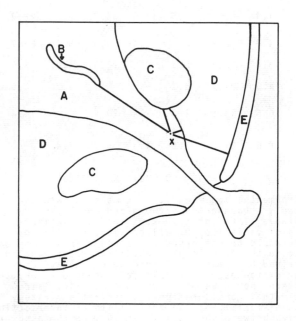

Figure 6. Idealized map pattern composed of 5 different regions. The nearest distances to the boundaries of the other regions for a random point X in region A are shown.

The pattern can be described by the average distances which separate the region boundaries. Table 2 contains the average distances expressed in miles which separate the nearest unlike type environments for the point pattern in Figure 2. Each distance represents how far on the average one would expect to travel from one type environment to another. This information provides the basis for an optimal sampling strategy.

Table 2

Average distances expressed in miles between
nearest unlike type environments for the
point pattern of Figure 2

Nearest Unlike Type Environment

	natural levee	point bar	swamp	marsh	beach	lacus-trine	bay-sound
natural levee		7.4	2.4	7.3	28.4	7.3	22.2
point bar	1.4		2.5	11.1	34.7	8.0	28.4
swamp	4.8	9.2		5.4	29.6	5.4	23.7
marsh	3.4	14.6	5.6		12.3	4.0	7.0
beach	14.5	24.7	8.1	5.8		9.7	1.9
lacus-trine	6.6	10.8	4.3	2.4	20.4		14.4
bay-sound	14.6	21.8	7.8	4.4	5.6	7.4	

A PROPOSED OPTIMAL STRATEGY

An environmental map when it is completed is a map
which depicts boundaries between regions having
recognizable differences in some selected variable
or group of variables. Of all possible maps the most
accurate would be one based on sample points taken on
or close to the true boundaries. If an underlying pattern
is described by a matrix of interpoint nearest unlike
neighbor distances, the sample data used to reconstruct
the pattern should be distributed similarly. Aside
from azimuthal considerations, a desirable strategy
consists of maximizing the probability of intersecting
boundaries between successive samples. On the assumption
that different subregions of the area being investigated
occupy a different percentage of the total area, it
follows that the spacing between successive samples
should be unequal. This argues against systematic
sampling when prior knowledge of the underlying pattern
exists.

By introducing the cost involved in sampling, an optimal
strategy is proposed whereby the greater cost involved
in travel to regions further removed where there is a
high probability of adding new information is balanced
against the lesser cost involved in travel to nearby
locations where there is a low probability of adding
new information. With this strategy, it is anticipated
that fewer samples will be needed to recover the
equivalent amount of information as compared to either

random or systematic sampling. An operational formulation
of this strategy is currently being developed.

REFERENCES

1. Kolb,C.R., and Van Lopik,J.R., 1958, Geology of the
   Mississippi River Deltaic Plain Southeastern Louisiana:
   Vicksburg, U.S. Corps Engr. Wtrwys. Expt. Sta. Tech.
   Rept. 3-483.

2. SYMAP, Harvard Center Environ. Design Studies,
   Cambridge, Mass.

3. McCammon,R.B.,1972, Environment pattern reconstruction
   from sample data. II. Spatial characteristics.
   Mississippi Delta region: ONR Tech. Rept. 2, Geog.
   Prog. Branch, Wash, D.C., 117 p.

ACKNOWLEDGMENTS

This research is sponsored by the Geography Programs
Branch of the Office of Naval Research, Washington,
D.C. I wish to thank my two graduate students, Andrea
Krivz and Richard Kolb, for their assistance with
the computer programming.

INDUSTRY'S ROLE IN COASTAL MAPPING

Mr. Albert V. Cocking
President
Teledyne Geotronics
725 East Third Street
Long Beach, California 90812

BIOGRAPHICAL SKETCH

Mr. Cocking has been President of Teledyne Geotronics since
founding the company in 1957 and has acted as consulting
geodesist for the U.S. Navy and many commercial companies,
both domestic and foreign. He has been responsible for
numerous innovations and improvements in the computer processing of photogrammetric surveying, and engineering fields.
He majored in physics and subsequently took advance courses
in photogrammetry and geodesy at UCLA. He holds State of
California teaching credentials and has taught geodetic and
advance surveying. He is a registered photogrammetric surveyor and consulting engineer in the State of California, a
member of American Society of Photogrammetry, and a Fellow
of American Congress of Surveying and Mapping.

ABSTRACT

Present capabilities are reviewed and new methods and ap-
proaches are examined. A typical project describing the in-
terfacing of these methods is examined in light of the
diversed usage to which such maps can be useful. An observation is also made as to the need for new equipment for developing contour maps of the ocean bottom. A description of a
hypothetical instrument is presented explaining how it might
be possible to use methods developed for photogrammetry, to
conveniently reduce side-looking sonar data. A conclusion
stating that industry's future in coastal mapping will be
developing and manufacturing instruments, as well as producing maps for design and construction for industry's needs.

DISCUSSION

Man has long been concerned about his environment and has
traditionally followed the changes and developments by recording this information on maps and charts. Over the years
this has proven to be a convenient method due primarily to
the apparent permanent and unchanging state of affairs that
takes place in nature. Of course, we all know that the earth
is a dynamic and changing body, subject to the forces of
nature that usually act in a sedate manner. There are some
exceptions to this subtle molding of our world and they primarily manifest themselves in coastal regions. We have all
experienced the dramatic changes that take place during the
day as the tide changes, as well as the seasonal fluctuations
that occur through the deposits of sand and debris that
accumulates along the shorelines, and the erosion that results from the constant forces of wave action. To those
people, commonly called "son's of beaches", who have studied
about or lived in a coastal region, larger more significant,
and more permanent changes are apparent over a period of
years. In coastal regions of submergence, we see spits,

bars, and islands appearing. We note in areas of emergence, changes in the harbors and beaches that affect docks, bridges and highways, as well as the individual land owner. As great as these changes are, in recent years, man's actions have clouded and overran nature's forces (Fig. 1) by dredging, by building groins, harbors, and islands, by thermal pollution, sewage disposal and oil spills, and by our laws. These actions will have an immediate and long range affect on our coastal areas. The resulting changes are being generated by private, corporate, and governmental agencies. As our population increases, as our thirst for energy accelerates, and our need for additional resources intensifies, our requirements for better and different types of maps and charts are more apparent than ever before. These pressures are increasing and industry is turning towards the ocean and marginal coastal regions for expansion. The oil industry, the mining industry, the fishing industry, the real estate industry, the recreational industry, and the transportation industry, all share a stake in the future development of coastal areas. This means that they require maps, laws, and technology adequate to record their interests and design their structures.

We, in the mapping industry, have recognized this challenge and are embarking on a program to cope with the anticipated demands. Traditionally, one of industry's main contributions to society has been the development of adequate hardware to solve man's problems and mapping is no exception. Irrespective of the use or user, whether it be for military, civil, or commercial needs, it has been industry's role to design and manufacture instruments commensurate with the requirements. I believe that this remains one of industry's prime functions.

In reviewing the requirements for coastal mapping, it becomes obvious that some sort of control network is essential. Most of our nets are established by triangulation, traverse and levels. These nets are permanent and fixed in relation to the land on which they are placed. Unfortunately, they are hard to recover and sometimes should be considered less than permanent due to the changes that take place on the land. Teledyne, through Teledyne Raydist, has produced a scheme that solves many of the problems that are associated with coastal control nets. With the Teledyne Radist's "T" System, a permanent network for an unlimited number of users is available on a 24-hour basis. With this system and Raydist's navigator, renting for about $1,000 a month, it is possible to determine your position to within ± 1 meter, continuously day or night, rain or fog. One such system is now being operated in the Chesapeake Bay and a similar system is planned for the coastal areas of California (Fig. 2). This equipment can be used in a boat or an airplane with equal efficiency. Utilizing this system of control, photogrammetry is an ideal means of mapping coastal areas that are above or near the surface of the ocean. With black and white infrared film, it is possible to achieve accurate positions of the water/beach interface. This is extremely important in establishing legal boundaries during mean lower low water.

FIGURE 1

IDENTICAL PHOTO COVERAGE OF THE LONG BEACH HARBOR
TOP PHOTO TAKEN IN 1929,   LOWER PHOTO TAKEN IN 1971
SCALE 1" = 350'

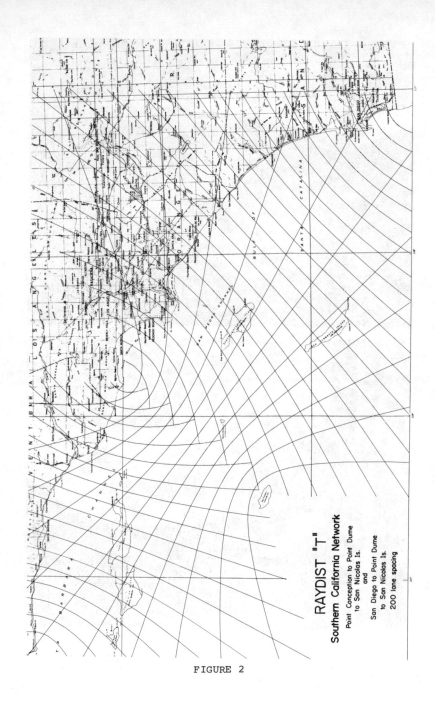

RAYDIST "T"
Southern California Network

Point Conception to Point Dume
to San Nicolas Is.
and
San Diego to Point Dume
to San Nicolas Is.
200 lane spacing

FIGURE 2

300

Color photography is helpful in mapping sub-surface as well as observing currents and turbidity. Infrared color photography is used in measuring the marine growth that occurs along and near our coastal lines. Black and white photography with Raydist positioning, extended through analytical techniques, make mapping of all visible features convenient, accurate, and reasonable in cost. The necessary equipment to do this type of mapping is available in abundance in both governmental and private groups.

Another area of interest to the mapper is the bottom and sub-bottom. With tankers getting larger and moving faster, many harbors and waterways are marginal and will require significant dredging and mapping. Once again the Raydist system will provide good positioning, while the Teledyne Exploration Model 305 Sparker will provide a profile of the bottom and information as to the material to be found beneath the bottom. Although I have confined my remarks to Teledyne equipment, it is primarily due to my experience with and knowledge of these instruments. There are many other manufacturers that make similar equipment at similar prices. The main point I want to make is that we can assume that industry and government has available a wide variety of equipment and techniques that can meet the coming requirements for coastal mapping. There are, however, some promising areas that require new development. One such instrument that is needed is a device to provide information of the bottom that can conveniently be reduced. I expect that in the near future, such an instrument will become available. I envision this equipment to be a sonar system utilizing continuous transmission frequency modulated techniques. The information can be recorded in a manner which will enable us to produce photos that can be used in a conventional stereo plotter and contour maps of the bottom could be conveniently made. In putting this in terms for a photogrammetrist, we could substitute the airplane with a boat and the camera with the sonar gear and produce stereo coverage of large areas. In order to satisfy our curiosity as to the practicability of clearing parallax and mapping from scanned imagery rather than photography, we flew a test in the dead of night and using an IR scanner, operating in the 8-14 micron range, made the following contour map and compared it with maps made from conventional photography (Fig. 3).

The other role that industry should provide in the coastal mapping field is one of service and map production for both industry and government. As industry's requirements become broader in scope and more stringent in regulations to be met, it becomes incumbent upon industry to develop the capability to provide the necessary maps and related surveys for industry's needs.

One such job that Teledyne Geotronics did was in the Gulf of Siam. It is typical of the type of work that industry is being called upon to execute. The maps required were multi-purposed and covered a large area and because of this the Harbor Department of the Thailand Government, as well as a major oil company, participated in the funding of the project. We used tellurometers and Raydist equipment for the positioning of a boat that was equipped with a Teledyne Exploration Sparker System, and a Bendix Depth Recorder.

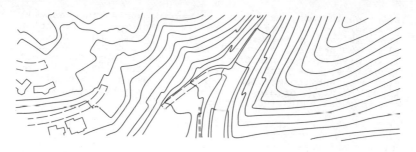

Compiled from Conventional Mapping Photography

Compiled from Infrared Scanner Imagery

FIGURE 3

The data was gathered simultaneously for both the Bathymetric and sub-bottom mapping and recorded in a form that was easy to process through our computers. This digital data was then processed by our Gerber Plotter and automatically compiled in the form of overlays presented at a common scale. Photogrammetric maps were compiled of the coastal areas and surface indications of current was presented in a similar fashion. With this information, current studies were undertaken and we were able to relate the data directly to the base maps that we had prepared. At this point, I wish to emphasize that all of the information was digital and stored in our computer for future reference to be used in determining such things as pay quantities if and when dredging operations were to begin. The project was successful and proved the cost effectiveness of utilizing a wide variety of disciplines to produce a useable set of maps and data on a common basis for a multiplicity of uses. The maps resulted in a good tool for exploration, navigation, construction, planning and military requirements. We produced maps of the ocean bottom and sub-bottom as well as depicting currents and tidal information useful for a wide range of users with greatly diversified requirements.

In conclusion, I believe that industry's role in coastal mapping can best be separated into the areas of 1) development and production of instruments to better cope with the accelerated emphasis on coastal mapping by government, industry, and the military, and 2) provide services for industry to develop maps of large scale and accuracies that are commensurate with the needs of design and ownership, while the government should continue to develop better and more accurate maps and charts on a regional basis, private industry should concentrate on local maps for specific projects. The projects will vary from route surveys for pipelines on the ocean bottom to property surveying for individual owners.

PETROLEUM EXPLORATION IN THE COASTAL ZONE

Alan M. Warren
Associate Washington Representative
Humble Oil & Refining Company
Washington, D. C.   20036

BIOGRAPHICAL SKETCH

Alan M. Warren is Associate Washington Representative for
Humble Oil & Refining Company. He received his B.S. degree
in Geology from Louisiana State University and his M.B.S.
from The University of Houston. Following graduation he
was employed by Humble Oil & Refining Company as a geophysicist in the Exploration Department concerned with the geological interpretation of marine seismic data. He progressed
through assignments of increasing responsibilities to Manager of the Louisiana Offshore District, the position he
held prior to his current assignment in Washington, D.C. He
is an active member of the Society of Exploration Geophysi-
cists, American Association of Petroleum Geologists, and
the Marine Technology Society.

ABSTRACT

Energy demand in the United States by 1985 is expected to
double what it is today. Petroleum exploration to find
adequate supplies must also accelerate. The bays and
estuaries of the coastal zones have in the past provided
excellent hunting grounds. Future reserves will be discovered in the continental margins along the Atlantic Seaboard, where the potential for natural gas is considered
particularly high. Seismic methods must be used to identify
areas of greatest potential. Accurate maps and surveys will
be a prerequisite. Legal boundaries must also be defined.
Exploratory wells and production facilities will be controlled
by rules and regulations promulgated by the respective states
and/or the United States Geological Survey.

ENERGY DEMAND

The demand for energy in the United States is increasing at
a fantastic rate. By 1985 it is expected to nearly double
what it is today. Where is this energy to come from?

Growth in hydroelectric power is limited by availability of
adequate and acceptable damsites. Though additional capacity
will be developed, hydroelectric power will provide only two
percent of the energy needed in the U.S. by 1985. Today,
nuclear energy supplies less than one percent of the total
U.S. demand. Providing technical and environmental problems
can be resolved and fast-breeder reactors can be built and
put in operation, nuclear power may supply 11 percent of this

nation's energy requirements in 1985. Coal will continue to
supply an important part of our energy needs. It is estimated that for the next 10 or 15 years, coal will supply
about 20 percent of the energy demand.

Oil and gas supply over three-fourths of our energy today,
and will still be supplying two-thirds of it in 1985. Although petroleum's share of total energy supply will decrease
slightly, consumption will almost double. As a result, we
must find and develop new major reserves of oil and gas to
replace our present rapidly dwindling supply.

EXPLORATION

Oil and gas exploration and development have been going on in
the U.S. since Col. Drake's discovery well near Titusville,
Pennsylvania, in 1859. Consequently, the sedimentary basins
of the land areas of the "lower 48" have been intensely
explored and drilled. These are mature areas where major
additions to oil and gas reserves are few and far between.
In fact, for many years inshore production has been increasing
(largely through secondary recovery projects), and the remaining reserves have been decreasing.

The bays and estuaries of the coastal zones have experienced
an exploration and development history similar to that of
adjacent dry land areas. In fact, it was the large accumulations of oil and gas discovered in the coastal marshes and
estuaries of Louisiana in the 1930's that prompted the exploration of the open waters of the Gulf of Mexico. So far,
the 16,000 wells which have been drilled for oil and gas in
United States waters have only tapped a fraction of the
potential thought to exist within the country's continental
shelf. The U.S. Geodetic Survey, for example, recently released estimates which place the total potential resource
base of the continental margin at 1.5 trillion to over 2
trillion barrels of oil, and from nearly 4.5 quadrillion to
more than 5 quadrillion cubic feet of natural gas. Of these
amounts, the USGS suggests that the oil industry, operating
under today's technology and economic structure, should be
able to find and recover from 160 to 190 billion barrels of
oil, and from 800 trillion to 1.1 quadrillion cubic feet of
natural gas. Much of this oil and gas is thought to exist
within the continental margins of the Atlantic Seaboard, where
the potential for natural gas is considered particularly high.

Exploration for these much needed reserves offshore depends,
in large measure, on projecting the geologic framework established onshore into the marine environment. The seaward
projection of productive trends and the evaluation of their
oil and gas potential involves the integration of subsurface
geologic data obtained from wells with geophysical information

provided by the reflection seismograph. The nearshore surf
zone poses a real problem in tying the coastal zone geology
to that of the open waters. The technological problems of
operating in this mixed land-sea environment are tremendous.
Longshore currents, tidal swells, breaking surf, and highly
variable bottom conditions all contribute to the difficulty
of establishing reliable correlations of geologic events in
a structurally complex area.

SEISMIC METHODS

The reflection seismograph is presently the primary exploration tool in the coastal zone. This method involves the
generation of acoustic energy by some means near the earth's
surface and the transmission of this energy downward through
the earth's layers with a portion of this energy being reflected upward at each interface which has a density or
velocity contrast. The reflected energy in turn is detected
by means of pressure or displacement-type detectors near the
surface, and the data is recorded in digital form on magnetic tape. These tapes are computer analyzed and presented
to the geophysicist in cross-section form for his interpretation.

Current deep water work involves basically three types of
energy sources - the air gun, gas gun, and hydraulic vibrator,
and these are placed approximately 30' below the water surface. The air gun utilizes the principle of a rapid discharge of air under high pressure, creating a compressional
wave front and eventually an air bubble, which is undesirable.
The gas gun involves the ignition of a flammable mixture of
two gases such as oxygen and propane, creating an expansion
of the gases. The expansion may occur directly into the water
or be confined to a flexible rubber housing. In either case,
the compressional wave front is transmitted to the water.
The direct transmission creates an undesirable gas bubble
similar to the air bubble, while the confined method does
not. The third method, the hydraulic vibrator, transmits a
wave front of varying frequencies into the water.

The detector system in deep water usually consists of a
neutrally buoyant "streamer cable" containing numerous piezoelectric transducers to detect the reflected compressional
waves. This cable, which is normally some 8000 feet long,
is under continuous tow behind the surveying vessel which
travels at a speed of 5 to 6 knots. At specified locations,
the energy sources emit a seismic compressional pulse, and
the transducers detect the reflected wave fronts for a period
of some 6 to 8 seconds.

The method in shallow water is similar in some respects to
that described for deep water. The energy sources and the

detectors are essentially the same, but the method of deploying the detector cable is different. The cable may be a bottom drag cable or one which lies directly on the ocean bottom. The bottom drag cable is for water depths from 10 to 40 feet, and the detectors are again pressure sensitive piezoelectric crystals. Weights are attached to the cable to force it to ride approximately 3 feet off the ocean bottom where it remains motionless during the period of energy transmission and detection. The cable that lies on bottom contains the piezoelectric transducers, but is moved from one location to the other by picking it up and completely relaying it in a new location. This cable is commonly called "bay" cable, and it may be used in water depths of as little as 5 feet.

As the seismic survey moves from the shallow water depth to land, the configuration of both the energy source and the cable detector system changes. The air and gas guns are placed in a housing which can be rammed or jetted approximately 15 feet into the ocean bottom or the marsh land. The vibrators are forced against the ocean bottom or the surface of the marsh. The cable deploying the detectors may be bay cable in the water, and lighter, more easily maneuverable cable on the higher ground. The detectors become velocity or displacement detectors, and are attached to the water bottom or marsh land by forcing their pointed end directly into the bottom or some sublayer of the marsh. These detectors record earth movement caused by the compressional wave fronts in much the same way that seismographs record earth movement caused by earthquakes.

These methods all share one common advantage - they do no damage to the environment. Many years ago, small charges of dynamite would have been used to provide acoustic energy, but this practice has been abandoned in favor of the ecologically safe techniques just described.

The transportation mode varies considerably over the three areas. In deep water, boats drawing from 6 to 15 feet are employed. These are usually 120-200 feet in length. In shallow water areas, powered jack-up barges drawing from 2 to 3 feet of water are used; and in the soft marsh areas, marsh buggies with large hollow wheels for flotation are used.

Of the three methods which I have described, the deep water method is the least expensive and least time consuming. Approximately 50 to 70 miles per day may be covered at a price of $150 to $200 per mile. The shallow water method may cover 10-20 miles per day at a cost of $1000 to $2000 per mile, and the marsh method may cover from 2-6 miles per day at a cost of $2000 to $4000 per mile.

The computer processing of the data for all these methods costs in the neighborhood of $125 to $200 per mile.

SURVEYING AND MAPPING

Several types of surveying methods can be applied to marine geophysical exploration of coastal areas. Each of these is designed to meet the needs and requirements of any particular coastal zone. These are radio-navigation, satellite positioning, radar, transit, and alidade.

The most frequently used surveying method is the radio-navigation system which is based on radio signals and contracted by Lorac, Offshore Navigation Inc. (Raydist), Decca Surveys, Cubic Corporation (Autho-Tape), and the long-range (Loran A & C) with base stations operated by the U.S. Government. Radio-navigation systems are most desirable in areas where existing onshore control is extended several miles offshore in deep water. Selection of these systems is based on existing nets, permanently established transmitters, and geographically oriented for the client's exploration needs.

Satellite positioning is very sophisticated and costly, and used only in remote areas where other surveying methods are not readily available.

Radar or electronic min-range surveying methods are not in great demand due to added costs of extra manpower to operate them. Land survey crews have to establish fixed sites at predetermined intervals for transponders to insure maximum accuracy fixes of shot point positions. Locating triangulation stations (bench marks) along shorelines also hinders the progress of land survey crews.

The transit and alidade, conventional means of surveys onshore, are sometimes employed in shallow bay areas. Being the most economical of all, success depends on the availability of existing triangulation stations in a particular coastal zone.

In all phases of coastal surveying, the U.S. Coast and Geological topographic 7½ minute quadrangle 1:24,000 feet is used as a tool in marine geophysical exploration. Exact descriptions of existing shorelines, water depths, underwater obstructions, and triangulation stations are a tremendous aid in planning seismic lines. Implemented with the topo quad is the U.S. Coast and Geodetic Nautical chart which is used in extended offshore areas. Marine geophysical (seismic lines) are plotted on a scale of 1:4000. State plane coordinate systems (x & y) are used in Texas and Louisiana. In the NE Gulf and East Coast, the Universal Mercator System (UTM) is used.

The need of triangulation stations or bench marks is
essential and critical in radar, electronic mini and long
range, transit, and alidade surveying. Most triangulation
stations are difficult to locate due to the nonexistence of
permanent landmarks along coastal areas. Some type of fix-
ture, such as a 6-foot galvanized pipe, might aid in locating
these bench marks.

A marine geophysical company will select a surveying method
which is both accurate and economical for its exploration
needs along coastal zones.

LEGAL PROBLEMS ESTABLISHING BOUNDARIES

The need for an accurate definition of a shoreline for
legal purposes, both for the State and Federal ownership
and for lease boundaries, becomes readily apparent upon examination of the area of dispute in Louisiana where the boundary
line will intersect producing fields. Operations in this
area have been conducted for many years on the basis of an
interim agreement where State and Federal governments have
provided a procedure for exploration and production in the
areas in dispute; however, the sums of money involved are of
such magnitude that a definite boundary must be established
to permit their release. The December 1971 supplemental
decree has provided for the release of much of the impounded
funds. In addition to lease ownership problems associated
with an indefinite boundary is the demarcation between State
and Federal Agency jurisdiction required for purposes of
well permits, drilling and producing regulations, environmental supervision, and production allowables. Along with
determining an accurate definition of the shoreline, a
solution must be found to deal with the ambulatory nature
of any State-Federal boundary caused by movement of the shoreline, which extends or recedes over a period of time from a
variety of natural causes.

EXPLORATION WELLS AND PRODUCTION FACILITIES

Exploratory wells in coastal waters are developed within the
framework of the Conservation Rules and Regulations Per-
taining to Oil and Gas Operations legislated by the respective
states. The wells are drilled as single-well locations with
a mobile drilling rig such as a bottom founded barge or a
shallow jack-up unit. An unsuccessful well is abandoned
after removing all equipment to a depth below the bay floor.
A successful prospect is completed with free standing well-
head equipment above the water surface.

Additional development wells would be drilled as either
single or as multiple well locations. Production flowlines
from the individual wells are routed to a centrally located,
permanent production platform for separation and metering.

The oil, water and gas from the platform is then separately
pipelined to a shore-based terminal for further distribution.

SUMMARY

In summary, it is hoped that this discussion has portrayed
the role of the petroleum industry in exploring for oil and
gas in the Coastal Zone, and has given an insight into the
need for such exploration. The Coastal Zone does present
unique problems for the industry, but modern technology has
made possible an operation which is completely compatible
with our environment.

THE AMERICAN SOCIETY OF PHOTOGRAMMETRY
publishes the following manuals and proceedings:

MANUALS	Price to members	Price to non-members
MANUAL OF PHOTOGRAMMETRY (3rd Edition) 1966 1220 pages in two volumes, 878 illustrations, 80 authors	$19.00	$22.50
MANUAL OF PHOTOGRAPHIC INTERPRETATION, 1960 868 pages, 600 photographs, 90 authors	12.00	15.00
MANUAL OF COLOR AERIAL PHOTOGRAPHY, 1968 550 pages, 50 full-color aerial photographs 40 authors	21.00	24.50

PROCEEDINGS

ANNUAL MARCH MEETINGS		
1970 Washington, D.C. 769 pages	2.50	5.00
1972 Washington, D.C. 636 pages	2.50	5.00
FALL TECHNICAL MEETINGS		
1970 Denver, CO, 542 pages, 33 pages	2.50	5.00
1971 San Francisco, CA, 770 pages, 71 papers*	2.50	5.00
1970 INTERNATIONAL SYMPOSIUM ON PHOTOGRAPHY & NAVIGATION, Sponsored by International Society for Photogrammetry Commission I, ASP, and the Dept. of Geodetic Science, The Ohio State University, 412 pages, illustrated, hard-cover bound	5.00	5.00
OPERATIONAL REMOTE SENSING, proceedings from the seminar held in Houston, Texas, February 1972	5.00	10.00
WORKSHOPS:		
COLOR AERIAL PHOTOGRAPHY IN THE PLANT SCIENCES & RELATED FIELDS, 20 papers, 288 pages, March 1971, Gainesville, Florida	5.00	10.00
ORTHOPHOTO WORKSHOP, January 1971, Washington, D.C., 133 pages, 22 papers	5.00	10.00
CLOSE-RANGE PHOTOGRAMMETRY, Urbana, Illinois 33 papers, 433 pages	5.00	10.00

*Includes papers from Symposium on Computational Photogrammetry.

Send orders, or requests for information, to ASP, 105 N. Virginia
Avenue, Falls Church, Va. 22046.

TOOLS FOR COASTAL ZONE MANAGMENT......

the proceedings of a two-day conference earlier this year, deals with the practicalities of managing coastal resources.

This special Marine Technology Society publication will become a basic reference for persons working on coastal planning as a result of probable new Federal legislation on coastal zone management.

Covered in this publication are the various tools and techniques available to coastal zone managers. Included are papers on new equipment and methods for gathering data, environmental baseline studies, information systems and data banks, matrices and inventories, and modeling techniques. Specific uses of each are presented and critically assessed by a panel of experts.

A highlight of "Tools for Coastal Zone Management" is the full text of an address by Gov. Russell W. Peterson of Delaware, explaining why and how that state enacted controversial legislation barring heavy industry from its coastline and subsequent reactions to this step.

Participants at the conference include leaders from government agencies, academic institutions, industries and research organizations. The conference was arranged by the MTS Coastal Zone Marine Management Committee.

Please send____ "Tools for Coastal Zone Management" to:

Name_____

Address_____

City_____State_____Zip_____

SEND ORDERS TO:

TOOLS FOR COASTAL ZONE
MANAGEMENT -- MTS
1730 M Street, N.W., Suite 412
Washington, D.C. 20036

Price:

$12.00

MTS/ASO mbrs.
(10% discount)

ORGANIZATION OF ACSM

AMERICAN CONGRESS ON SURVEYING AND MAPPING
National Headquarters, Suite 430 Woodward Building
733 – 15th Street, N.W., Washington, D.C. 20005
Telephone: Area Code 202 DIstrict 7-0029

ACSM

The objectives of ACSM are to: (a) advance the sciences of surveying and mapping in their several branches, in furtherance of the public welfare and in the interests of both those who use maps and surveys and those who make them, and establish a central source of reference and union for its members; (b) contribute to public education in the use of surveys, maps and charts and encourage the prosecution of basic surveying, mapping and charting programs; (c) encourage improvement of college curriculums for the teaching of all branches of surveying and mapping both in the technological sciences and the professional philosophies; (d) honor the leaders in the sciences of surveying and mapping; and (e) support a program of publications that will represent the professional and technical interests of surveying and mapping.

ACSM PUBLICATIONS AVAILABLE

	Members	Non-Members
Bound Papers: ACSM Annual Meetings, Washington, D.C.		
1968—March 10–15, 615 pp.	$2.50	$5.00
1969—March 9–14, 500 pp.	out of stock	
1970—March 1– 6, 695 pp.	2.50	5.00
1971—March 7–12, 791 pp.	out of stock	
1972—March 12–17, 430 pp.	2.50	5.00
Bound Papers: ACSM Fall Conventions		
1968—September 18–21, Minneapolis, 226 pp.	1.00	2.50
1969—September 23–26, Portland, Oregon, 378 pp.	2.50	5.00
1970—October 7–10, Denver, Colorado, 542 pp.	2.50	5.00
1971—September 7–11, San Francisco, 454 pp.	3.75	7.50
Monographs		
Cartography Division		
CA-3—Cartographic Scribing Materials, Instruments and Techniques by Lionel C. Moore, Revised Edition, 1968	1.00	2.50
CA-4—Dot Area Symbols in Cartography by Henry W. Castner and Arthur H. Robinson, 1969, 78 pp.	1.00	2.50
CA-5—Method-Produced Error in Isarithmic Mapping by Joel Morrison, 1971, 76 pp.	1.00	2.50
Control Surveys Division		
CS-1—Suggested Specifications for Local Horizontal Control Surveys by Joseph F. Dracup, 1969, 17 pp.	1.00	2.50
CS-2—Electronic Distance Measuring Instruments by Raymond Tomlinson and Thomas Burger, 1971, 60 pp.	1.00	2.50
Land Surveys Division		
Manual of Prevailing Fees for Land Surveying Services, 1971, 210 pp.	6.00	12.00
Other Publications		
Bibliography of Property Survey Literature by Winfield H. Eldridge, 1963, 142 pp.	2.50	5.00
Bound Papers from the Orthophoto Workshop, Washington, D.C. January 18–21, 1971, 133 pp.	5.00	5.00
Guide for Professional Employment Practices, Joint Committee on Employment Practices, 1970, 18 pp.	2.00	2.00
Index to Surveying and Mapping, 1941–1960, Volumes I–XX	1.00	3.00
Policy on Matters of Professional Practice, 40 pp., punched for loose leaf binding	1.00	2.50
Proceedings, Symposium on Automation of Field Survey Instrumentation and Data Acquisition, ACSM-C&GS, Gaithersburg, Maryland, December 7–10, 1969, 272 pp.	5.00	5.00
Definitions of Surveying and Associated Terms, a cooperative ACSM-ASCE committee updating of terms, scheduled for publication early 1972.	(price not set)	

N O T E S

NOTES

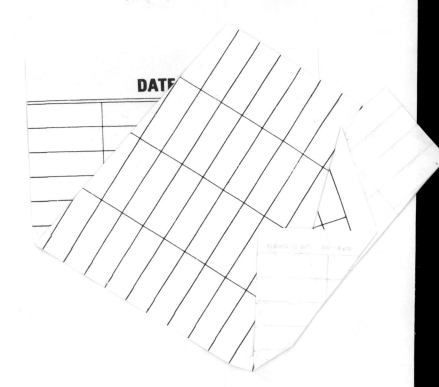

DATE